A2-Level
Chemistry

The Revision Guide

Exam Board: OCR B

Editors:
Mary Falkner, Sharon Keeley, David Hickinson, Paul Jordin, Simon Little,
Michael Southorn, Hayley Thompson.

Contributors:
Mike Bossart, Robert Clarke, Ian H. Davis, John Duffy, Lucy Muncaster,
Paul Warren, Chris Workman.

Proofreaders:
Barrie Crowther, Julie Wakeling.

Published by Coordination Group Publications Ltd.

ISBN: 978 1 84762 268 6

With thanks to Laura Stoney for the copyright research.

Groovy website: www.cgpbooks.co.uk
Jolly bits of clipart from CorelDRAW®
Printed by Elanders Hindson Ltd, Newcastle upon Tyne.

Contents

The Scientific Process

'How Science Works' is all about the scientific process — how we develop and test scientific ideas.
It's what scientists do all day, every day (well except at coffee time — never come between scientists and their coffee).

Scientists Come Up with **Theories** — Then **Test Them**...

Science tries to explain **how** and **why** things happen. It's all about seeking and gaining **knowledge** about the world around us. Scientists do this by **asking** questions and **suggesting** answers and then **testing** them, to see if they're correct — this is the **scientific process**.

1) **Ask** a question — make an **observation** and ask **why or how** whatever you've observed happens.
E.g. Why does sodium chloride dissolve in water?

2) **Suggest** an answer, or part of an answer, by forming a **theory** or a **model** (a possible **explanation** of the observations or a description of what you think is actually happening).
E.g. Sodium chloride is made up of charged particles, which are pulled apart by the polar water molecules.

3) Make a **prediction** or **hypothesis** — a **specific testable statement**, based on the theory, about what will happen in a test situation.
E.g. A solution of sodium chloride will conduct electricity much better than water does.

4) Carry out **tests** — to provide **evidence** that will support the prediction or refute it.
E.g. Measure the conductivity of water and of sodium chloride solution.

The evidence supported Quentin's Theory of Flammable Burps.

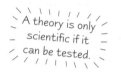

A theory is only scientific if it can be tested.

...Then They **Tell** Everyone About Their **Results**...

The results are **published** — scientists need to let others know about their work. Scientists publish their results in **scientific journals**. These are just like normal magazines, only they contain **scientific reports** (called papers) instead of the latest celebrity gossip.

1) Scientific reports are similar to the **lab write-ups** you do in school. And just as a lab write-up is **reviewed** (marked) by your teacher, reports in scientific journals undergo **peer review** before they're published.

Scientists use standard terminology when writing their reports. This way they know that other scientists will understand them. For instance, there are internationally agreed rules for naming organic compounds, so that scientists across the world will know exactly what substance is being referred to.

2) The report is sent out to **peers** — other scientists who are experts in the **same area**. They go through it bit by bit, examining the methods and data, and checking it's all clear and logical. When the report is approved, it's **published**. This makes sure that work published in scientific journals is of a **good standard**.

3) But peer review **can't guarantee** the science is **correct** — other scientists still need to **reproduce** it.

4) Sometimes **mistakes** are made and bad work is published. Peer review **isn't perfect** but it's probably the best way for scientists to self-regulate their work and to publish **quality reports**.

...Then **Other Scientists** Will **Test** the Theory Too

1) Other scientists read the published theories and results, and try to **test the theory** themselves. This involves:
   - Repeating the **exact same experiments**.
   - Using the theory to make **new predictions** and then testing them with **new experiments**.

2) If all the experiments in the world provide evidence to back it up, the theory is thought of as **scientific 'fact'** (for now).

3) If **new evidence** comes to light that **conflicts** with the current evidence the theory is questioned all over again. More rounds of **testing** will be carried out to try to find out where the theory **falls down**.

This is how the scientific process works — evidence supports a theory, loads of other scientists read it and test it for themselves, eventually all the scientists in the world **agree** with it and then bingo, you get to **learn** it.

This is exactly how scientists arrived at the structure of the atom — and how they came to the conclusion that electrons are arranged in shells and orbitals. It took years and years for these models to be developed and accepted — this is often the case with the scientific process.

The Scientific Process

If the **Evidence** Supports a Theory, It's **Accepted** — for Now

Our currently accepted theories have survived this '**trial by evidence**'. They've been tested **over and over again** and each time the results have backed them up. **BUT**, and this is a big but (teehee), they never become totally indisputable fact. Scientific **breakthroughs or advances** could provide new ways to question and test the theory, which could lead to **changes and challenges** to it. Then the testing starts all over again...

And this, my friend, is the **tentative nature of scientific knowledge** — it's always **changing** and **evolving**.

In 1865, when Kekulé suggested the structure of benzene was a ring of carbon atoms, joined by alternating single and double bonds, it was widely accepted — it was the best fit for the evidence at the time. It was only once electrons had been discovered and orbital theory was developed that scientists came up with the modern 'delocalised model', which explains the behaviour of benzene better than Kekulé's model. See page 84.

Evidence Comes From **Lab Experiments**...

1) Results from **controlled experiments** in **laboratories** are **great**.

2) A lab is the easiest place to **control variables** so that they're all **kept constant** (except for the one you're investigating).

3) This means you can draw meaningful **conclusions**.

For example, if you're investigating how temperature affects the rate of a reaction you need to keep everything but the temperature constant, e.g. the pH of the solution, the concentration of the solution, etc.

...But You **Can't** Always do a Lab Experiment

There are things you **can't** study in a lab. And outside the lab controlling the variables is tricky, if not impossible.

- *Are increasing CO_2 emissions causing climate change?*
  There are other variables which may have an effect, such as changes in solar activity. You can't easily rule out every possibility. Also, climate change is a very **gradual process**. Scientists won't be able to tell if their predictions are correct for donkey's years.

- *Does eating food containing trans fatty acids increase the risk of heart disease and strokes?*
  There are always differences between groups of people. The best you can do is to have a **well-designed study** using **matched groups** — **choose two groups** of people (those who eat a lot of trans fats and those who don't) which are **as similar as possible** (same mix of ages, same mix of diets etc.). But you still can't rule out every possibility. Taking newborn identical twins and treating them identically, except for making one consume a lot of trans fats and the other none at all, might be a fairer test, but it would present huge **ethical problems**.

Samantha thought her study was very well designed — especially the fitted bookshelf.

Science Helps to Inform **Decision-Making**

Lots of scientific work eventually leads to **important discoveries** that **could** benefit humankind — but there are often **risks** attached (and almost always **financial costs**).

Society (that's you, me and everyone else) must weigh up the information in order to **make decisions** — about the way we live, what we eat, what we drive, and so on. Information is also used by **politicians** to devise policies and laws.

- Scientific advances mean **hydrogen fuel cells** can now be used to power cars (see page 110). They sound better for the **environment** than conventional engines because their only waste product is **water**. But you need lots of **energy** to produce the **hydrogen** and **oxygen** in the first place, so maybe they're not so good after all.

- Pharmaceutical drugs are really expensive to develop, and drug companies want to make money. So they put most of their efforts into developing drugs that they can sell for a good price. Society has to consider the **cost** of buying new drugs — the **NHS** can't afford the most expensive drugs without **sacrificing** something else.

- **Synthetic polymers** are very useful — they're **cheap** to produce and very **durable**. But they're **hard to dispose of** (they don't break down easily). So we need to make choices about how we can best dispose of plastics (see page 33) and whether we should try to **reduce** the amount that we use, or work to develop more **biodegradeable plastics**.

So there you have it — how science works...

Hopefully these pages have given you a nice intro to how science works, e.g. what scientists do to provide you with 'facts'. You need to understand this, as you're expected to know how science works yourself — for the exam and for life.

Acids, Bases and Bonding

You might think you know what acids and bases are — but don't be too sure. There are quite a few different definitions. The most widely used definition is called the Brønsted-Lowry theory, and that's what this page is about.

Acids are Substances That Can **Give Away Protons**

The Brønsted-Lowry theory says that an acid is a **proton donor**.

1) A proton is an **H⁺ ion** — when a hydrogen atom loses an electron to form an ion, a proton is all that's left.

2) So all Brønsted-Lowry acids must contain **hydrogen**, and be able to release it as an **H⁺ ion**. For example:

> **HCl is an acid** because when the molecule dissolves in water the H–Cl bond breaks, forming H⁺ and Cl⁻ ions — so it's a proton donor.
>
> $$H\text{--}Cl_{(g)} \; + \; (aq) \; \rightarrow \; H^+_{\;(aq)} \; + \; Cl^-_{\;(aq)}$$
>
>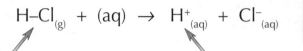
>
> You don't really get H+ ions in solution. They join up with water molecules to form hydroxonium, H_3O^+, ions.
>
> As HCl dissolves in water, the bond holding the H and Cl atoms together breaks...   ...and an H⁺ ion (proton) is released.
>
> **CH₄ isn't an acid**, even though it contains hydrogen, because it doesn't release H⁺ ions.

Bases are Substances That Can **Take Away Protons**

The Brønsted-Lowry theory says that a base is a **proton acceptor**.

1) So bases are the opposite of acids — instead of giving out H⁺ ions they take them away from other substances.

2) **Ammonia, NH₃,** is a base since it can take a H⁺ from other things to become an ammonium ion, NH_4^+.

> You might have heard that bases release OH⁻ ions in solution. That was the Arrhenius definition. The Brønsted-Lowry definition doesn't contradict this — OH⁻ ions accept H⁺ ions and form water. One problem with the Arrhenius definition though is that it means a substance can't be a base unless it's in solution.

Acids and Bases React Together by **Transferring Protons**

1) Since acids are proton donors and bases are proton acceptors, they're ideally suited to reacting together.

2) During an **acid-base reaction**, H⁺ ions move from the acid to the base.

> When the gases HCl and NH₃ meet, a proton moves from HCl to NH₃, forming the ions NH_4^+ and Cl⁻. These make ammonium chloride, NH₄Cl — this is seen as a cloud of white smoke.
>
>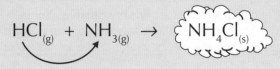
>
> $$HCl_{(g)} \; + \; NH_{3(g)} \; \rightarrow \; NH_4Cl_{(s)}$$
>
> A proton moves from acid to base.

Acids, Bases and Bonding

You learnt all about bonding at AS — sadly you still need to know it at A2. Here's a quick recap of ionic and metallic:

Ionic Bonding is When Ions are Stuck Together by Electrostatic Attraction

1) Ions are formed when **electrons** are **transferred** from one atom to another.
   Atoms want to lose or gain electrons so that they have a **full outer shell**.

Ionic bonding happens between a metal and a non-metal.

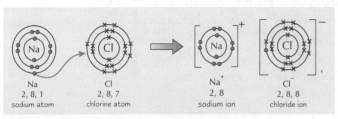

Na
2, 8, 1
sodium atom

Cl
2, 8, 7
chlorine atom

Na⁺
2, 8
sodium ion

Cl⁻
2, 8, 8
chloride ion

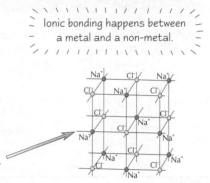

2) **Electrostatic attraction** holds positive and negative ions together in a lattice.

Metals Have Giant Structures

Metal elements exist as **giant metallic lattice structures**.

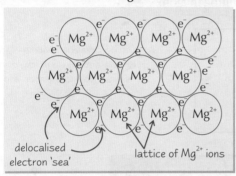

delocalised electron 'sea'

lattice of Mg^{2+} ions

1) In metallic lattices, the electrons in the outermost shell of the metal atoms are **delocalised** — they're free to move. This leaves a **positive metal ion**, e.g. Na^+, Mg^{2+}, Al^{3+}.

2) The positive metal ions are **attracted** to the delocalised negative electrons. They form a lattice of closely packed positive ions in a **sea** of delocalised electrons — this is **metallic bonding**.

Practice Questions

Q1 What is transferred from acids to bases when they react together?

Q2 What is transferred from one atom to another when an ionic bond forms?

Exam Questions

1 Sodium ethoxide is a white, ionic solid.
  When it is added to water, the ethoxide ion reacts according to the following equation:

$$C_2H_5O^-_{(aq)} + H_2O_{(l)} \rightarrow C_2H_5OH_{(aq)} + OH^-_{(aq)}$$

  This is an acid-base reaction.
  a) Identify the base and explain your answer in terms of the Brønsted-Lowry theory of acids and bases. [2 marks]
  b) What is the role of water in this reaction? Explain how you know. [2 marks]

2 This question is about the definition of acids and bases.
  a) What is the Brønsted-Lowry definition of acids and of bases? [2 marks]
  b) According to some acid-base theories, aluminium chloride ($AlCl_3$) is an acid.
     Could $AlCl_3$ be an acid according to the Brønsted-Lowry theory? Explain your answer. [2 marks]
  c) In these reactions, say whether water is acting as an acid, a base, or neither according to the Brønsted-Lowry theory.
     i) $HNO_3 + H_2O \rightarrow H_3O^+ + NO_3^-$ [1 mark]
     ii) $NH_3 + H_2O \rightarrow NH_4^+ + OH^-$ [1 mark]

A chemist's last words — now which flask was my mineral water in?...

So remember — according to Mr Brønsted and Mr Lowry, acids give away protons and bases accept them. You need to be able to look at a reaction and say which substance is the acid and which is the base. And in an exam, both substances will almost definitely have hydrogen in, so it won't be completely obvious. There's more on this type of acid and base in Unit 5.

More on Bonding

Here's a quick whizz through covalent bonding, to make sure you remember exactly what's what.

Molecules *are Groups of Atoms* Bonded *Together*

A molecule is held together by **covalent bonds**.

In covalent bonding, two atoms **share** electrons, so they've **both** got full outer shells of electrons. Both the positive nuclei are attracted **electrostatically** to the shared electrons.

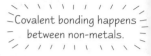
Covalent bonding happens between non-metals.

Water, H_2O

Ammonia, NH_3

Oxygen, O_2

Dative Covalent *Bonding is Where* Both Electrons *Come From* One Atom

In a **dative** (or **coordinate**) covalent bond, one atom donates **both electrons** to a bond.

The **ammonium ion** (NH_4^+) is formed by dative covalent bonding — the nitrogen atom in an ammonia molecule **donates a pair of electrons** to a proton (H^+).

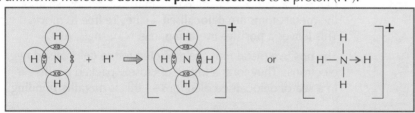

Dative covalent bonding is shown in diagrams by an arrow, pointing away from the 'donor' atom.

Some Covalently *Bonded Substances Have* Giant Structures

Carbon is one element that can form giant networks of **covalently** bonded atoms.

<u>Graphite</u> — each carbon forms 3 covalent bonds. The spare electrons are free to move through the layers and can carry a current. The layers are held together by intermolecular forces (see p27).

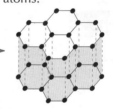

<u>Diamond</u> — each carbon forms 4 strong covalent bonds.

Learn the Properties *of the Main Substance Types*

Bonding	Examples	Melting and boiling points	Typical state at STP	Does solid conduct electricity?	Does liquid conduct electricity?	Is it soluble in water?
Ionic	NaCl $MgCl_2$	High	Solid	No (ions are held firmly in place)	Yes (ions are free to move)	Yes
Simple molecular (covalent)	CO_2 H_2O I_2	Low (have to overcome van der Waals forces or hydrogen bonds, not covalent bonds)	Sometimes solid, usually liquid or gas (water is liquid because it has hydrogen bonds)	No	No	Depends on how polarised the molecule is
Giant molecular (covalent)	Diamond Graphite SiO_2	High	Solid	No (except graphite)	— (will generally sublime)	No
Metallic	Fe Mg Al	High	Solid	Yes (delocalised electrons)	Yes (delocalised electrons)	No

More on Bonding

Electron Pairs **Repel** Each Other

The shape of a molecule (or molecular ion) depends on the **number of electron pairs** in the outer shell of the central atom.

1) Electron pairs **repel** each other as much as they can and different **types** of electron pair repel more than others.

2) Lone pairs repel **more** than bonding pairs. So, the **greatest** angles are between **lone pairs** of electrons, and bond angles between bonding pairs are often **reduced** because they are pushed together by lone-pair repulsion.

| Lone-pair/lone-pair bond angles are the biggest. | Lone-pair/bonding-pair bond angles are the second biggest. | Bonding-pair/bonding-pair bond angles are the smallest. |

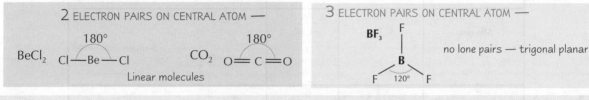

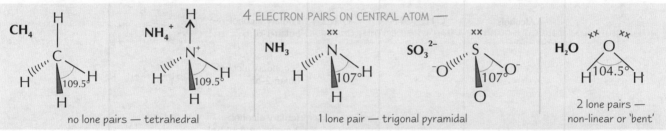

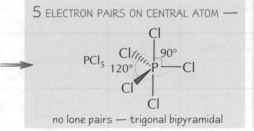

Some atoms can have more than eight bonding electrons.

For example, in PCl$_5$, phosphorus has 10 electrons (5 pairs). And in SF$_6$, sulfur has 12 electrons (6 pairs) in its outermost shell.

Practice Questions

Q1 What's the difference between a covalent bond and a dative covalent bond?

Q2 Silicon dioxide and carbon dioxide are both covalent compounds. Why do they have very different melting points?

Q3 Name the shape formed by a molecule with 4 electron pairs around its central atom (and no lone-pairs).

Exam Questions

1 The molecule ICl contains a covalent bond.
   a) Showing outer-shell electrons only, draw a 'dot-and-cross' diagram to show the bonding in ICl. [2 marks]
   b) State what a covalent bond is and why forming such bonds makes atoms more stable. [3 marks]
   c) In terms of attractive forces, explain how a covalent bond holds the atoms in molecules
   such as F$_2$ and O$_2$ together. [1 mark]

2 a) The molecules BCl$_3$ and NCl$_3$ both consist of a central atom surrounded by three Cl atoms – but they
   are not the same shape. Predict the shapes of the two molecules and explain why they are different. [3 marks]
   b) Sodium chloride and silicon dioxide consist of different types of giant lattice structure.
   Name the structures and describe a test that you could do to tell them apart. [4 marks]

Do you expect me to talk? No, Mr Bond — I expect you to form molecules...

There's nowt here that you didn't meet at AS. You've just got to make sure it's not been pushed out of your brain by all the new A2 stuff. When you're predicting the shapes of molecules, watch out for lone pairs. It's easy to be fooled into thinking that NH$_3$ must be trigonal planar, but there are four electron pairs on the central nitrogen atom, so it's pyramidal.

Organic Reactions

Organic chemistry is concerned with chemicals built around carbon chains. You might think this restriction would limit the amount that could be said. But no... there's a surprising amount to say about carbon chains. Whoop-di-doo.

You Need to Know the **Homologous Series** from AS...

The organic compounds that you learned about at AS might well come up in A2 exam questions. So here they are. Oh — and you best make sure you know how to name them too.

Name of Homologous Series	General Formula	Functional Group	Examples
Alkanes	C_nH_{2n+2}	None*	2-methylpentane
Alkenes	C_nH_{2n}	C=C	3-methylbut-1-ene
Alcohols	$C_nH_{2n+1}OH$	–OH	Primary alcohol: butan-1-ol Secondary alcohol: butan-2-ol Tertiary alcohol: 2-methylpropan-2-ol
Diols	$C_nH_{2n}(OH)_2$	–OH	ethane-1,2-diol
Ethers	—	–O–	ethyl methyl ether or methoxyethane
Arenes	—	⬡	methylbenzene
Cycloalkanes	C_nH_{2n}	None*	cyclohexane
Halogenoalkanes	—	C–X (X = F, Cl, Br or I)	1,3-dibromopropane

* Strictly speaking, alkanes do have functional groups — the C–C and C–H bonds (all the reactions of alkanes involve one of these). But they're so unreactive that they're not normally considered as functional groups.

Handy Hints for Naming Organic Compounds:

1) Count the carbon atoms in the **longest continuous chain** — this gives you the **stem** e.g. if there's **1 carbon atom**, the stem will be **meth-**, if there are **2 carbon atoms** the stem will be **eth-**, etc.

2) The **main functional group** of the molecule usually gives you the end of the name (the **suffix**) e.g. alkanes end in **-ane**, alkenes end in **-ene**, alcohols end in **-ol**.

3) Number the carbon atoms on the **longest chain**, so that the one with the main functional group attached has the **lowest** number. Write the carbon number that the main functional group is on **before** the suffix e.g. butan-2-ol.

These aren't the only rules. If you're a bit rusty, I'd suggest digging out your AS level notes and having a flick through.

Organic Reactions

...And These Reactions Too

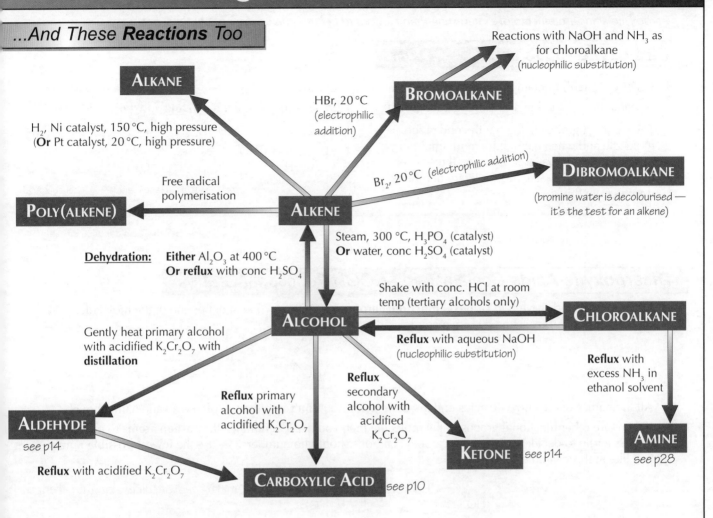

Practice Questions

Q1 What's the functional group in an alkene?

Q2 Name two homologous series whose functional groups contain C–O bonds.

Q3 What is produced when a halogenoalkane reacts with an aqueous solution of sodium hydroxide?

Q4 Name the organic product in the reaction of ethene with bromine.

Exam Questions

1   An organic compound has the molecular formula C_3H_6O. The structural formula is thought to be either A or B shown below:

   A: $CH_2=CHCH_2OH$ **B: CH_3CH_2CHO**

   a) Name all of the functional groups in molecule A.   [2 marks]
   b) Describe a test that would give a positive result with compound A but not with compound B.
      State what reagent you would use and the results of the test with compound A.   [2 marks]

2   1,2-dibromoethane can be made from ethanol by the following series of reactions:

   Ethanol   →   X   →   1,2-dibromoethane

   a) X is produced by dehydration of ethanol.
      Name X and state the reagents and conditions required to produce it from ethanol.   [3 marks]
   b) What reagents and condition are required to convert X into 1,2-dibromoethane?   [2 marks]

Chemist / goalkeeper wanted — must have fast reactions and good refluxes...

I hope this stuff is all coming flooding back to you — even oozing back will do. You should have detailed notes on all of these homologous series and reactions in your AS notes, so do check back for extra details. If you're given a structural formula in an exam question, it often helps to draw out the displayed formula — this makes the functional groups clearer.

Carboxylic Acids and Esters

Carboxylic acids are much more interesting than cardboard boxes — as you're about to discover...

Carboxylic Acids contain –COOH

Carboxylic acids contain the **carboxyl** functional group **–COOH**.

To name them, you find and name the longest alkane chain, take the '-e' off the end and add '**–oic acid'**.

The carboxyl group's always at the **end** of the molecule and when naming it's more important than other functional groups — so all the other functional groups in the molecule are numbered starting from this carbon.

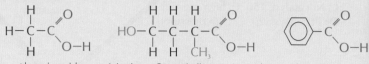

ethanoic acid   4-hydroxy-2-methylbutanoic acid   benzoic acid

Benzoic acid can also be called benzene carboxylic acid.

Dicarboxylic Acids Contain Two –COOH Functional Groups

1) Dicarboxylic acids have **two carboxyl functional groups** (-COOH) — one at either end of the molecule. The smallest dicarboxylic acid is ethanedioic acid:

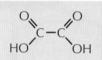

2) All the names of dicarboxylic acids end in **–dioic acid**. You **don't** lose the '-e' off the alkane name though.

3) If there are other functional groups in the molecule then you need to **number the carbon atoms** to name it. There's a rule to decide which of the carboxyl carbons should be number 1 — use the **lowest possible numbers** just like in this example.

$$\underset{HO}{\overset{O}{\diagdown}}C-CH_2-CH_2-\overset{2}{\underset{\underset{CH_3}{|}}{C}}H-\overset{1}{C}\overset{\diagup O}{\diagdown}OH$$ This is **2-methylpentanedioic acid** (not **4-methyl**)

Carboxylic Acids are Weak Acids

Carboxylic acids are **weak acids** — in water they partially dissociate into a **carboxylate ion** and an **H⁺ ion**.

The equilibrium lies to the left because most of the molecules don't dissociate.

$$R-C\overset{\diagup O}{\underset{O-H}{\diagdown}} \rightleftharpoons R-C\overset{\diagup O}{\underset{O^-}{\diagdown}} + H^+$$

carboxylic acid   carboxylate ion

Carboxylic Acids React with Alkalis and Carbonates to Form Salts

1) Carboxylic acids are **neutralised** by **aqueous alkalis** to form **salts** and **water**.

Salts of carboxylic acids are called carboxylates and their names end with –oate.

ethanoic acid   sodium ethanoate

$$CH_3COOH_{(aq)} + NaOH_{(aq)} \rightarrow CH_3COONa_{(aq)} + H_2O_{(l)}$$

2) Carboxylic acids react with **carbonates, CO₃²⁻,** or **hydrogencarbonates, HCO₃⁻,** to form a **salt, carbon dioxide** and **water**.

In these reactions, carbon dioxide fizzes out of the solution.

ethanoic acid   sodium ethanoate

$$2CH_3COOH_{(aq)} + Na_2CO_{3(s)} \rightarrow 2CH_3COONa_{(aq)} + H_2O_{(l)} + CO_{2(g)}$$

$$CH_3COOH_{(aq)} + NaHCO_{3(s)} \rightarrow CH_3COONa_{(aq)} + H_2O_{(l)} + CO_{2(g)}$$

Carboxylic Acids and Esters

Esters have the Functional Group –COO–

Esters are made from carboxylic acids and alcohols. Their names have two parts —
the first bit comes from the **alcohol** and the second bit from the **carboxylic acid**.

Just to confuse you, the name's written the opposite way round from the structural and displayed formulae.

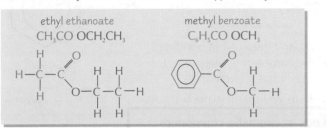

ethyl ethanoate
$CH_3CO\ OCH_2CH_3$

methyl benzoate
$C_6H_5CO\ OCH_3$

1-methylpropyl methanoate
$HCO\ OCH(CH_3)CH_2CH_3$

When numbering the carbons to name
the attached groups, count out from
the ester link in the middle. So here,
the methyl group's on carbon 1.

Alcohols React with Carboxylic Acids to form Esters

If you heat a **carboxylic acid** with an **alcohol** in the presence of an **acid catalyst**, you get an ester.
It's called an **esterification** reaction. Concentrated sulfuric acid is usually used as the acid catalyst.

This oxygen comes from the alcohol.

carboxylic acid   alcohol   ester   water

It's also a condensation
reaction as it releases water.

Here's how ethanoic acid reacts with ethanol to make the ester, ethyl ethanoate:

ethanoic acid   ethanol   ethyl ethanoate   water

Practice Questions

Q1 What is the name of the –COOH functional group?

Q2 How could you use sodium carbonate as a test for carboxylic acids?

Q3 Which two functional groups can be reacted together to form an ester?

Exam Questions

1 Ethyl butanoate, $CH_3CH_2CH_2COOCH_2CH_3$, is used as an artificial pineapple flavouring in drinks.

a) What is the name of the homologous series to which ethyl butanoate belongs?   [1 mark]

b) Ethyl butanoate can be formed by reacting an alcohol with a carboxylic acid.
   i)   Name the alcohol.   [1 mark]
   ii)   Draw the **displayed** formula of the carboxylic acid and name it.   [3 marks]
   iii) When the alcohol reacts with the carboxylic acid, two products are formed –
         ethyl butanoate and one other. What is the other product?   [1 mark]

2 The plastic PET (also called Terylene®) is made by heating
   together benzene-1,4-dicarboxylic acid and molecule A:

   a) Name molecule A.   [1 mark]

   b) Benzene-1,4-dicarboxylic acid reacts with excess sodium hydroxide to form a salt and water.
      Write an equation for this reaction.   [2 marks]

Ethyl, Ester and a whole lot of acid — what a s-COO-p...

*'Esters' is where molecular structures get rather complicated. And to make matters worse, you've got to remember which
bit of the ester came from the alcohol and which bit came from the carboxylic acid. Eeeee... They don't have to learn this
type of stuff in Media Studies. There is something pleasingly symmetrical about those dicarboxylic acids though...*

Phenols

Phenols are the aromatic versions of alcohols. Don't drink them though — they'd get your insides a bit too clean. Aromatic compounds have benzene rings, so first of all you've got to make sure you know what these are...

Benzene has a Ring of Delocalised Electrons

1) The symbol for **benzene** (C_6H_6) is shown on the right. At each point on the hexagon is a carbon atom.

   There's more on benzene and its structure on page 84.

2) Each carbon has one spare **electron** in its outer shell, which isn't involved in bonding to another atom. These electrons are **delocalised** around the carbon ring (they're not attached to any particular carbon atom). That's why the symbol has a **circle** in it.

   Delocalisation makes benzene more **stable** (less reactive) than you might expect.

> Compounds with **benzene ring structures** are called **arenes**, or **aromatic compounds**. All other organic compounds (e.g. alkanes and alkenes) are called **aliphatic compounds**.

benzene

This is a skeletal formula — the C and H atoms aren't shown.

Phenols Have Benzene Rings with –OH Groups Attached

Phenol has the formula C_6H_5OH. Other phenols have various groups attached to the benzene ring:

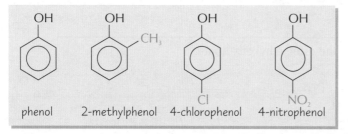

phenol   2-methylphenol   4-chlorophenol   4-nitrophenol

Number the carbons starting from the one with the –OH group.

I see benzene rings everywhere — am I going nuts?

Test for Phenol Using Iron(III) Chloride Solution

If you add phenol to **iron(III) chloride solution** and shake, you get a **purple** solution. Other phenols give other colours.

Iron(III) chloride + phenol

SHAKE

Phenol Dissolves to Form a Weakly Acidic Solution

1) Phenol dissolves a little bit in water, as the hydroxyl group's able to form **hydrogen bonds** with water molecules.

2) The solution formed is **weakly acidic** because phenol dissociates in water to form a **phenoxide ion** and an **H^+ ion**:

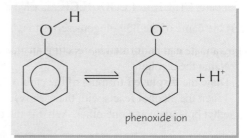

phenoxide ion

Phenol Reacts with Strong Bases to form Salts

1) Phenol reacts with **sodium hydroxide solution** at room temperature to form **sodium phenoxide** and **water**. The hydrogen ion on the phenol is removed by the OH^- ion.

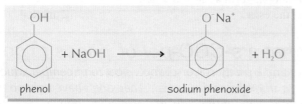

phenol   sodium phenoxide

2) Phenol **doesn't react** with **sodium carbonate** solution though — sodium carbonate is not a strong enough base to remove the hydrogen ion from phenol.

Phenols

Acyl Chlorides have the Functional Group –COCl

1) Acyl chlorides react with phenols, so you need to know what they are.
2) **Acyl (or acid) chlorides** have the functional group **COCl** — their general formula is $C_nH_{2n-1}OCl$.
3) All their names end in **–oyl chloride**.

ethanoyl chloride   4-hydroxy-2,3-dimethylpentanoyl chloride

Like a carboxylic acid or an ester, the carbon atoms are numbered from the end with the acyl functional group.

Acyl Chlorides React with Phenols to Form Esters

The usual way of making an **ester** is to react an alcohol with a carboxylic acid (see page 11).
Phenols react **very** slowly with carboxylic acids though, so it's faster to use an **acyl chloride**, such as ethanoyl chloride.

Ethanoyl chloride reacts slowly with phenol at room temperature, producing the ester **phenyl ethanoate** and **hydrogen chloride** gas.

ethanoyl chloride   phenyl ethanoate

Practice Questions

Q1 How can you test a compound to see if it is a phenol?

Q2 Are phenols acidic, alkaline or neutral? Explain your answer.

Q3 Why are phenols reacted with acyl chlorides instead of carboxylic acids to make esters?

Exam Questions

1 Salicylic acid is a precursor of aspirin.
 Aspirin is produced when the phenol group of salicylic acid reacts
 with ethanoyl chloride. This is an esterification reaction.

salicylic acid

 a) Draw the structure of aspirin. [1 mark]

 b) What other product is formed in this reaction? [1 mark]

2 Carboxylic acids and phenols both have pH values below 7, and both react with strong bases such as sodium hydroxide.
 Describe **two** tests that could be used to tell a phenol and a carboxylic acid apart.

 In your answer you should state the reagents you would use in each test and the
 results that you would expect to see for both the carboxylic acid and the phenol. [6 marks]

3 A food chemist wishes to make the ester phenyl ethanoate, $CH_3COOC_6H_5$, to test as an artificial flavouring.

 a) The chemist first tries to make the ester using a carboxylic acid. Name the carboxylic acid that
 he should use and a compound that he should try to react this with to make phenyl ethanoate. [2 marks]

 b) The reaction involving the carboxylic acid is very slow, so the chemist tries to find a more reactive compound
 that will produce the same ester.
 i) Give the structural formula and name of a suitable compound. [1 mark]
 ii) In this reaction, what else would be produced apart from the ester? [2 marks]

It's the phenol countdown — only... let's see... rather a lot of pages to go...

Some nice straightforward chemistry here — some funky molecules and a pretty colour change. You can't complain too much. You just have to knuckle down and learn it. If you're asked to draw the product of a reaction between a phenol and an acyl chloride, remember — whatever else is attached, it's the H from the OH attached to the benzene ring that falls off.

Aldehydes and Ketones

Aldehydes and ketones are both carbonyl compounds. They've got their carbonyl groups in different positions though.

Aldehydes *and* Ketones *contain a* Carbonyl Group

Aldehydes and ketones are **carbonyl compounds** — they contain the **carbonyl** functional group, **C=O**.

Aldehydes have their carbonyl group at the **end** of the carbon chain. Their names end in **–al**.

Ketones have their carbonyl group in the middle of the carbon chain. Their names end in **–one**, and often have a number to show which **carbon** the carbonyl group is on.

R represents a carbon chain of any length.

methanal   propanal

propanone   pentan-2-one

Aldehydes and Ketones are Made by Oxidising Alcohols

1) If you **gently heat** a **primary alcohol** with an oxidising agent, you make an **aldehyde**.

   Acidified potassium dichromate(VI) is usually used as the oxidising agent.

   Aldehydes easily oxidise further to make **carboxylic acids**, so you've got to **distil** the aldehyde out of the reaction as soon as it's formed to stop it oxidising further.

   primary alcohol   aldehyde   carboxylic acid

   $+ H_2O$

2) You can reflux (see below) a **secondary alcohol** with an oxidising agent to make a **ketone**.

   Ketones are very difficult to oxidise further — so you don't have to worry about oxidising it too far.

   secondary alcohol   ketone

   $+ H_2O$

   R and R' are two (possibly different) carbon chains.

Refluxing *Makes Sure You Don't Lose Any* Volatile *Organic Substances*

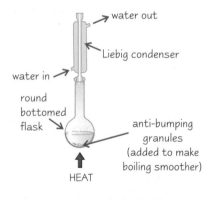

water out

Liebig condenser

water in

round bottomed flask

anti-bumping granules (added to make boiling smoother)

HEAT

1) **Organic reactions** are slow and the substances are usually **flammable** and **volatile** (they've got **low boiling points**). If you stick them in a beaker and heat them with a Bunsen burner they'll **evaporate** or **catch fire** before they have **time to react**.

2) You can **reflux** a reaction to get round this problem.

3) The mixture's **heated in a flask** fitted with a **vertical Liebig condenser** — this condenses the vapours and **recycles** them back into the flask, giving them **time to react**.

4) The **heating** is usually **electrical** — hot plates, heating mantles, or electrically controlled water baths are normally used. This **avoids naked flames** that might ignite the compounds.

Volatile Liquids Can be Purified by Distillation

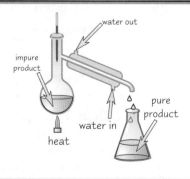

water out

impure product

pure product

water in

heat

1) Distillation is used to **separate** a liquid from any impurities, such as unreacted starting materials, other products, catalysts, etc.

2) You heat the impure liquid in a flask fitted with a thermometer and a **condenser**.

3) When the liquid you want **boils** (this is when the thermometer is at the boiling point of the liquid), you place a flask at the open end of the condenser ready to collect your product.

4) When the thermometer shows the temperature is changing, put another flask at the end of the condenser because a **different liquid** is about to be delivered.

Aldehydes and Ketones

Hydrogen Cyanide will React with Carbonyls by Nucleophilic Addition

Hydrogen cyanide reacts with carbonyl compounds to produce **cyanohydrins** (molecules with a CN and an OH group). It's a **nucleophilic addition reaction** — a **nucleophile** attacks the molecule, causing an extra group to be **added**.

Hydrogen cyanide's a **weak acid** — it partially dissociates in water to form H^+ ions and CN^- ions.

$$HCN \rightleftharpoons H^+ + CN^-$$

1) The CN^- group **attacks** the partially positive carbon atom and **donates** a pair of electrons. Two electrons from the double bond transfer to the oxygen.

2) H^+ (from either hydrogen cyanide or water) bonds to the oxygen to form the **hydroxyl group** (OH).

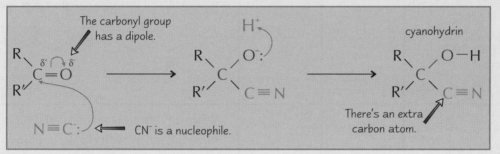

The carbonyl group has a dipole.

cyanohydrin

Cyanohydrins are also known as hydroxynitriles.

CN^- is a nucleophile.

There's an extra carbon atom.

Watch out — hydrogen cyanide is a **highly poisonous gas**, so the reaction needs to be carried out in a **fume cupboard**.

Practice Questions

Q1 What is the difference between an aldehyde and a ketone?

Q2 What two pieces of equipment are used to reflux a reacting mixture?

Q3 Name the mechanism by which a CN^- ion reacts with an aldehyde or ketone.

Exam Questions

1 Ethanol is heated with acidified potassium dichromate.
As soon as the product forms it is removed from the reaction mixture by distillation.

   a) Name the type of reaction that is occurring. [1 mark]

   b) Name the product and the functional group that it contains. [2 marks]

   c) i) Explain why it is important that the product is not left in the reaction mixture when it forms. [2 marks]

   ii) Why is this not a problem when the same reaction is performed with propan-2-ol in place of ethanol? [2 marks]

2 An alcohol, **X**, is refluxed with an oxidising agent to form compound **Y**, which when reacted with HCN forms 2-hydroxy-2-methylbutanenitrile (shown right). Draw the displayed formulae and give the names of **X** and **Y**.

$$H-\overset{\overset{\displaystyle H}{|}}{\underset{\underset{\displaystyle H}{|}}{C}}-\overset{\overset{\displaystyle H}{|}}{\underset{\underset{\displaystyle H}{|}}{C}}-\overset{\overset{\displaystyle CH_3}{|}}{\underset{\underset{\displaystyle OH}{|}}{C}}-C\equiv N$$

[6 marks]

3 Look at the structural formulae of the carbonyl compounds, **A**, **B** and **C** below.

   A: CH_3CHO **B:** CH_3COCH_3 **C:** $(CH_3)_2CHCHO$

   For each one state
   i) The name of the compound. [3 marks]
   ii) The name of the alcohol that is oxidised to produce the compound. [3 marks]

Aldehydes and ketones need company — they're -al-one...

Make sure you know how aldehydes differ from ketones, what you have to oxidise to get each of them, and what you get if you oxidise aldehydes and ketones themselves. There's a dipole involved in the reaction at the top of this page. Check back to your AS stuff if you've forgotten how dipoles are caused by differences in electronegativities.

Reaction Type and Atom Economy

Like all scientists, chemists just love to categorize things. I bet they even have a separate drawer for 'sparkly trousers'.

Organic Reactions Can be **Grouped Together** into Different Types

There are **five types** of organic reaction that you need to know about:

Reaction Type	Number of Reactant Molecules	Number of Product Molecules	Examples
REARRANGEMENT No atoms are added or removed. The atoms just change the order in which they're connected.	1	1	There aren't any specific ones you need to know at A-level, but this one will give you the idea:
ADDITION Molecules add together. *One of the reactants is likely to have a C=C or C=O double bond.*	2	1	Aldehydes/ketones reacting with HCN (see p15). Alkenes reacting with H_2, Br_2 or HBr. E.g.
SUBSTITUTION One functional group is 'swapped' for another. *In aliphatic compounds –OH, – halogen, –NH$_2$ can exchange. Benzene reactions often involve groups exchanging for a H on the ring.*	2	2	Halogenoalkanes refluxed with NaOH or NH_3. E.g. Tertiary alcohol shaken with HCl. Free-radical chlorination of alkanes.
ELIMINATION Atoms are removed from a molecule. *This usually results in a double bond.*	1	2	Alcohol dehydrated with hot Al_2O_3 or conc H_2SO_4.
CONDENSATION This is addition followed by elimination.	2	2	Carboxylic acids reacting with alcohols to form esters (see p11). Two amino acids reacting to form a dipeptide (see p46).

Make sure you can work out which type a reaction belongs to.

Reaction Type and Atom Economy

Atom Economy is a Measure of the Efficiency of a Reaction

1) Atom economy tells you how wasteful a **reaction** is. It's a measure of the proportion of **reactant atoms** that become part of the **desired product** (rather than by-products) in the **balanced** chemical equation.

2) It's calculated using this formula:

$$\% \text{ atom economy} = \frac{\text{molecular mass of desired product}}{\text{sum of molecular masses of all products}} \times 100$$

This is the same as the "sum of molecular masses of all reactants".

3) Don't muddle this up with **percentage yield** (see p82). Percentage yield tells you how wasteful the **process** is — it's based on how much of the product is lost because of things like reactions not completing or losses during purification.

Some Reaction Types Have Higher Atom Economies than Others

1) Reactions with only **one product** have an atom economy of **100%**. It makes sense — if there's only one product, then **all** of the reactant atoms must end up in the product that you want.

2) Look at the table on the previous page — **rearrangement** and **addition** reactions have only one product, so they've got atom economies of 100%.

3) In **substitution** and **condensation** reactions two reactant molecules form two product molecules. One of these products is going to be a by-product, so the atom economy is going to be less than 100%.

4) **Elimination** reactions have an even lower **atom economy**. This is because atoms are removed from the single reactant molecule and aren't replaced.

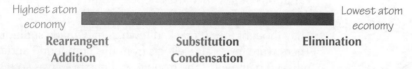

Highest atom economy		Lowest atom economy
Rearrangent	**Substitution**	**Elimination**
Addition	**Condensation**	

Practice Questions

Q1 List five types of organic reaction in order of atom economy. Give an example for each reaction type.

Q2 What is atom economy a measure of?

Q3 Give the equation used to calculate atom economy.

Q4 Why do addition reactions have high atom economies?

Exam Questions

1 Chlorine can be reacted with ethane or ethene to make a chloroalkane:

   Ethane: $C_2H_6 + Cl_2 \rightarrow C_2H_5Cl + HCl$ Ethene: $C_2H_4 + Cl_2 \rightarrow C_2H_4Cl_2$

   a) Classify each reaction above as rearrangement, addition, substitution or elimination.   [2 marks]

   b) Calculate the atom economy of both reactions.   [3 marks]

   c) Explain why one reaction has a lower atom economy than the other.   [2 marks]

2 Maleic anhydride, $C_4H_2O_3$, is a very versatile chemical used to make oil additives, artificial sweeteners, and many other things. It can be prepared industrially by oxidising benzene or but-2-ene. There are very few commercial chemical companies that use the oxidation of benzene any more — during the 1970s and 80s most companies switched from benzene to but-2-ene oxidation.

   Using the equations below, calculate the atom economy for each process and use you answer to suggest why butene oxidation might be the preferred method for producing maleic anhydride.

   Benzene oxidation: $C_6H_6 + 4.5O_2 \rightarrow C_4H_2O_3 + 2CO_2 + 2H_2O$

   Butene oxidation: $C_4H_8 + 3O_2 \rightarrow C_4H_2O_3 + 3H_2O$ [6 marks]

Boost the atom economy — invest in bonds...

Greenness and sustainability is all the rage these days. So atom economy will almost definitely make an appearance in your exam. If things aren't done efficiently, we'll use up all the raw ingredients and make heaps of waste. The waste will end up miles high and we'll all have to go off and live in a spaceship for centuries while robots clean up the planet.

Making Medicines

Medicines are chemicals that alter the way your body functions in order to treat or prevent disease. There are an awful lot of possible chemicals out there, so finding one that does exactly what you want with no bad side-effects is tricky.

Medicines Can be *Improved* by *Changing Their Structure*

When chemists find out that a particular molecule has **medicinal properties**, they try to improve the properties by **tweaking** the molecular structure. A tiny difference in structure can mean a **big** difference in properties.

The development of aspirin shows this really well (you don't need to learn the structures).

For thousands of years, it's been known that chewing the bark of willow trees relieves pain. In the 19th century, scientists discovered that a compound in willow bark was converted to **salicylic acid** when the bark was chewed, and it was this chemical that relieved pain.

Doctors tried giving salicylic acid to their patients — it worked a treat as a painkiller, but had some nasty side effects, such as irritating the mouth and stomach (sometimes leading to ulcers).

salicylic acid

Sodium salicylate — its bite was worse than its bark.

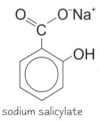

sodium salicylate

Rather than give up on the molecule, chemists tried to make **variations** of it, which they hoped would relieve pain without the side effects.

They thought they'd cracked it when they made **sodium salicylate**. There were fewer side effects from this compound and it still relieved pain well. The trouble was, the taste was so disgusting that it made some patients vomit.

The best variant of salicylic acid turned out to be this one: An **ester functional group** has been added, and this compound is now known as **aspirin**.

Its painkilling effect is still there, but it's much less irritating than salicylic acid and doesn't taste as bad as sodium salicylate.

aspirin

Today *Large Numbers* Of *Similar Molecules are Made and Tested*

1) The aspirin example shows how useful it is to test a load of **similar molecules** to find one that has the **most powerful medicinal properties** and the **least nasty side effects**.

2) In the case of aspirin, not many variations had to be tested before a safe and effective painkiller was found. But, when pharmaceutical companies develop modern drugs, they usually have to test a **HUGE** number of molecules before they find one that might just work as a new medicine.

3) When chemists were trying to find a new medicine in the past, they'd prepare one compound at a time for testing — this could take years.

4) To speed things up, modern drug-discovery chemists use a technique called **combinatorial chemistry**. Instead of making compounds one at a time, they make **hundreds** of similar molecules all at once. This set of compounds is called a **library**. The many chemicals in a library are all tested in the hope that at least one of them will be a safe and effective drug.

Making Medicines

Medicines Go Through *A Lot of Testing* Before They Can Be Sold

Before a drug is licensed to be sold, or prescribed by a doctor, it has to go through a lengthy series of tests.
Clinical trials (tests on human volunteers) are a large part of this series. They're designed to answer three questions:

> **1. Is it safe?**
> If the drug's found to be toxic or to have damaging side effects it's removed from the trials at this stage.

> **2. Does it work?**
> If it doesn't have the medicinal effects that the trials are looking for (such as the ability to reduce pain) then a chemical will be rejected at this stage.

> **3. Is it better than anything currently available?**
> If a chemical is safe and works, researchers then compare it to other medicines that are available. It's only worth marketing a new drug if it offers something that other medicines don't — such as curing problems more quickly, or with fewer side effects.

High Atom Economy Reactions are More Environmentally Friendly

1) Medicine production can be damaging to the environment if it uses **lots of natural resources** or produces **large amounts of waste chemicals** that have to be disposed of.

2) To avoid these environmental problems it's important to try to find reactions with a **high atom economy** (see page 17).

Practice Questions

Q1 Why might it be necessary to change the molecular structure of a drug even if it works well?

Q2 Why do pharmaceutical companies often make large numbers of very similar molecules when they are developing new drugs?

Q3 What is the technique of making large numbers of very similar molecules at once called?

Q4 List three reasons why a drug may fail during clinical trials.

Exam Questions

1 The diagram shows three molecules that were tested as candidates for a drug to relieve high blood pressure and how active (effective at lowering blood pressure) they were.

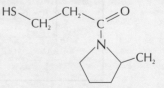

    Molecule 1: medium activity   **Molecule 2: very low activity**   **Molecule 3: very low activity**

a) Write the formulae of any functional groups that you think must be present for the drug to work well. [2 marks]

b) For each of the functional groups that you identified in part a) explain how you can tell that it has to be present for the drug to work. [2 marks]

2 Combinatorial chemistry is used by pharmaceutical companies.

a) Explain what the term 'combinatorial chemistry' means. [2 marks]

b) How does combinatorial chemistry help chemists when they are looking for new drugs? [2 marks]

Laughter isn't the best medicine — it didn't get through the cynical trials...

Developing a new medicine can take years — not only do they have to find suitable molecules, but with some serious diseases, it can take years to find out if the drug is successful. Before clinical trials start, the drugs are tested on animals. But even if they don't seem to do any harm to animals, there's always a risk that they'll act differently in humans...

Infrared Spectra and Chromatography

You met infrared spectra at AS, and I bet you've bumped into chromatography before. But do learn all these A2 details.

Infrared Spectroscopy Lets You Identify Organic Molecules

1) In infrared (IR) spectroscopy, a beam of **IR radiation** goes through the sample.
2) The IR energy is absorbed by the **bonds** in the molecules, increasing their **vibrational** energy.
3) **Different bonds** absorb **different wavelengths**. Bonds in different **places** in a molecule absorb different wavelengths too — so the O–H group in an **alcohol** and the O–H in a **carboxylic acid** absorb different wavelengths.
4) This table shows what **frequencies** different groups absorb:

This tells you what the trough on the graph will look like.

Functional group	Where it's found	Frequency/ Wavenumber (cm^{-1})	Type of absorption
O–H	alcohols	3200 – 3750	strong, broad
O–H	carboxylic acids	2500 – 3300	medium, very broad
C–O	alcohols, carboxylic acids and esters	1100 – 1310	strong, sharp
C=O	aldehydes, ketones, carboxylic acids and esters	1680 – 1800	strong, sharp
C=O	amides	1630 – 1700	medium
C=C	alkenes	1620 – 1680	medium, sharp
N–H	primary amines	3300 – 3500	medium to strong
N–H	amides	about 3500	medium

O–H groups tend to have broad absorptions — it's because they take part in hydrogen bonding.

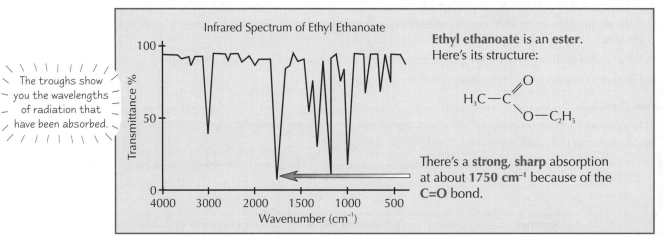

The troughs show you the wavelengths of radiation that have been absorbed.

Infrared Spectrum of Ethyl Ethanoate

Ethyl ethanoate is an **ester**. Here's its structure:

$$H_3C - C \underset{O-C_2H_5}{\overset{O}{<}}$$

There's a **strong, sharp** absorption at about **1750 cm^{-1}** because of the **C=O** bond.

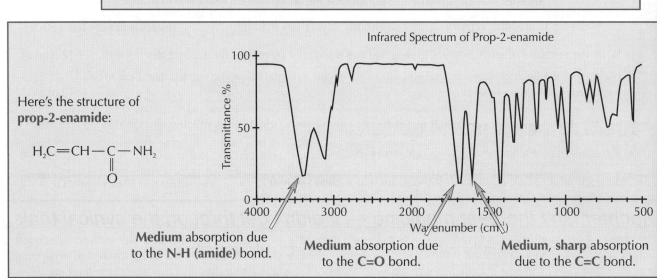

Here's the structure of **prop-2-enamide**:

$$H_2C = CH - \underset{\underset{O}{\|}}{C} - NH_2$$

Infrared Spectrum of Prop-2-enamide

Medium absorption due to the **N-H (amide)** bond.

Medium absorption due to the **C=O** bond.

Medium, sharp absorption due to the **C=C** bond.

Infrared Spectra and Chromatography

Molecules can be Separated and Identified Using **Chromatography**

Chromatography is used in chemistry to separate mixtures of molecules. There are many different forms of chromatography — but they all involve a **mobile phase** (a liquid or gas) that moves over a second material called the **stationary phase** (which doesn't move).

Thin-Layer Chromatography is a Simple Way of Separating Mixtures

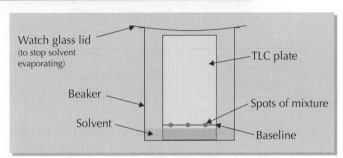

1) In thin layer chromatography (TLC), the **stationary phase** is a thin layer of **silica (silicon dioxide)** or **alumina (aluminium oxide)** fixed to a glass or metal plate.

2) A line is drawn **in pencil** near the bottom of the TLC plate (the baseline) and a small drop of each mixture to be separated is put on the line.

3) The plate is placed in a beaker with a small volume of solvent (this is the **mobile phase**). The solvent level must be **below** the baseline.

4) The beaker is left until the solvent has moved almost to the top of the plate. The plate is then removed from the beaker and allowed to dry. Before it's evaporated you should mark how far the solvent travelled up the plate (this line is called the **solvent front**).

5) As it moves up the plate, the solvent will carry the substances in the mixture with it — but some chemicals will be carried **faster** than others and so travel further up the plate.

6) You can use the **positions of the chemicals** to identify what the chemicals are.

Colourless Chemicals are Revealed Using UV Light or Iodine

1) If the chemicals in the mixture are **coloured** (such as the dyes that make up an ink) then you'll see them as a **set of coloured dots** at different heights on the TLC plate...

... something like this:

2) But if there are **colourless chemicals** in the mixture, you need to find a way of making them **visible**. Here are two ways:

> Many TLC plates have a special **fluorescent dye** added to the silica or alumina layer that glows when **UV light** shines on it. Where there are spots of chemical on the plate, they cover the fluorescent dye and don't glow. You can put the plate under a **UV lamp** and draw around the dark patches to show where the spots of chemical are.

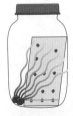

> Another way of showing the position of the spots is to expose them to **iodine vapour** (leaving the plate in a sealed jar with a couple of iodine crystals does the trick). The iodine sticks to the chemicals on the plate and shows up as **purple spots**.

Chromatography can be used to Purify Substances

1) The TLC above separates **very small quantities** of chemicals — ideal for identifying what makes up a mixture.

2) You can also use chromatography to separate **large quantities** of a mixture in an **organic synthesis**.

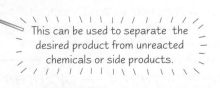

This can be used to separate the desired product from unreacted chemicals or side products.

3) You need larger-scale equipment though, such as a **glass column** (e.g. a burette) packed with silica or alumina (the same **stationary phase** that is used in TLC). You then pour your mixture into the column and run solvent (the **mobile phase**) through it continually.

4) The different chemicals in the mixture move down the column at **different rates**, so they come out at different times, meaning you get pure chemicals.

Infrared Spectra and Chromatography

The **Position** of the Spots on a Plate Can Help to **Identify Substances**

1) If you just want to know **how many** chemicals are present in a mixture, all you have to do is **count the number of spots** that form on the plate.

2) But if you want to find out what each chemical **is**, you can calculate something called an R_f value. The formula for this is:

$$R_f = \frac{\text{distance travelled by spot}}{\text{distance travelled by solvent}}$$

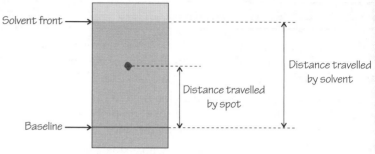

3) R_f values are **always the same** no matter how big the plate is or how far the solvent travels — they're properties of the chemicals in the mixture and so can be used to identify those chemicals.

4) BUT — if the composition of the TLC plate, the solvent, or the temperature change even slightly, you'll get **different R_f values**.

5) It's really hard to keep the conditions identical. So, if you suspect that a mixture contains, say, chlorophyll, it's best to put a spot of chlorophyll on the baseline of the **same plate** as the mixture and run them both at the **same time**.

Practice Questions

Q1 Why do different organic functional groups absorb different frequencies of IR radiation?
Q2 What are the names of the two phases that are used in all forms of chromatography?
Q3 What is the formula for calculating R_f values?
Q4 Apart from identifying substances, what else can chromatography be used for?

Exam Questions

1   A molecule with a molecular mass of 74 gives the following IR spectrum.

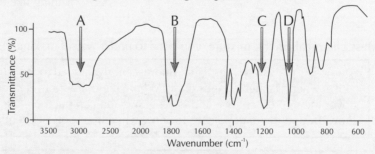

a)   Which functional groups produced the troughs labelled A – D?   [4 marks]
b)   Suggest a molecular formula and a name for this molecule. Explain your suggestions.   [3 marks]

2   The diagram below shows a chromatogram of four known substances (1 to 4) and two unknowns, labelled X and Y. One of the unknowns is pure and the other is a mixture.

a) Which of the unknowns, X or Y is a pure substance?   [1 mark]

b) Suggest which of the known substances (1 to 4) are present in the unknown that is a mixture. Explain your answer.   [2 marks]

c) The solvent front on the chromatogram was measured at 8 cm from the baseline, and Substance 1 travelled 5.6 cm. Calculate the R_f value of Substance 1.   [2 marks]

Cromer-tography — pictures from my holiday in Norfolk...

You don't have to learn any of the IR-spectra data — you'll be given it in your exam. Just make sure you're happy using it. Working out R_f values is easy marks if you remember that it's the distance travelled by the spot divided by distance travelled by the solvent, and not the other way around — it might help to think of it as a fraction (and it'll always be less than 1).

Mass Spectrometry

If you've got some stuff and don't know what it is, don't taste it. Try mass spectrometry instead.
And to give you something to look forward to, there's a little twist at the end.

Mass Spectrometry Can Help to Identify Compounds

1) **Mass spectrometry** can be used to find the **relative molecular mass**, M_r, of a compound.

2) To find the relative molecular mass of a compound you look at the **molecular ion peak** (the **M⁺ peak**) on the spectrum. Molecular ions are formed when molecules have **electrons** knocked off. The mass/charge value of the molecular ion peak is the molecular mass.

Assuming the ion has 1+ charge, which it normally will have.

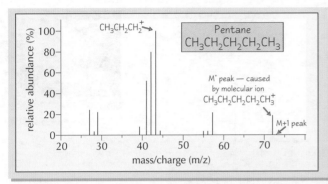

Here's the mass spectrum of pentane. Its M⁺ peak is at 72 — so the compound's M_r is 72.

For most <u>organic compounds</u> the M⁺ peak is the one with the second highest mass/charge ratio. The smaller peak to the right of the M⁺ peak is called the M+1 peak — it's caused by the presence of the carbon isotope ^{13}C.

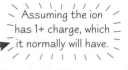

Fragment (consider revising)

Mr Clippy's grammar advice also applies to chemistry.

The Molecular Ion can be Broken into Smaller Fragments

The bombarding electrons make some of the molecular ions break up into **fragments**.
The fragments that are **positive ions** show up as peaks on the mass spectrum, making a **fragmentation pattern**.
Fragmentation patterns are actually pretty cool because you can use them to identify **molecules**, and even their **structure**.

For propane, the molecular ion is $CH_3CH_2CH_2^+$, and the fragments it breaks into include CH_3^+ ($M_r = 15$) and $CH_3CH_2^+$ ($M_r = 29$).

Only the **ions** show up on the mass spectrum — the **free radicals** are 'lost'.

$CH_3CH_2CH_3^+$

$CH_3CH_2\bullet + CH_3^+$
free radical   ion

$CH_3CH_2^+ + \bullet CH_3$
ion   free radical

There are Some Common Fragments You Should Know

So the peaks on mass spectra are due to positive ions. You've got to work out what **ion** could have made each peak from its **m/z value**. (You assume that the m/z value of a peak matches the **mass** of the ion that made it.)
There are some m/z values you should be able to recognise:

Fragment	CH_3^+	$C_2H_5^+$	$C_3H_7^+$	OH^+	$C_6H_5^+$ (phenyl ion)
Molecular Mass	15	29	43	17	77

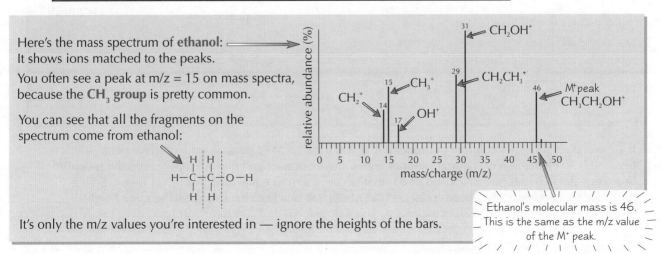

Here's the mass spectrum of **ethanol**:
It shows ions matched to the peaks.

You often see a peak at m/z = 15 on mass spectra, because the **CH₃ group** is pretty common.

You can see that all the fragments on the spectrum come from ethanol:

It's only the m/z values you're interested in — ignore the heights of the bars.

Ethanol's molecular mass is 46. This is the same as the m/z value of the M⁺ peak.

Mass Spectrometry

The **Difference** Between Peaks Tells You About 'Lost' Fragments

1) Just because a free radical fragment is lost it doesn't mean that it can't be detected.

2) If you look at the **difference** between the m/z values of two peaks on a mass spectrum you can work out the mass of the fragment that was 'lost'. This'll be clearer from the example below.

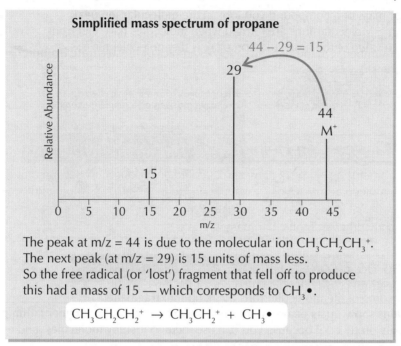

Simplified mass spectrum of propane

$44 - 29 = 15$

The peak at m/z = 44 is due to the molecular ion $CH_3CH_2CH_3^+$.
The next peak (at m/z = 29) is 15 units of mass less.
So the free radical (or 'lost') fragment that fell off to produce
this had a mass of 15 — which corresponds to $CH_3\bullet$.

$$CH_3CH_2CH_2^+ \rightarrow CH_3CH_2^+ + CH_3\bullet$$

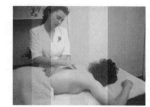

A massage spectrum

3) If a fragment is unstable or doesn't form with a positive charge easily, then there mightn't be a peak for it at all either In such a case, the difference between the m/z values of other peaks will be the **only** evidence for that fragment.

4) Look at the mass spectrum of **bromobenzene** below. There are no really clear peaks at 79 or 81 representing a **Br^+ ion** (remember Br has two isotopes – ^{79}Br and ^{81}Br). **BUT**, the difference between the M^+ ion at 156 and the peak at 77 is **79** — showing that a ^{79}Br atom has been lost.

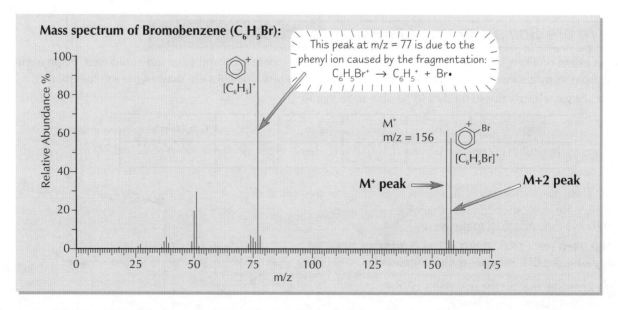

Mass spectrum of Bromobenzene (C_6H_5Br):

$[C_6H_5]^+$

This peak at m/z = 77 is due to the
phenyl ion caused by the fragmentation:
$C_6H_5Br^+ \rightarrow C_6H_5^+ + Br\bullet$

M^+
m/z = 156

$[C_6H_5Br]^+$

M^+ peak ⟹

M+2 peak

5) If a molecule's got either **chlorine** or **bromine** in it you'll get an **M+2 peak** as well as an M^+ peak — this is because both elements have **natural isotopes** with different masses and they all show up on the spectrum. Bromine's got two isotopes, **Br-79** and **Br-81**, that occur in almost **equal amounts** (~ 1:1 ratio). So if a molecule contains bromine, the M^+ peak and the M+2 peak will both have roughly the **same height**.

Mass Spectrometry

High Resolution Mass Spectrometry *Measures Very Accurate Masses*

1) Normally a mass spectrometer records the m/z values as **whole numbers** on a mass spectrum. However, **high-resolution** mass spectrometers can measure m/z values to at least **4 decimal places**.

2) Very **accurate measurements** of m/z values are useful because they allow you to compare elements and compounds using **relative isotopic masses**. The relative isotopic mass of ^{12}C is defined as **exactly 12** — everything else is measured **relative** to this. The relative masses of protons and neutrons are not exactly equal to 1, so **nothing else** apart from ^{12}C has a relative isotopic mass that's a whole number. On the right are a few examples of the **accurate isotopic** ⟹ **masses** of some common atoms.

> $^{1}H = 1.0078$
> $^{12}C = 12.0000$
> $^{14}N = 14.0031$
> $^{16}O = 15.9949$

*This isn't the same as relative atomic mass (which is an average of the masses of all the different isotopes of an element) — these masses are the **relative masses of a single isotope**.*

Accurate Molecular Masses *Can Help in Working out a Formula*

1) In low-resolution mass spectrometry, an M^+ peak at **m/z = 28** could be produced by several different molecules — N_2, CO and C_2H_4 all have molecular masses of 28 when rounded to the nearest whole number.

2) If you use the accurate masses given above, however, you find the three molecules have slightly different molecular masses:

> $N_2 = 28.0062$
> $CO = 27.9949$
> $C_2H_4 = 28.0312$

So a high-resolution mass spectrum could tell you which one of the three it was.

Practice Questions

Q1 Which peak in the mass spectrum of a molecule tells you the M_r?

Q2 What process causes peaks in a mass spectrum to have m/z values less than the molecular mass?

Q3 Why do you sometimes need to look at the difference in m/z value of these peaks?

Q4 Why do you sometimes need high-resolution mass spectrometry?

Exam Questions

1 Below is the mass spectrum of an organic compound, Q.

a) What is the M_r of compound Q? [1 mark]

b) What fragments are the peaks marked X and Y most likely to correspond to? [2 marks]

c) Suggest a structure for compound Q. [1 mark]

d) Why is it unlikely that this compound is an alcohol? [2 marks]

relative abundance

Y

X

0   5   10   15   20   25   30   35   40   45

mass/charge (m/z)

2 The mass spectrum of methyl ethanoate, CH_3COOCH_3, has major peaks at m/z values of 43 and 74.

a) What is the name of the process that creates the species responsible for the peak at 43 units of mass? [1 mark]

b) Write out the formula of the species responsible for the peak at 43. [1 mark]

c) How many units of mass have been lost from the molecular ion to produce the peak at m/z = 43? What species does this provide evidence for? [2 marks]

3 a) Explain why obtaining the M_r value from a low resolution mass spectrometer would not provide enough information to determine whether an unknown compound was propane or ethanal. [1 mark]

b) A high-resolution mass spectrum measures the M_r of a compound to be 44.0261. Use the accurate atomic masses below to decide if it is propane or ethanal. Show your working. [3 marks]

$^{1}H = 1.0078$ $^{12}C = 12.0000$ $^{16}O = 15.9949$

Use the clues, identify the fragments — mass spectrometry my dear Watson...

It's handy if you can learn the molecular masses of those common fragments, but if you forget them, just take a deep breath and work them out from the relative atomic masses of the atoms in the fragment. And don't worry, I haven't forgotten I said there was twist at the end... erm... hydrogen was my sister all along... and all the elements went to live in Jamaica. The End.

Electronegativity and Intermolecular Forces

Pulling power... that's what we're talking about here. The ability to pull electrons.

Some Atoms **Attract** Bonding Electrons More than Other Atoms

The ability to attract the bonding electrons in a covalent bond is called **electronegativity.**

1) Electronegativity is usually measured using the **Pauling scale**
— the higher the value, the more electronegative the element.

2) **Fluorine** is the most electronegative element.
Oxygen, nitrogen and chlorine are also strongly electronegative.

3) In general, electronegativity **increases across periods**
and **decreases down groups** (ignoring the noble gases).

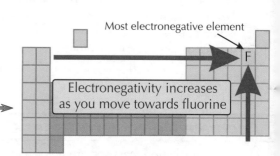

Most electronegative element

Electronegativity increases
as you move towards fluorine

Covalent Bonds may be Polarised by **Differences** in **Electronegativity**

In a covalent bond between two atoms of **different** electronegativities,
the bonding electrons are **pulled towards** the more electronegative atom.
This makes the bond **polar.**

*So most molecules aren't **purely covalent** — they have some **ionic character.***

1) The covalent bonds in diatomic elements (e.g. H_2, Cl_2) are **non-polar** because the atoms have **equal** electronegativities. So the electrons are equally attracted to both nuclei.

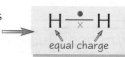

equal charge

2) Some elements, like carbon and hydrogen, have pretty **similar** electronegativities, so bonds between them are essentially **non-polar**.

3) But in a **polar bond**, the difference in electronegativity between the two atoms causes a **dipole**. A dipole is a **difference in charge** between the two atoms caused by a shift in **electron density** in the bond.

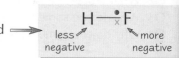

less negative   more negative

4) So what you need to remember is that the **greater the difference** in electronegativity between two atoms, the **more polar** the bond between them will be.

Polar Bonds **Don't** Always Make **Polar Molecules**

Whether a molecule has a **permanent dipole** depends on its **shape** and the **polarity** of its bonds.

1) In a simple molecule, like **hydrogen chloride**, the polar bond gives the whole molecule a permanent dipole — it's a **polar molecule.**

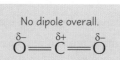

polar

'δ' (delta) means 'slightly', so 'δ+' means 'slightly positive'.

2) A more complicated molecule may have **several polar bonds**. If the polar bonds are arranged so they point in opposite directions, they'll **cancel each other out** — the molecule is **non-polar** overall.

No dipole overall.

$$\overset{\delta-}{O} = \overset{\delta+}{C} = \overset{\delta-}{O}$$

3) If the polar bonds all point in roughly the **same direction**, then the molecule is **polar.**

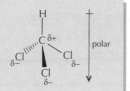

polar

4) **Lone pairs of electrons** on the central atom also have an effect on the overall polarity and may **cancel out** the dipole created by the bonding pairs.

No dipole overall.

Electronegativity and Intermolecular Forces

Intermolecular Forces are **Very Weak**

Intermolecular forces are forces **between** molecules. They're much **weaker** than covalent, ionic or metallic bonds.
There are three types you need to know about:

Permanent Dipole-Permanent Dipole Bonding

The $\delta+$ and $\delta-$ charges on **polar molecules** cause **weak electrostatic forces** of attraction **between** molecules.
The polar molecules in **hydrogen chloride gas** interact in this way.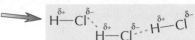

Instantaneous Dipole-Induced Dipole Bonding

These forces cause **all** atoms and molecules to be **attracted** to each other.

1) **Electrons** in charge clouds are always **moving** really quickly.
   At any one moment, the electrons in an atom are likely to be more to one
   side than the other. At this moment, the atom has a **temporary dipole**.

2) This dipole can create **another** temporary dipole in the opposite direction
   on a neighbouring atom. The two dipoles are then **attracted** to each other.

3) Because the electrons are constantly moving, the dipoles are being **created** and **destroyed** all the time.
   This means that dipole-dipole attractions are only temporary — this is the weakest type of intermolecular bonding.

> The **size** and **shape** of molecules affects the **strength** of the **intermolecular forces** between them.
> * In organic molecules, the **longer** the carbon chain is, the **stronger** the induced dipole forces
>   will be, because there's **more molecular surface area** and more **electrons** to interact.
> * Branched-chain molecules can't **pack closely** together, and they also have smaller **molecular
>   surface areas** — so the instantaneous dipole-dipole forces between them are small.

Hydrogen Bonding

1) Hydrogen bonding happens when **hydrogen** is covalently bonded to **fluorine,
   nitrogen or oxygen**. They're all very **electronegative**, so they draw the bonding
   electrons away from the hydrogen atom.

2) The bond is so **polarised** that the hydrogen atoms form weak bonds with **lone
   pairs of electrons** on the fluorine, nitrogen or oxygen atoms of **other molecules**.

3) Hydrogen bonding is the strongest of the three types of intermolecular bonding.

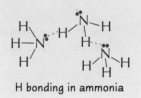

H bonding in ammonia

Practice Questions

Q1 Write a definition of electronegativity.
Q2 Which element is the most electronegative?
Q3 List the three types of intermolecular bond in order of increasing strength.

Exam Questions

1 a) Draw a diagram of two water molecules with a hydrogen bond between them.
   Show the δ^+ and δ^- charges on all the oxygen and hydrogen atoms. [2 marks]
  b) What is the strongest type of intermolecular bonding holding the molecules
   in liquid hydrogen bromide together? [1 marks]

2 a) Which element would you expect to be more electronegative — sulfur or oxygen? Explain your answer. [2 marks]
  b) The structure of sulfur trioxide is shown on the right. Label each of
   the S and O atoms with δ^+ or δ^- to show the polarity of the S=O bonds. [2 marks]
  c) Is the sulfur trioxide molecule polar or non-polar overall?
   Explain your answer. [2 marks]

| |
| O || S Sulfur trioxide O O |

Electronegativity — how I feel when I listen to techno...

*All those electrons being pulled around, left, right and centre. Makes me dizzy just thinking about it. It's all pretty logical
really though — where you have opposite charges, even the tiny ones that you get from differences in electronegativity,
stuff sticks together. And that's how you end up with intermolecular bonding. Delta negative meets delta positive. Ahhh...*

Amines, Amides and Hydrolysis

Amines, meet the amines. They're a nitrogen-containing family.
From the list of bases, they're a page right out of organic chemistry...

Amines are Organic Derivatives of Ammonia

If one or more of the **hydrogens** in **ammonia** (NH_3) is replaced with an organic group, R, you get an **amine**.

Primary amine   Secondary amine   Tertiary amine

R can be any organic group, like CH_3, or a benzene ring.

Holmes thought he'd sniffed out a clue in The Case of the Large Amine Aroma — but it was a red herring.

Small amines smell similar to **ammonia**, with a **slightly 'fishy'** twist.
Larger amines smell very **'fishy'**.

You Can Name Amines Using the Prefix 'Amino-'

1) To name a **primary amine** all you need to do is find and name the **longest alkane chain** in the molecule, and add '**amino-**' to the front.

aminoethane

You can also name amines by adding the suffix '-amine' to the name of the alkyl group the NH_2 is attached to. So this would be ethylamine.

2) If the alkane chain is more than two carbons long, you should include a **number** to show which carbon the amino group is attached to.
Number the carbon chain so that the amino group has the **smallest possible number**.

1-aminopropane   2-aminopentane

3) If the molecule has **two amino groups** then it's a **diamine**, and so you use the prefix '**diamino-**' instead.

1,3-diaminopropane   2,4-diaminohexane

An Amine is a Base Because it has a Lone Pair of Electrons

Amines act as **bases** because they **accept protons**.
An amine has a **lone pair of electrons** on the **nitrogen** atom that can form a **dative covalent (coordinate) bond** with an H+ ion.

Amines React with Acids to Form Salts

You can **neutralise** an amine by reacting it with an **acid** to make an **ammonium salt**.
For example, **aminoethane** reacts with **hydrochloric** acid to form ethylammonium chloride:

$$CH_3CH_2NH_2 + HCl \rightarrow CH_3CH_2NH_3^+Cl^-$$

Amides Contain a Carbonyl Group

Amides contain the functional group $-CONH_2$.
The **carbonyl group** pulls electrons away from the rest of the group, so amides behave differently from amines.

amide   N-substituted amide

one of the hydrogens is replaced with an alkyl group

Amines, Amides and Hydrolysis

Amines can be **Acylated** to form **N-substituted Amides**

Acylation is when an **acyl group**, $R-C\overset{O}{\diagdown}$, is substituted for a **hydrogen atom**.

When an **amine** reacts with an **acyl chloride**, an H atom from the NH_2 group is swapped for the acyl group to give an **N-substituted amide** (see page 28).
The hydrochloric acid formed will react with any excess amine to form a **salt**, as in the equation on page 28.

$$H_3C-C\overset{O}{\underset{Cl}{\diagdown}} + CH_3NH_2 \longrightarrow H_3C-C\overset{O}{\underset{NHCH_3}{\diagdown}} + HCl$$

ethanoyl chloride   aminoethane   N-methylethanamide

Amides can be **Hydrolysed** Under **Acidic** or **Basic** Conditions

To **hydrolyse** an amide you can:

Heat it with **dilute acid** to get a **carboxylic acid** and an **ammonium salt**...

$$H_3C-C\overset{O}{\underset{NH_2}{\diagdown}} + H_2O + HCl \longrightarrow H_3C-C\overset{O}{\underset{OH}{\diagdown}} + NH_4Cl$$

Ethanamide   Ethanoic acid

...or heat it with a **dilute alkali** to get a **carboxylate ion** and **ammonia gas given off**.

$$H_3C-C\overset{O}{\underset{NH_2}{\diagdown}} + NaOH \longrightarrow H_3C-C\overset{O}{\underset{O^-Na^+}{\diagdown}} + NH_3$$

Ethanamide   Sodium ethanoate

Esters are **Hydrolysed** to Form **Alcohols**

The **esters** are another group of molecules that can hydrolysed by using either **acid** or **alkali**.
With both types of hydrolysis you get an **alcohol**, but the second product in each case is different.

ACID HYDROLYSIS

Acid hydrolysis splits the ester into an **acid** and an **alcohol** — it's just the **reverse** of the esterification reaction on page 11.

You have to **reflux** the ester with a **dilute acid**, such as hydrochloric or sulfuric.

For example:

$$\text{ethyl ethanoate} + H_2O \underset{reflux}{\overset{H^+}{\rightleftharpoons}} \text{ethanoic acid} + \text{ethanol}$$

ethyl ethanoate   ethanoic acid   ethanol

These conditions might be a bit too basic...

As it's a reversible reaction, you need to use lots of water to push the equilibrium over to the right.

BASE HYDROLYSIS

This time you have to **reflux** the ester with a **dilute alkali**, such as sodium hydroxide.
You get a carboxylic acid salt and an alcohol.

For example:

$$\text{ethyl ethanoate} + NaOH \underset{reflux}{\rightleftharpoons} \text{sodium ethanoate} + \text{ethanol}$$

ethyl ethanoate   sodium ethanoate   ethanol

Amines, Amides and Hydrolysis

Organic Solids can be Purified by Recrystallisation

If the product of an organic reaction is a solid, then the simplest way of purifying it is a process called **recrystallisation**.

First you dissolve your solid in a solvent to make a **saturated** solution. Then you let it cool. As the solution cools, the solubility of the product falls. When it reaches the point where it can't stay in solution, it starts to form crystals. Here's how it's done:

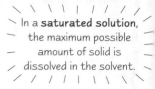

In a **saturated solution**, the maximum possible amount of solid is dissolved in the solvent.

1) **Very hot solvent** is added to the **impure** solid until it **just** dissolves – it's really important not to add too much solvent.

2) This should give a **saturated solution** of the **impure product**.

3) This solution is left to **cool** down **slowly**. **Crystals** of the **product** form as it cools.

4) The **impurities** stay in solution. They're present in much smaller amounts than the product, so they'd take much longer to crystallise out.

5) The crystals are removed by **filtration** and **washed** with ice-cold solvent. Then they are dried — leaving you with crystals of your product that are **much purer** than the original solid.

The ****ing answer is ****ing ethanol.

Tara noticed a couple of impurities in Ian's solution.

The Choice of Solvent for Recrystallisation is Very Important

1) When you **recrystallise** a product, you must use an **appropriate solvent** for that particular substance. It will only work if the solid is **very soluble** in the **hot** solvent, but **nearly insoluble** when the solvent is **cold**.

2) If your product **isn't soluble enough** in the hot solvent you **won't** be able to dissolve it at all.

3) If your product **is too soluble** in the cold solvent, most of it will **stay in the solution** even after cooling. When you filter it, you'll **lose** most of your product, giving you a very low **yield**.

Practice Questions

Q1 What is the functional group present in an amine? What is the functional group present in an amide?

Q2 Explain why amines are basic.

Q3 Describe how an amide can be hydrolysed using a weak alkali.

Q4 Describe how you would hydrolyse an ester under acidic conditions.

Exam Questions

1 Look at the structural formulas of the three amines shown below.

A $CH_3-CH_2-CH-CH_3$ with NH_2

B CH_3-N-CH_3 with CH_3

C $CH_3-CH-CH_2-NH_2$ with NH_2

   a) Name amine A and amine C. [2 marks]

   b) Classify amine A and amine B as primary, secondary or tertiary. [2 marks]

2 Aminoethane, $CH_3CH_2NH_2$, and ethanamide, CH_3CONH_2, will both react with dilute hydrochloric acid.

   a) Write a balanced equation for the reaction of aqueous aminoethane with aqueous hydrochloric acid. [1 mark]

   b) Write a balanced equation for the reaction of aqueous ethanamide with aqueous hydrochloric acid. [2 marks]

3 Esters can be hydrolysed under either acidic or basic conditions.

   a) Name the products formed when ethyl ethanoate is refluxed with:

      i) dilute hydrochloric acid, [2 marks]

      ii) dilute sodium hydroxide. [2 marks]

   b) A scientist refluxes ethyl ethanoate with dilute sodium hydroxide, and obtains an impure solid product. Describe how he could purify this solid by recrystallisation from an appropriate solvent. [4 marks]

When you're with the amides, have a CONH₂ time — an NH₂ time...

'Amine' and 'amide' might sound pretty similar, but that C=O group makes a world of difference to their chemical reaction. Check that you can tell the difference between them. There are a few reactions to learn on these pages too — make sure you know them all, inside out and back to front. Actually you probably only need to know the reversible ones back to front.

Polymers

There are two ways of making polymers that you need to know about — addition polymerisation and condensation polymerisation. But whichever one you use you'll still end up with a satisfyingly long chain of molecules...

Addition Polymers are Formed from Alkenes

The double bonds in alkenes can open up and join together to make long chains called **addition polymers**.
It's kind of like they're holding hands in a big line. The individual, small alkenes are called **monomers**.

Poly(phenylethene) is formed from **phenylethene**.

the double bond opens up

phenylethene monomer   poly(phenylethene) polymer

This is what a section of the poly(phenylethene) chain would look like.

Poly(chloroethene) is formed from **chloroethene**.

chloroethene monomer   poly(chloroethene) polymer

Poly(chloroethene) is also known as poly(vinyl chloride), or PVC.

Condensation Polymers Include Polyesters, Polyamides and Polypeptides

1) **Condensation polymerisation** usually involves two different types of monomer.

2) Each monomer has at least **two functional groups**. Each functional group reacts with a group on another monomer to form a link, creating polymer chains.

3) Each time a link is formed, a water molecule is lost — that's why it's called **condensation** polymerisation.

There are loads of **natural** condensation polymers — proteins are condensation polymers (see page 46).

Here are a couple of examples of how **synthetic** condensation polymers are made. You don't need to remember the details of these examples — just the basic idea of how you form links between molecules by eliminating water.

Reactions Between Dicarboxylic Acids and Diamines Make Polyamides

Carboxyl groups react with **amino** groups to form **amide links**.

a water molecule is eliminated

dicarboxylic acid   diamine   amide link

Dicarboxylic acids and diamines have functional groups at each end of the molecule, so long chains form.

Example   **Nylon 6,6** — made from **1,6-diaminohexane** and **hexanedioic acid**.

1,6-diaminohexane   hexanedioic acid   nylon 6,6 $+ 2nH_2O$

Reactions Between Dicarboxylic Acids and Diols Make Polyesters

Carboxyl groups react with **hydroxyl** groups to form **ester links**.

a water molecule is eliminated

dicarboxylic acid   diol   ester link

Example   **PET** — made from **benzene-1,4-dicarboxylic acid** and **ethane-1,2-diol**.

PET stands for polyethylene terephthalate

benzene-1,4-dicarboxylic acid   ethane-1,2-diol   PET $+ 2nH_2O$

Polymers

The Structural Formula of a Polymer Depends on its Monomers

If you know the structural formulas of a pair of monomers, you can work out the structural formula of the condensation polymer that they would form.

> **Example:** A condensation polymer is made from 1,4-diaminobutane, $H_2N(CH_2)_4NH_2$, and decanedioic acid, $HOOC(CH_2)_8COOH$. Draw the structural formula of the polymer that is formed.
>
> 1) Draw out the two **monomer** molecules next to each other.
>
> 2) Remove an **OH** from the **dicarboxylic acid**, and an **H** from the **diamine** — that gives you a water molecule.
>
> 3) Join the C and the N together to make an **amide link**.
>
> 4) Take another **H** and **OH** off the ends of your molecule. Draw brackets around it, and there's your **repeat unit**.

If the monomer molecules are a dicarboxylic acid and a diol, then you take an H atom from the diol, and an OH group from the dicarboxylic acid, and form an ester link instead.

You Can Also Work Out the Structural Formula of the Monomers From the Polymer

You can find the formulas of the **monomers** used to make a condensation polymer by looking at its formula.

1) First find the amide **(HN–CO)** or ester **(CO–O)** link. Break it down the middle.

2) Then add an **H** or an **OH** to **both ends** of **both molecules** to find the monomers.
   (Always add Hs to O or N atoms, and OH groups to C atoms.)

Green Chemistry is an Important Part of Polymer Production

Lots of chemicals that are used in the manufacture of polymers are pretty dangerous.
The way that a polymer is made should be designed to minimise the impact on human health and the environment.

There are a set of principles that industrial chemists follow when they design a 'green' polymer manufacturing process:

1) Use **reactant** molecules that are as **safe** and **environmentally friendly** as possible.

2) Use as few **other materials**, like **solvents**, as possible. If you have to use other chemicals, choose ones that **won't** harm the environment. Poly(ethene) is usually made with the reactants suspended in an **organic solvent**. But the reactions can take place when all the reactants are in the **gas phase** — then **no** solvent at all is needed.

3) **Renewable raw materials** should be used wherever possible. Currently, most monomers are made from oil-fractions. Polymers made from renewable resources are being developed — poly(lactic acid) monomers can be made from corn starch.

4) **Energy use** should be kept to a **minimum**. Catalysts are often utilised in green polymer synthesis to lower energy use.

5) The process should generate no **waste products** that are **hazardous** to **human health** or the **environment**.

> **Example:** The industrial production of **nylon-6,6**.
>
> 1) When you react **hexanedioic acid** with **1,6-diaminohexane**, the only two products that you get are **nylon-6,6** and **water** — so it sounds pretty **environmentally friendly**.
>
> 2) But the process used to make hexanedioic acid produces lots of **nitrous oxide** as a waste product. Nitrous oxide is a greenhouse gas, and is also involved in ozone depletion — so it's really environmentally unfriendly.
>
> 3) Scientists are developing **new** ways of making hexanedioic acid that emit **less** nitrous oxide — by **trapping** and **recycling** it, or by using different reactions that don't produce **any** nitrogen oxides.
>
> 4) One of the new ways of making hexanedioic acid that's being developed is to make it from **glucose**. That would swap from a **fossil fuel** source to a **renewable plant** source. And this method doesn't produce any nitrous oxide — making it even **greener**.

Polymers

Recycling and Reusing Polymers Reduces CO₂ Emissions

1) Producing polymers on an industrial scale uses lots of **energy**.

> • Extracting the **raw materials**, and turning them into the **monomers** you want, uses energy.
> • Many polymers (including nylon-6,6 and PET) are produced at **high temperature** and **pressure**. Creating these conditions usually requires large amounts of **electricity**.
> • This often means burning **fuel**, and releasing **carbon dioxide**, a greenhouse gas, into the atmosphere.

2) Once they've been used, many plastic items are **thrown away**. A lot of this waste is just buried as **landfill**, where it can take a very long time to decompose.

3) Burying plastic means more has to be manufactured to make **new products** — using more **energy** and **raw materials**.

4) There are some other options for getting rid of plastic waste:

> Many plastics can be **recycled**.
> • Lots of plastics are made from **non-renewable** resources, like **oil**. Recycling them means less **raw materials** being used, and **less waste** going to landfill. Some plastics are **melted** down and remoulded. Others are chemically treated to break them back down to their monomers, and reused.
> • But **sorting** and **processing** the plastic does use a lot of **energy**.

> Waste plastics can also be **burned**.
> • Burning plastic **reduces** the amount of waste going to **landfill**, and **produces heat energy**, which can be used to generate **electricity**.
> • But it produces lots of **carbon dioxide**, and some **toxic waste gases** too.

Jo enjoyed Green Chemistry, but she preferred Fairway Physics.

Practice Questions

Q1 Draw a diagram showing how the addition polymer poly(ethene) is formed from ethene monomers.

Q2 Draw the structural formula of the polyamide made from 1,6-diaminohexane, $H_2N(CH_2)_6NH_2$, and octanedioic acid, $HOOC(CH_2)_6COOH$.

Q3 Name three different methods that are used to dispose of waste plastics.

Exam Questions

1 NOMEX® is a polymer fibre that is used in fire-resistant materials. The diagram shows a section of a molecule of NOMEX®.

a) Draw out the structural formulas of both monomers. [2 marks]

b) Is NOMEX® a polyester or a polyamide? Explain your answer. [2 marks]

2 a) The monomers shown on the right are used to make a polymer called poly(butylene succinate), or PBS.

$$HO \overset{O}{\underset{}{C}} (CH_2)_2 \overset{O}{\underset{}{C}} OH$$
butanedioic acid

$$HO-\overset{H}{\underset{H}{C}}-(CH_2)_2-\overset{H}{\underset{H}{C}}-OH$$
butane-1,4-diol

   i) Draw the structural formula of the polymer made from these two monomers. (It is not necessary to draw the carbon chains out in full.) [2 marks]

   ii) Give a name for the type of link formed between the monomers. [1 mark]

b) Explain why the formation of PBS from its monomers is described as a 'condensation reaction'. [1 mark]

c) When polymers, like PBS, reach the end of their useful life, they can be disposed of by burning. Give one advantage and one disadvantage of disposing of waste plastics using this method. [2 marks]

Never miss your friends again — form a polymer...

Clever things these polymers. They get used for making all sorts of things, from plastic bags to bulletproof vests. But most of them are made from some pretty nasty chemicals. And once you've made 'em, you've got to figure out how to get rid of 'em too. So considering the environmental impact of what you make is a really important part of the design process.

Polymer Properties

If you actually want to make something out of a polymer, you need to choose one with the right properties for the job...

Structure and Bonding Control the Properties of All Materials

1) The **physical properties** of polymers depend on the **intermolecular bonds** between chains — and these depend on the **structure** of the polymer.

2) This isn't just true for polymers — the properties of all materials (like **strength**, **density**, **flexibility**, and **melting and boiling points**) depend on how their atoms and molecules are arranged and bonded.

3) You need to be able to explain the **properties** of a material from information about its **structure** and **bonding**.

Most of the polymers you need to know about are **thermoplastics** — these are polymers that don't have any covalent bonds, or **cross-links**, between chains. So it's only **intermolecular forces** (see page 27) that hold their chains together.

Plastics With Longer Chains are Stronger and Less Flexible

1) **Thermoplastics** are **soft** and **flexible** when the polymer chains can **slide** over one another easily. If the chains can't move in this way the plastic will be **rigid**.

2) It's the **intermolecular forces** that attract the polymer chains to one another and prevent them from moving. If you **increase** the **number** or the **strength** of these forces, then the plastic will become **stronger** and more **rigid**.

3) The number of intermolecular bonds between chains **increases** as the chains get **longer**. Plastics with very **long** polymer chains tend to be **more rigid** than those made up of **short** chains.

Polymers Soften and Melt When You Heat Them Above T_m

Thermoplastics all have a **melting point**, T_m.

If you heat a thermoplastic polymer to a temperature above its T_m it will soften, and then **melt**.

The heat energy that you're adding disrupts the **intermolecular bonds** that hold the polymer chains together. The chains start to be able to **slide** over one another — so the plastic can **change shape** more easily.

Polymers Become Brittle and Shatter When You Cool Them Below T_g

If you cool a thermoplastic to below a certain temperature called its **glass transition temperature**, T_g, its physical properties will change. Cooling a polymer strengthens the **intermolecular bonds** that hold the chains together, so the plastic will become very **rigid**.

If you try to **bend** a plastic that is **colder** than its T_g, the polymer chains will not slide past each other to allow the plastic to change shape, and it will eventually **snap** or **shatter**.

Crystalline Polymers Are Stronger Than Amorphous Polymers

Polymers can be **crystalline** or **amorphous**.

In a **crystalline** polymer, the arrangement of the chains is **ordered** — they all run in the **same direction**, or fold up neatly and stack next to each other

In an **amorphous** polymer, the arrangement of the chains is **random** — they all run in **different directions**.

1) In a **crystalline** polymer, where the chains are neatly packed, they can get very close together.

2) This means that the **intermolecular forces** between the polymer chains are much **greater** in crystalline polymers than in amorphous polymers. So crystalline polymers are **stronger** than **amorphous** polymers.

3) Most polymers are a mixture — they'll have some **crystalline regions** and some **amorphous regions**.

Polymer Properties

Polymer Properties can be **Modified** to Meet a **Particular Need**

You can alter the **properties** of a polymer **physically** or **chemically** in several different ways.

1) You can make a polymer using a mixture of **monomer** molecules. You will end up with a **polymer chain** that has different properties from a polymer made from any of the monomers alone — this is called **copolymerisation**.

> **Example:** Making a **styrene-butadiene copolymer**
> - **Polystyrene** has a **high** glass transition temperature, so it is very **hard**, but **brittle**, at room temperature.
> - **Polybutadiene** has a **low** glass transition temperature, and is **rubbery** and **flexible** at low temperatures.
> - If you make a polymer from a **mixture** of styrene and butadiene monomers, you produce a plastic that is very **tough** and **hard-wearing**, but also **flexible**. It's used to make **tyres** and **shoe soles**.

2) Adding a **plasticiser** makes a polymer **bendier**. The plasticiser molecules get **between** the polymer chains and push them apart. This **reduces** the strength of the **intermolecular forces** between the chains — so they can slide around more. Plasticers are added to polymers with **high** glass transition temperatures to make them more **flexible**.

> **Example:** Using plasticisers to make **flexible PVC**
> - **Poly(chloroethene)** (or **PVC**) has a **high** T_g. It has long, closely packed polymer chains, making it **hard** but **brittle** at room temperature. **Rigid PVC** is used to make drainpipes and window frames.
> - If you add a **plasticiser** to the PVC it **spaces out** the polymer chains. This **lowers** the T_g, and the plastic becomes **flexible**. **Plasticised PVC** is used to make electrical cable insulation, flooring tiles and clothing.

3) **Cold-drawing** increases the **crystallinity** of a polymer.

> The chains of an **amorphous polymer** are **randomly tangled**. They don't lie close together, and the intermolecular forces between them are **weak**.
>
> By pulling, or **drawing**, the polymer chains out in straight lines, they are forced to **straighten out** and lie close together. The intermolecular forces between chains **increase**, so the polymer is **more crystalline** and **stronger**.

Before cold-drawing the chains are randomly twisted After cold-drawing, chains are aligned and close together

Cold-drawing is used to make strong polymer fibres — nylon fibre is usually cold-drawn to increase its strength.

Practice Questions

Q1 Describe what happens to a polymer if you cool it below its glass transition temperature.

Q2 Explain why amorphous polymers are less strong than crystalline ones.

Q3 What is a plasticiser and why would you add it to a polymer?

Exam Questions

1 Poly(ethene) can be made in two different forms. Low density poly(ethene) (LDPE) is not very strong, but it is light and has a low melting point. High density poly(ethene) (HDPE) is very strong and has a high melting point. A scientist examines samples of the two forms of poly(ethene), which have been labelled A and B. She finds that Polymer A is 85% crystalline, and Polymer B is 50% crystalline.
 a) Which of the polymer samples is HDPE? Explain your answer. [3 marks]
 b) Suggest why increasing the crystallinity of a polymer increases its melting point. [3 marks]
 c) Name a technique that can be used to make a polymer more crystalline. [1 mark]

2 Poly(chloroethene), or PVC, is a hard, brittle plastic. Adding a plasticiser lowers its glass transition temperature.
 a) Why is unplasticised PVC so hard and strong at room temperature? [2 marks]
 b) Explain why adding a plasticiser lowers the T_g of PVC, and how it changes the properties of the plastic. [3 marks]

I had a plasticised PVC drainpipe business — it folded...

...and I thought bendy guttering was going to be this season's big thing. Don't make the same mistake that I did. Make sure that you understand how the strength of its intermolecular bonds affects the properties of a polymer, and how you can alter them to get a polymer that's fit for a particular task. That way lies the path to lots of exam marks...

Rates of Reaction

The rate of a reaction is just how quickly it happens. This page'll give you a few ways you can follow a reaction when you're working in the lab — just what you've always wanted.

There are **Loads** of Ways to **Follow the Rate of a Reaction**

The **reaction rate** is the **change in the amount** of reactants or products **per unit time** (normally per second). If the reactants are in **solution**, the rate'll be **change in concentration per second** and the units will be **mol dm^{-3} s^{-1}**.

Although there are quite a few ways to follow reactions, not every method works for every reaction. You've got to **pick a property** that **changes** as the reaction goes on.

1) pH measurement

If one of the reactants or products is an **acid or base** you could follow the reaction by monitoring the pH of the reaction mixture. The simplest way to do this is by using a **pH meter** or pH probe connected to a datalogger.

2) Gas volume

If a **gas** is given off, you could **collect it** in a gas syringe and record how much you've got at **regular time intervals**. For example, this'd work for the reaction between an **acid** and a **carbonate** in which **carbon dioxide gas** is given off.

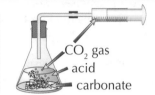
CO_2 gas
acid
carbonate

3) Loss of mass

If a **gas** is given off, the system will **lose mass**. You can measure this at regular intervals with a **balance**.

CO_2 gas
Balance

4) Colour change

Experimenting with colour isn't always a good idea.

You can sometimes track the colour change of a reaction using a gadget called a **colorimeter**. This measures the strength of colour by measuring light **absorbance**. For example, in the reaction between propanone and iodine, the **brown** colour fades.

$$CH_3COCH_{3(aq)} + I_{2(aq)} \rightarrow CH_3COCH_2I_{(aq)} + H^+_{(aq)} + I^-_{(aq)}$$
colourless   brown   colourless

5) Titration

You can monitor the **concentration** of a reactant or product in a solution by taking small samples of the reaction mixture at regular time intervals and **titrating** them. Once you've taken a sample, you need to **slow** the reaction happening in it right down — otherwise the concentration will be changing while you're trying to measure it. One easy way to do this is to add the sample to a large known volume of distilled water so that the chemicals become very dilute. The **problem** with titration is it's quite **slow**, so you can only use it to follow reactions that take a long time to finish (say half an hour).

Different Reactions Need **Different Techniques** for Calculating the **Rate**

Here's a handy summary to help you decide which technique to use when you're designing an experiment:

Reactant/ product	Technique to use	How to calculate rate
gas	loss of mass	rate = $\dfrac{\text{loss of mass}}{\text{time}}$
	volume of gas	rate = $\dfrac{\text{volume of gas produced}}{\text{time}}$
coloured	colorimeter	rate = $\dfrac{\text{change in absorbance}}{\text{time}}$
acid or base	pH meter	Concentration of H$^+$ ions = 10^{-pH} rate = $\dfrac{\text{change in concentration of H}^+ \text{ ions}}{\text{time}}$
in solution	titration	rate = $\dfrac{\text{change in concentration}}{\text{time}}$

Rates of Reaction

You Can Use **Graphs** to Calculate Rate

If you plot a graph of mass/volume/absorbance/concentration against **time** you can calculate the rate from the graph.

The **gradient** of the line — or the tangent if the graph's a curve — is proportional to the **rate** at that point in the reaction.

> A tangent is a line that just touches a curve and has the same gradient as the curve does at that point.

A graph of the **concentration of a reactant against time** might look something like this:

The gradient of the blue tangent is the rate of the reaction after **30 seconds**.

$$\text{Gradient} = \frac{-0.8}{60} = -0.013 \text{ mol dm}^{-3}\text{s}^{-1}$$

So, the rate after 30 seconds is **0.013 mol dm^{-3}s^{-1}**.

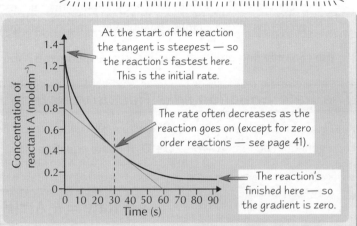

At the start of the reaction the tangent is steepest — so the reaction's fastest here. This is the initial rate.

The rate often decreases as the reaction goes on (except for zero order reactions — see page 41).

The reaction's finished here — so the gradient is zero.

The sign of the gradient doesn't matter when you're thinking about rate — it's **negative** when you're measuring **reactant** concentration because the reactant decreases. If you measured **product concentration**, instead, it'd be positive.

Practice Questions

Q1 What two methods could be used to measure the rate of any reaction that produces a gas?

Q2 How can you calculate the rate of a reaction that produces a coloured compound?

Q3 Why is it difficult to follow a fast reaction by titration?

Q4 How can a graph be used to work out the rate of a reaction?

Exam Questions

1 The rate of the acid-catalysed reaction between bromine, Br_2, and methanoic acid, HCOOH, was investigated.

$$Br_{2(aq)} + HCOOH_{(aq)} \xrightarrow{\text{H}^+_{(aq)}} 2H^+_{(aq)} + 2Br^-_{(aq)} + CO_{2(g)}$$

   a) Suggest one method that could be used to follow the reaction rate. [2 marks]

   b) If the concentration of Br_2 was recorded during the reaction, outline how the rate of reaction, at any particular time, could be determined. [3 marks]

2 The rate of decomposition of a chemical, X, in solution was followed by monitoring the concentration of X.

$$X_{(aq)} \rightarrow Y_{(l)} + Z_{(g)}$$

Time (minutes)	0	20	40	60	80	100
[X] (mol dm^{-3})	2.00	1.00	0.50	0.25	0.125	0.0625

   a) Suggest an alternative method that could have been used to follow the rate of this reaction. [2 marks]

   b) Using the data above, plot a graph and determine the rate of the reaction after 30 minutes. [6 marks]

This stuff'll speed up your revision rate...

In the exam you're going to have to be able to suggest suitable methods for following a reaction — and you'll have to explain how to calculate the rate from the results. Thrilling as these pages are, make sure you learn 'em...

Orders and Rate Equations

Never my favourite part of chemistry, here's where all the little letters and square brackets come in...

Orders *Tell You How a Reactant's* Concentration *Affects the* Rate

1) The **order of reaction** with respect to a particular reactant tells you how the **reactant's concentration** affects the **rate**.

   If you double the reactant's concentration and the rate **stays the same**, the order with respect to that reactant is **0**.
   If you double the reactant's concentration and the rate **also doubles**, the order with respect to that reactant is **1**.
   If you double the reactant's concentration and the rate **quadruples**, the order with respect to that reactant is **2**.

2) You can only find **orders of reaction** from **experiments**. You **can't** work them out from chemical equations.

The Rate Equation *links* Reaction Rate *to* Reactant Concentrations

Rate equations look ghastly, but all they're really telling you is how the **rate** is affected by the **concentrations of reactant**.
For a general reaction: **A + B → C + D**, the **rate equation** is:

The units of rate are mol dm⁻³ s⁻¹.

$$\text{Rate} = k[A]^m[B]^n$$

Remember — square brackets mean the concentration of whatever's inside them.

1) **m** and **n** are the **orders of the reaction** with respect to reactant A and reactant B.
   m tells you how the **concentration of reactant A** affects the **rate** and **n** tells you the same for **reactant B**.
2) The **overall order of the reaction** is **m + n**.
3) *k* is the **rate constant** — the bigger it is, the **faster** the reaction. The rate constant is **always the same** for a certain reaction at a **particular temperature**.
4) The **units** vary, so you have to **work them out**. The example on the next page shows you how.

Example:

The chemical equation below shows the acid-catalysed reaction between propanone and iodine.

$$CH_3COCH_{3(aq)} + I_{2(aq)} \xrightarrow{H^+_{(aq)}} CH_3COCH_2I_{(aq)} + H^+_{(aq)} + I^-_{(aq)}$$

This reaction is **first order** with respect to propanone and $H^+_{(aq)}$ and **zero order** with respect to iodine. Write down: a) the rate equation, b) the overall order of the reaction.

Even though $H^+_{(aq)}$ is a catalyst, rather than a reactant, it can still be in the rate equation.

a) The **rate equation** is: rate = $k[CH_3COCH_{3(aq)}]^1[H^+_{(aq)}]^1[I_{2(aq)}]^0$
   But $[X]^1$ is usually written as **[X]**, and $[X]^0$ equals **1** so is usually **left out** of the rate equation.
   So you can **simplify** the rate equation to: **rate = $k[CH_3COCH_{3(aq)}][H^+_{(aq)}]$**

Think about the indices laws from maths.

b) The overall order of the reaction is 1 + 1 + 0 = **2**

A Higher Temperature *Means a* Higher Rate Constant

1) Increasing the **temperature** means that the particles will tend to have more **kinetic energy**, so:
   - they'll fly about **faster** and will **collide more often**, speeding up the reaction.
   - a **greater proportion** of them will have the **activation energy** to **react**.
2) This means the **rate of reaction** increases.
3) But, according to the rate equation, reaction rate depends only on the rate constant and reactant concentrations. Since the reactant concentrations **don't** change, the rate constant **must** change.
4) So basically, the rate constant for a reaction is **higher** when the temperature is higher.

Fancy bumping into you here...

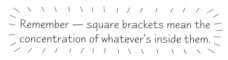

Higher temperatures mean that collisions happen more often.

Orders and Rate Equations

You can Calculate the Rate Constant from the Orders and Rate of Reaction

Once the rate and the orders of the reaction have been found by experiment, you can work out the **rate constant, k**.

Example:

The reaction below was found to be second order with respect to NO and zero order with respect to CO and O_2.
The rate is 1.76×10^{-3} mol dm^{-3} s^{-1}, when $[NO_{(g)}] = [CO_{(g)}] = [O_{2(g)}] = 2.00 \times 10^{-3}$ mol dm^{-3}.

$$NO_{(g)} + CO_{(g)} + O_{2(g)} \rightarrow NO_{2(g)} + CO_{2(g)}$$

First write out the **rate equation**:

$$Rate = k[NO_{(g)}]^2[CO_{(g)}]^0[O_{2(g)}]^0 = k[NO_{(g)}]^2$$

Next insert the **concentration** and the **rate**. **Rearrange** the equation and calculate the value of k:

$$Rate = k[NO_{(g)}]^2, \text{ so, } 1.76 \times 10^{-3} = k \times (2.00 \times 10^{-3})^2 \Rightarrow k = \frac{1.76 \times 10^{-3}}{(2.00 \times 10^{-3})^2} = 440$$

Find the **units for k** by putting the other units in the rate equation:

$$Rate = k[NO_{(g)}]^2, \text{ so mol dm}^{-3}\text{s}^{-1} = k \times (\text{mol dm}^{-3})^2 \Rightarrow k = \frac{\text{mol dm}^{-3}\text{ s}^{-1}}{(\text{mol dm}^{-3})^2} = \frac{\text{s}^{-1}}{\text{mol dm}^{-3}} = \text{dm}^3\text{ mol}^{-1}\text{ s}^{-1}$$

So the answer is: $k = 440$ dm^3 mol^{-1} s^{-1}

Practice Questions

Q1 What is the general form of a rate equation for a reaction between reactants A and B?

Q2 How do you work out the overall order of a reaction from its rate equation?

Q3 What happens to the rate of a reaction if the rate constant gets smaller?

Q4 Do all rate constants have the same units?

Exam Questions

1 The following reaction is second order with respect to NO and first order with respect to H_2.

$$2NO_{(g)} + 2H_{2(g)} \rightarrow 2H_2O_{(g)} + N_{2(g)}$$

   a) Write a rate equation for the reaction and deduce the overall order for the reaction. [3 marks]

   b) The rate of the reaction at 800 °C was determined to be 0.00267 mol dm^{-3} s^{-1} when:
$[H_{2(g)}] = 0.0020$ mol dm^{-3} and $[NO_{(g)}] = 0.0040$ mol dm^{-3}.

     i) Calculate a value for the rate constant at 800 °C, including units. [3 marks]

     ii) Predict the effect on the rate constant of decreasing the temperature of the reaction to 600 °C. [1 mark]

2 The ester ethyl ethanoate, $CH_3COOC_2H_5$, is hydrolysed by heating with dilute acid to give ethanol and
ethanoic acid. The reaction is first order with respect to the concentration of H$^+$ and the ester.

   a) Write the rate equation for the reaction. [1 mark]

   b) When the initial concentration of the acid is 2.0 mol dm^{-3} and the ester is 0.25 mol dm^{-3}, the initial rate
is 2.2×10^{-3} mol dm^{-3} s^{-1}. Calculate a value for the rate constant at this temperature and give its units. [2 marks]

   c) Calculate the initial rate at the same temperature if more solvent is added to the
initial mixture so that the volume doubles. [2 marks]

Describe the link between concentration and rate, soldier. That's an order...

Welcome to the wonderful world of the rate equation. They'll be springing up all over the place now. If the mere
mention of anything mathsy fills you with dread, don't panic — they're not as scary as they seem. Just remember to
learn all the main points and if in doubt: practise, practise, pra— well you get the idea anyway...

Experimental Data and Rate Equations

Wouldn't it be nice if you could go to sleep with this book under your pillow and when you woke up you'd know it all.

The **Initial Rates Method** can be used to work out **Rate Equations**

The **initial rate of a reaction** is the rate right at the **start** of the reaction.
You can find this from a **concentration-time** graph by calculating the
gradient of the **tangent** at **time = 0**.

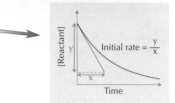

Here's a quick explanation of how to use the **initial rates method**:

1) Repeat the experiment several times using **different initial concentrations** of reactants.
   You should only change **one** of the concentrations at a time, keeping the rest constant.

2) Calculate the **initial rate** for each experiment using the method above.

3) Finally, see how the **initial concentrations** affect the **initial rates** and figure out the **order** for each reactant.
   The example below shows you how to do this. Once you know the **orders**, you can work out the rate equation.

Example:
The table on the right shows the results of a
series of initial rate experiments for the reaction:

$$NO_{(g)} + CO_{(g)} + O_{2(g)} \rightarrow NO_{2(g)} + CO_{2(g)}$$

Write down the rate equation for the reaction.

Experiment number	$[NO_{(g)}]$ (mol dm^{-3})	$[CO_{(g)}]$ (mol dm^{-3})	$[O_{2(g)}]$ (mol dm^{-3})	Initial rate (mol dm^{-3} s^{-1})
1	2.0×10^{-2}	1.0×10^{-2}	1.0×10^{-2}	0.176
2	4.0×10^{-2}	1.0×10^{-2}	1.0×10^{-2}	0.704
3	2.0×10^{-2}	2.0×10^{-2}	1.0×10^{-2}	0.176
4	2.0×10^{-2}	1.0×10^{-2}	2.0×10^{-2}	0.176

1) Look at experiments 1 and 2 — when $[NO_{(g)}]$ doubles (but all the other concentrations stay constant), the rate **quadruples**. So the reaction is **second order** with respect to NO.

2) Look at experiments 1 and 3 — when $[CO_{(g)}]$ doubles (but all the other concentrations stay constant), the rate **stays the same**. So the reaction is **zero order** with respect to CO.

3) Look at experiments 1 and 4 — when $[O_{2(g)}]$ doubles (but all the other concentrations stay constant), the rate **stays the same**. So the reaction is **zero order** with respect to O_2.

4) Now that you know the order with respect to each reactant you can write the rate equation: **rate = $k[NO_{(g)}]^2$** .

k can be calculated by inserting the concentrations and the initial rate from one of the experiments into the rate equation.

A **Half-life** is the Time Taken for a Reactant to Halve in Quantity

It's easy to calculate half-life from a **concentration-time** graph :

Example: The graph below shows how the concentration of chloroethane (CH_3CH_2Cl) changes
during the following reaction at 492 °C: $CH_3CH_2Cl_{(g)} \rightarrow CH_2CH_{2(g)} + HCl_{(g)}$

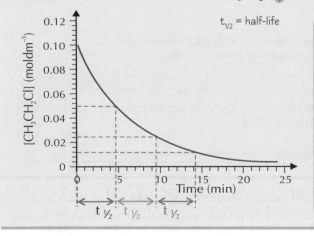

1) The initial concentration of CH_3CH_2Cl is **0.10 mol dm^{-3}**. According to the graph, it takes about **4.75 minutes** for this to fall to **0.05 mol dm^{-3}** — i.e. the half-life is about 4.75 minutes.

2) You can measure several half-lives from one graph — just keep picking different values for the concentration of the reactant and find how long it takes that value to fall by half.

3) As you can see the half-life for CH_3CH_2Cl is **constant** — it always takes around 4.75 minutes for the reactant's concentration to halve in quantity.

Experimental Data and Rate Equations

Orders can be Worked Out from Half-Lives and Concentration-Time Graphs

You can figure out the **order of reaction** with respect to a reactant by looking at the shape of a **concentration-time graph** and seeing whether the **half-life**, $t_{1/2}$, is **constant**.

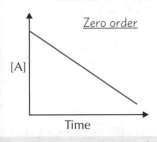

Zero order

[A] / Time

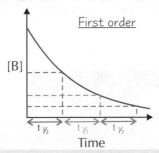

First order

[B] / $t_{1/2}$ $t_{1/2}$ $t_{1/2}$ / Time

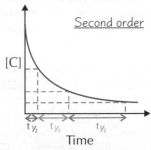

Second order

[C] / $t_{1/2}$ $t_{1/2}$ $t_{1/2}$ / Time

If it's zero order, the rate **doesn't change** as concentration falls — the graph is a **straight line**.

If it's first order, the graph is **curved**. The rate decreases as the concentration does, but $t_{1/2}$ is **constant**.

If it's second order, the graph is curved again, but the half-life **increases** as the reaction goes on.

You Need to Know the Order for Each Reactant to Write a Rate Equation

You need to know the order with respect to all the reactants to write a rate equation.

1) In the example on the last page the half-life of CH_3CH_2Cl is constant — making it a **first order** reaction with respect to CH_3CH_2Cl. This is the only reactant, so the rate equation's going to be: **rate = $k[CH_3CH_2Cl]$**.

2) If more than one reactant is involved, you need to work out the order for each reactant separately. In the **above example**, the graphs show that the reaction is **zero order** with respect to A, **first order** with respect to B and **second order** with respect to C. So the **rate equation is: rate = $k[B][C]^2$** (remember, zero order terms don't appear in the equation).

Practice Questions

Q1 How can you calculate the initial rate of a reaction from a concentration-time graph?

Q2 How can you calculate the half-life for a reaction from a concentration-time graph?

Q3 What do the initial rates of reaction, measured at different initial concentrations of reactant, tell you?

Q4 Sketch reactant concentration-time graphs for zero, first and second order reactions.

Exam Questions

1 The table shows the results of a series of initial rate experiments for the reaction between substances X and Y.

Experiment	[X] (mol dm⁻³)	[Y] (mol dm⁻³)	Initial rate × 10⁻³ (mol dm⁻³ s⁻¹)
1	0.2	0.2	1.30
2	0.4	0.2	5.19
3	0.2	0.4	2.61

a) Find the order of the reaction with respect to reactants X and Y. Explain your reasoning. [4 marks]

b) Write the rate equation for the reaction. [1 mark]

c) Calculate a value for the rate constant, k, including units. [3 marks]

2 In a reaction between A and B, the concentration of each reactant is measured at regular intervals and concentration-time graphs are plotted for A and for B. Neither graph is a straight line. The data in the table is obtained from the concentration-time graphs.

a) Calculate the first three half-lives for each reactant and find the order of the reaction:

i) with respect to A, [3 marks]

ii) with respect to B.

b) Write a rate equation for the reaction. [3 marks]

[A] mol dm⁻³	Time (s)	[B] mol dm⁻³	Time (s)
1	0	1	0
0.5	17	0.5	21
0.25	34	0.25	58
0.125	51	0.125	117

Yes — it's another page on rates...

This stuff about half-lives sounds like something from Lord of the Rings. Sadly there's not a hobbit in sight. Don't let that put you off though — you'll need to be able to work out the order of reaction from a concentration-time graph in the exam, so half-lives are a must. The initial-rates method is a key one too — make sure you know how to do it.

Rates and Reaction Mechanisms

Ever wondered exactly how your favourite reaction happens? Probably not, but work out the rate equation and it'll give you a clue about the reaction mechanism.

The **Rate-Determining Step** is the **Slowest Step** in a Multi-Step Reaction

Mechanisms can have **one step** or a **series of steps**. In a series of steps, each step can have a **different rate**. The **overall rate** is decided by the step with the **slowest** rate — the **rate-determining step**.

Otherwise known as the rate-limiting step.

Reactants in the **Rate Equation** Affect the **Rate**

The rate equation is handy for working out the **mechanisms** of a chemical reaction.

You need to be able to pick out which reactants from the chemical equation are involved in the **rate-determining step**. Here are the **rules** for doing this:

> If a reactant appears in the **rate equation**, it must be affecting the **rate**. So this reactant, or something derived from it, must be in the **rate-determining step**.
>
> If a reactant **doesn't** appear in the **rate equation**, then it **won't** be involved in the **rate-determining step** (and neither will anything derived from it).

Catalysts can appear in rate equations, so they can be in rate-determining steps too.

Some **important points** to remember about rate-determining steps and mechanisms are:

1) The rate-determining step **doesn't** have to be the first step in a mechanism.

2) The reaction mechanism **can't** usually be predicted from **just** the chemical equation.

You Can Predict the **Rate Equation** from the **Rate-Determining** Step...

> The **order of a reaction** with respect to a reactant shows the **number of molecules** of that reactant which are involved in the **rate-determining step**.

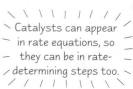

So, if a reaction's second order with respect to X, there'll be two molecules of X in the rate-determining step.

For example, the mechanism for the reaction between **chlorine free radicals** and **ozone**, O_3, consists of **two steps**:

$$Cl\bullet_{(g)} + O_{3(g)} \rightarrow ClO\bullet_{(g)} + O_{2(g)} \text{ — slow (rate-determining step)}$$

$$ClO\bullet_{(g)} + O\bullet_{(g)} \rightarrow Cl\bullet_{(g)} + O_{2(g)} \text{ — fast}$$

$Cl\bullet$ and O_3 must both be in the rate equation, so the rate equation will be of the form: **rate** $= k[Cl\bullet]^m[O_3]^n$.

There's only **one** $Cl\bullet$ radical and **one** O_3 molecule in the rate-determining step, so the **orders**, m and n, are both **1**.

So the rate equation is **rate** $= k[Cl\bullet][O_3]$.

...And You Can Predict the **Mechanism** from the **Rate Equation**

Knowing exactly which reactants are in the **rate-determining step** gives you an idea of the reaction **mechanism**.

For example, the nucleophile **OH⁻** can substitute for **Br** in 2-bromo-2-methylpropane. Here are two possible mechanisms:

$$CH_3-\underset{\underset{CH_3}{|}}{\overset{\overset{CH_3}{|}}{C}}-Br \;+\; OH^- \;\rightarrow\; CH_3-\underset{\underset{CH_3}{|}}{\overset{\overset{CH_3}{|}}{C}}-OH \;+\; Br^-$$

or

$$CH_3-\underset{\underset{CH_3}{|}}{\overset{\overset{CH_3}{|}}{C}}-Br \;\rightarrow\; CH_3-\underset{\underset{CH_3}{|}}{\overset{\overset{CH_3}{|}}{C}}{}^+ \;+\; Br^- \text{ — slow (rate-determining step)}$$

$$CH_3-\underset{\underset{CH_3}{|}}{\overset{\overset{CH_3}{|}}{C}}{}^+ \;+\; OH^- \;\rightarrow\; CH_3-\underset{\underset{CH_3}{|}}{\overset{\overset{CH_3}{|}}{C}}-OH \text{ — fast}$$

The actual **rate equation** was worked out using rate experiments: **rate** $= k[(CH_3)_3CBr]$

OH⁻ isn't in the **rate equation**, so it **can't** be involved in the rate-determining step.

The **second mechanism** is more likely to be correct because OH⁻ **isn't** in the rate-determining step.

Rates and Reaction Mechanisms

You have to *Take Care* when Suggesting a *Mechanism*

If you're suggesting a mechanism, **watch out** — things might not always be what they seem.

E.g. when nitrogen(V) oxide, N_2O_5, decomposes, it forms nitrogen(IV) oxide and oxygen: $2N_2O_{5(g)} \rightarrow 4NO_{2(g)} + O_{2(g)}$

From the chemical equation, it looks like **two** N_2O_5 molecules react with each other. But this isn't the case. Experimentally, it's been found that the reaction is **first order** with respect to N_2O_5 — the rate equation is: **rate = $k[N_2O_5]$**. This shows that there's only one molecule of N_2O_5 in the rate-determining step. One **possible mechanism** is:

Only one molecule of N_2O_5 is in the rate-determining step, fitting in with the rate equation.

$N_2O_{5(g)} \rightarrow NO_{2(g)} + NO_{3(g)}$ — **slow (rate-determining step)**

$NO_{3(g)} + N_2O_{5(g)} \rightarrow 3NO_{2(g)} + O_{2(g)}$ — **fast**

The two steps add up to the overall chemical equation. You can cancel the $NO_{3(g)}$ as it appears on both sides.

Enzyme-Catalysed Reactions Don't Behave as You'd Expect

Enzymes are biological molecules that can **catalyse** certain reactions.

- An enzyme molecule works by joining to a reactant molecule — called a **substrate** — and forming an **enzyme-substrate complex**.
- The substrate reacts more easily while attached to the enzyme. Once the product is formed, the enzyme **detaches** and goes on to connect to another substrate molecule.

There's more on enzymes on page 54

1) In a very simple **first order** reaction, a **substrate, S**, might become a molecule of **product, P**:

$$S \rightarrow P$$

2) As the concentration of S increases, the reaction speeds up. In fact, because it's a first order reaction, doubling the concentration of S should double the rate of reaction. If you plotted this as a rate-concentration graph it would be a straight line — showing that rate is **directly proportional** to substrate concentration.

3) However when the above reaction is **catalysed by an enzyme**, something odd happens...

4) At first doubling the concentration of S still doubles the rate of reaction. Eventually though, the reaction reaches a stage where it can't go any faster — no matter how you increase the amount of S.

Enzyme-Catalysed Reactions *Change Order* as Substrate is Added

The graph shows how the rates of an **un-catalysed** and an **enzyme-catalysed** reaction change as more substrate is added.

1) The **un-catalysed** reaction is **first order** so the graph is just a straight line.

2) The **enzyme-catalysed** reaction is first order when the substrate concentration is **low** — the graph is straight at the start — but it changes as more substrate is added.

3) Towards the end, the line of the graph levels out until it is horizontal. At this point the rate is **no longer affected** by the concentration of S. The reaction has become **zero order**.

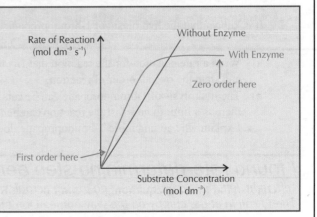

Rates and Reaction Mechanisms

The Order Changes Because the Rate-Determining Step Changes

Remember that the **order of the reaction** is connected to the **reaction mechanism**.

- When the enzyme-catalysed reaction is **first order**, then **one** molecule of S must be involved in the rate-determining step of the mechanism.
- When the reaction becomes **zero** order then **no** molecules of S can be involved in the rate-determining step.

> In the simple enzyme-catalysed reaction where S becomes P,
> S combines with an **enzyme molecule, E**, to make the **enzyme-substrate complex, ES**:
>
> $$S + E \rightarrow ES \qquad \text{step 1}$$
>
> Then the substrate changes into the product, which detaches from the enzyme:
>
> $$ES \rightarrow EP \qquad \text{step 2}$$
> $$EP \rightarrow E + P \qquad \text{step 3}$$

1) When **S concentration** is **low**, there are lots of free enzyme molecules waiting to attach to the S molecules. As there isn't much S around, it doesn't bump into the enzyme very often, making **step 1 slow**. Step 1 determines the overall rate, so the reaction is **first order** with respect to S.

2) For a while, as you **increase** the amount of S, step 1 **speeds up** and the rate of reaction increases.

3) Eventually though, you reach a stage where almost all of the enzyme molecules have become ES complexes. At this point, the enzyme is said to be **saturated**. Adding more S **can't** make the reaction any faster — there are no free enzyme molecules for the extra S to attach to.

4) The rate of reaction now depends on how fast the ES can convert into EP — **step 2** has become the **rate-determining step**. Since S is not involved in step 2, the reaction becomes **zero order** with respect to S.

Practice Questions

Q1 What does the term 'rate-determining step' mean?
Q2 How does the rate equation help you decide what the mechanism for a reaction is?
Q3 What happens to the order of an enzyme-catalysed reaction as the substrate concentration increases?
Q4 Why does the rate of an enzyme-catalysed reaction reach a limit as substrate concentration is increased?

Exam Questions

1   The following reaction is first order with respect to H_2 and first order with respect to ICl.

$$H_{2(g)} + 2ICl_{(g)} \rightarrow I_{2(g)} + 2HCl_{(g)}$$

a)   Write the rate equation for this reaction. [1 mark]

b)   The mechanism for this reaction consists of two steps.
   i) Identify the molecules that are in the rate-determining step. Justify your answer. [3 marks]
   ii) A chemist suggested the following mechanism for the reaction.

$$2ICl_{(g)} \rightarrow I_{2(g)} + Cl_{2(g)} \qquad \text{slow}$$
$$H_{2(g)} + Cl_{2(g)} \rightarrow 2HCl_{(g)} \qquad \text{fast}$$

Suggest, with reasons, whether this mechanism is likely to be correct. [2 marks]

2   It is known that the hydrolysis of 1-bromopropane occurs according to the following one-step mechanism:
$$CH_3CH_2CH_2Br + OH^- \rightarrow CH_3CH_2CH_2OH + Br^-$$

a)   Write a rate equation for the reaction that fits the mechanism given above and state the overall order of reaction. [4 marks]

b)   The hydrolysis of 1-bromopropane can be catalysed by an enzyme. In the enzyme-catalysed reaction there is a limit to how fast the reaction can be made to go by increasing the concentration of the reactants. Explain why adding more 1-bromopropane does not increase the rate beyond this limit. [2 marks]

I found rate-determining step aerobics a bit on the slow side...

Left, right, left, right. Yes it's true, I go to step aerobics. Nothing wrong with a bit of exercise bouncing to the latest beats. Then I call in at the chippy on the way home. Don't judge me. It get's late and I'm hungry. This enzyme-order business is pretty tricky to get your head around, but stick with it and it'll soon start making sense — unlike why I go to aerobics.

Amino Acids and Proteins

And now we hurtle headlong into the world of biochemistry. First up, it's proteins...

Amino Acids have an **Amino Group** and a **Carboxyl** Group

An amino acid has a **basic amino group** (NH_2) and an **acidic carboxyl group** (COOH).
This makes them **amphoteric** — they've got both acidic and basic properties.

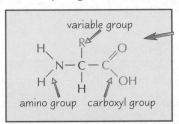

variable group

The R group is different for different amino acids

amino group   carboxyl group

Amino Acids Can Exist As Zwitterions

A zwitterion is a **dipolar ion** — it has both a **positive** and a **negative charge** in different parts of the molecule.
Zwitterions only exist near an amino acid's **isoelectric point**. This is the **pH** at which the **average overall charge** on the amino acid is zero. It's different for different amino acids — it depends on their R-group.

In conditions more **acidic** than the isoelectric point, the $-NH_2$ group is likely to be **protonated**.	At the isoelectric point, both the carboxyl group and the amino group are likely to be ionised — forming an ion called a **zwitterion**.	In conditions more **basic** than the isoelectric point, the –COOH group is likely to **lose** its proton.

low pH   zwitterion   high pH

Paper Chromatography is used to Identify Unknown Amino Acids

You can easily identify amino acids in a mixture using a simple paper chromatography experiment. Here's how:

1) Draw a **pencil line** near the bottom of a piece of chromatography paper and put a **concentrated spot** of the mixture of amino acids on it.

2) Dip the bottom of the paper (not the spot) into a solvent.

3) As the solvent spreads up the paper, the different amino acids move with it, but at **different rates**, so they separate out.

4) When the solvent's **nearly** reached the top, take the paper out and **mark** the **solvent front** with pencil.

5) Amino acids aren't **coloured** — so you have to spray **ninhydrin solution** on the paper to turn them purple.

6) You can work out the R_f values of the amino acids using this formula:

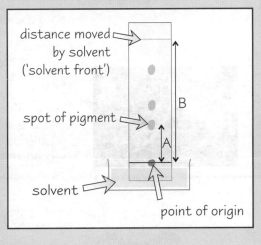

distance moved by solvent ('solvent front')

spot of pigment

B

A

solvent

point of origin

$$R_f \text{ value of amino acid} = \frac{A}{B} = \frac{\text{distance travelled by spot}}{\text{distance travelled by solvent}}$$

Now you can use a **table of known amino acid R_f values** to identify the amino acids in the mixture.

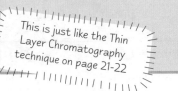

This is just like the Thin Layer Chromatography technique on page 21-22

Amino Acids and Proteins

Proteins are Condensation Polymers of Amino Acids

Proteins are made up of **lots** of amino acids joined together. The chain is put together by **condensation** reactions and broken apart by **hydrolysis** reactions. **Peptide links** are made between the amino acids.

Here's how two amino acids join together to make a **dipeptide**:

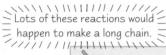
Lots of these reactions would happen to make a long chain.

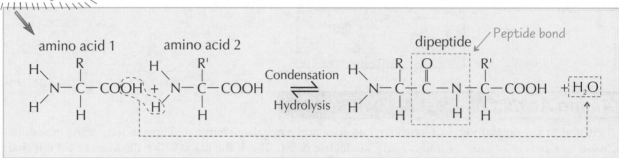

amino acid 1   amino acid 2   Condensation / Hydrolysis   dipeptide / Peptide bond   + H_2O

Proteins are really polyamides — the monomers are joined by amide groups. In proteins these are called peptide bonds though.

To break up the protein (**hydrolyse** it) you need to use pretty harsh conditions.
Hot aqueous 6 mol dm^{-3} hydrochloric acid is added, and the mixture is heated under reflux for 24 hours.
The final mixture is then neutralised.

Proteins have Different Levels of Structure

Proteins are **big**, **complicated** molecules. They're easier to explain if you describe their structure in four 'levels'. These levels are called the **primary**, **secondary**, **tertiary** and **quaternary** structures. You only need to know about the first three though.

 (1)

The **primary structure** is the **sequence of amino acids** in the long chain that makes up the protein (the **polypeptide chain**).

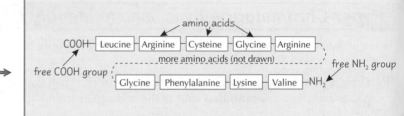

amino acids

COOH— Leucine — Arginine — Cysteine — Glycine — Arginine
free COOH group   more amino acids (not drawn)   free NH$_2$ group
Glycine — Phenylalanine — Lysine — Valine —NH$_2$

Lucy's giant alpha-helix replica was spiralling out of control.

(2)

The **peptide links** can form **hydrogen bonds** with each other, meaning the chain isn't a straight line. The shape of the chain is called its **secondary structure**. The most common secondary structure is a **spiral** called an **alpha (α) helix**.

α helix chain

(3)

The chain of amino acids is itself often coiled and folded in a characteristic way that identifies the protein. **Extra bonds** can form between different parts of the polypeptide chain, which gives the protein a kind of **three-dimensional shape**. This is its **tertiary structure**.

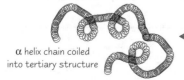

α helix chain coiled into tertiary structure

Amino Acids and Proteins

Different Bonds *Hold Proteins Together*

The **secondary** structure is held together by **hydrogen bonds** between the peptide links.

The **tertiary** structure is **held together** by quite a few different types of force.
These all exist between the **side chains** (R-groups) of the amino acids.

These forces hold the tertiary structure together:

1) **Instantaneous dipole-induced dipole** forces — weak attractions between two **non-polar** side groups, e.g. CH_3.
2) **Ionic interactions** between **charged** side groups, like CO_2^- and NH_3^+.
3) **Hydrogen bonding** — between groups such as –OH and $-NH_2$.
4) **Disulfide bridge** — a covalent bond between two sulfur-containing side groups (–SH). This type of bond is stronger than the others.

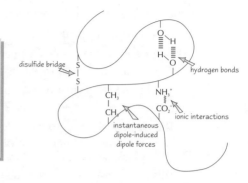

It's the **three-dimensional structure** that gives proteins their properties.
So these intermolecular bonds are really important — because they're what causes the three-dimensional structure.

Practice Questions

Q1 What word describes something that can act as an acid and a base?

Q2 What is a zwitterion?

Q3 What's a peptide bond?

Q4 Name the four types of force that are involved in holding together the tertiary structures of proteins.

Exam Questions

1   The amino acid glycine is shown below.

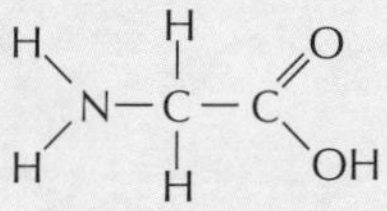

glycine

a)   The amino acid serine is otherwise known as 2-amino-3-hydroxypropanoic acid.
Draw the structure of serine.   [1 mark]

b)   When two amino acids react together, a dipeptide is formed.
i) Explain the meaning of the term dipeptide.   [2 marks]
ii) Draw the structures of the two dipeptides formed when serine and glycine react together.   [2 marks]

c)   The dipeptides formed can be hydrolysed to give the original amino acids again.
Give the reagent(s) and conditions for this reaction.   [2 marks]

2   Helen is investigating the structure of a protein in a school lab. She first refluxes a sample
of the protein for 24 hours in 6 mol dm^{-3} hydrochloric acid to break it up into monomer units.

a)   What type of reaction is this?   [1 mark]

b)   What is the name of the monomer units that make up a protein?   [1 mark]

c)   Describe a simple technique that Helen could use to separate and identify
the specific monomer units present in the protein.   [5 marks]

My top three tides of all time — high tide, low tide and peptide...

The word zwitterion is such a lovely word — it flutters off your tongue like a butterfly. These pages aren't too painful — another organic structure, a nice experiment and some stuff on proteins. There's even a two-for-the-price-of-one equation — forwards it's condensation; backwards it's hydrolysis. Remember to learn the conditions for the hydrolysis though.

DNA

DNA — the molecule of life. And unfortunately, just like life, it's complicated.

DNA is a **Polymer** of **Nucleotides**

DNA, <u>D</u>eoxyribo<u>N</u>ucleic <u>A</u>cid, contains all the genetic information of an organism.

DNA is made up from lots of **monomers** called **nucleotides**.
Nucleotides are made from the following:

1) **A phosphate group.**

2) **A pentose sugar** — a five-carbon sugar. It's deoxyribose in DNA.

3) **A base** — one of four different bases. In DNA they are **adenine** (A), **cytosine** (C), **guanine** (G) and **thymine** (T).

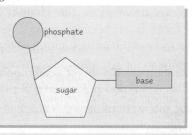

The nucleotides join together to form a **polynucleotide chain**. The bond between each pair of nucleotides forms between the phosphate group of one nucleotide and the sugar of another. This makes what's called a **sugar-phosphate backbone**.

The bases can be in any order, and it's the order of them that holds all the information.

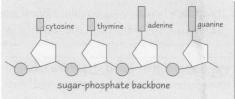

sugar-phosphate backbone

DNA Forms by **Condensation Polymerisation**

The **sugar-phosphate backbone** is formed by condensation polymerisation. The diagram below shows you how:

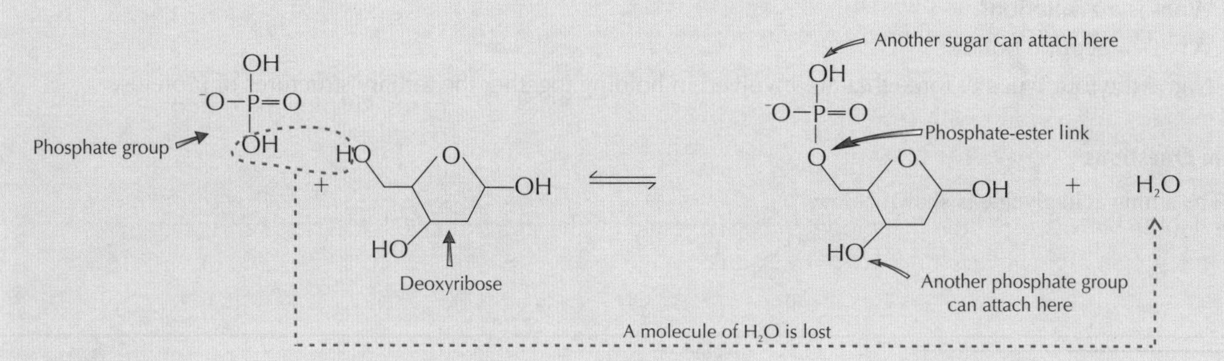

1) The lone pair of electrons on an oxygen atom in the deoxyribose sugar molecule makes a **dative covalent bond** with the phosphorus atom in a phosphate group.

2) A molecule of water is lost and a **phosphate-ester link** is formed.

3) There are still OH groups in the phosphate-ester, so further ester links can be formed. This allows the molecule to grow and make a polymer.

DNA **Bases** Join to the **Sugar** Via a **Condensation** Reaction too

It is also a **condensation reaction** that connects **base molecules** (like **adenine**, shown below) to sugars in the sugar-phosphate backbone. All of the bases have an **NH group** somewhere in their structure. It's the N atom of the NH group that bonds to deoxyribose — eliminating an OH group from the sugar and H from the NH group to form water.

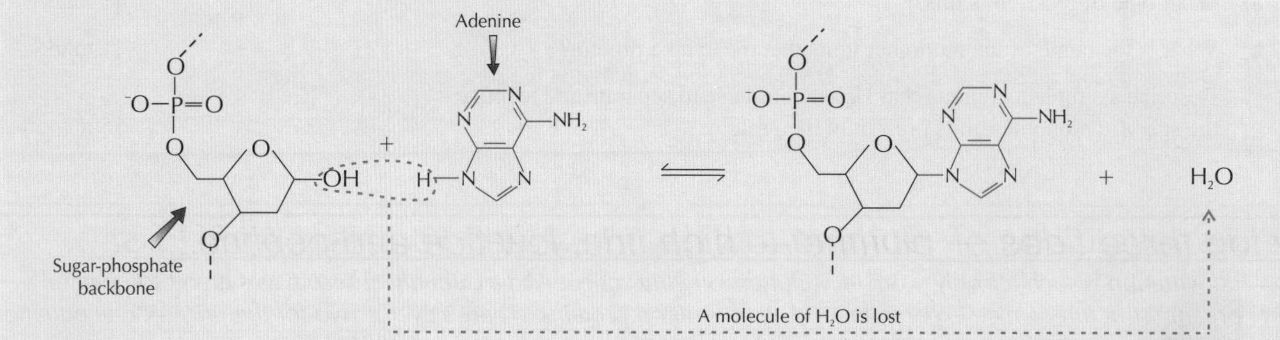

DNA

DNA Contains the Basis of the Genetic Code

The **sequence** of bases **determines** the sequence of **amino acids** in a protein.
The way that DNA codes for it is called the **genetic code**.

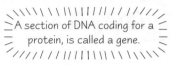
A section of DNA coding for a protein, is called a gene.

1) DNA codes for specific amino acids with sequences of three bases, called **base triplets**. Different sequences of bases code for different amino acids.

2) There are **64** possible **base triplet combinations**, but only about **20** amino acids in human proteins so there are some base triplets to spare. These aren't wasted though: ⟹

3) The **order** in which the amino acids are connected together (the primary structure) determines the secondary and tertiary structures of a protein — and so, all the **properties** of the protein.

4) There's a huge number of possible arrangements of amino acids and this creates the **enormous diversity** of proteins in living organisms.

- some amino acids are coded for by more than one base triplet.
- some base triplets act as 'punctuation' to stop and start production of an amino acid chain.

DNA Forms a Double Helix

DNA is made of **two polynucleotide strands**.

The two strands spiral together to form a **double helix** structure, which is held together by **hydrogen bonds** between the bases.

Each base can only join with one particular partner — this is called **specific** or **complementary base pairing**.

Adenine always pairs with **thymine** (A - T) and **guanine** always pairs with **cytosine** (G - C).

There's more on this on the next page.

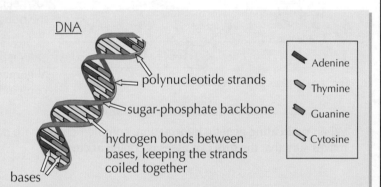

DNA

polynucleotide strands

sugar-phosphate backbone

hydrogen bonds between bases, keeping the strands coiled together

bases

⬛ Adenine
⬛ Thymine
⬛ Guanine
⬛ Cytosine

The double helix was **not** the first model to be suggested for the structure of DNA. There were other ideas — including a triple helix — that were tried and rejected before the currently accepted model was arrived at.

Practice Questions

Q1 What are the monomers that make up DNA called?

Q2 What are the three components of these monomers?

Q3 Name the reaction by which these components connect together.

Q4 Which type of intermolecular force holds the two strands of DNA together in a double helix?

Exam Question

1   A phosphate group, the base guanine and the sugar deoxyribose are shown below.

$$\text{O-P=O} \quad \text{(guanine)} \quad \text{(deoxyribose)}$$

a)   Draw and label a diagram showing a DNA nucleotide containing the base guanine using these three structures.   [2 marks]

b)   Explain how DNA codes for proteins using bases like guanine.   [2 marks]

The Genetic Code — Coming to Theatres Near You Next April First...

Let's face it, I'm a geek, but this DNA stuff never ceases to amaze me. It's just so flippin' clever. Sadly, even if you don't share my enthusiasm, you do have to know it. If you happen to be skipping the dead useful exam questions (naughty, naughty), then have a go at this one. Seriously, try it. You can have a biscuit afterwards.

More DNA

Yup, still on DNA I'm afraid...

Hydrogen Bonding Causes the Bases to Form Specific Pairs

You saw on the last page that in the DNA double helix, opposite bases always pair up **adenine (A) to thymine (T)** and **guanine (G) to cytosine (C)**. This is called **complementary base pairing**. It happens because of the arrangement of atoms in the base molecules that are capable of forming **hydrogen bonds**.

A **hydrogen bond** forms between a polar positive **H atom** (that's an H attached to anything highly electronegative like N) and a lone pair of electrons on a nearby **O** or **N atom**. To bond, the two atoms have to be the **right distance apart**.

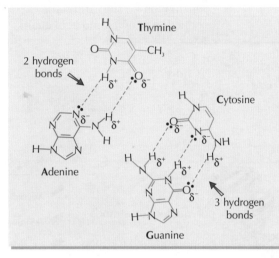

1) A and T have the right atoms — in the right places — to each form **2 hydrogen bonds**. This allows them to pair up. G and C can each form **3 hydrogen bonds**, so they pair up as well.

2) These are the **only** possible base combinations. Other base pairings would put the partially charged atoms too close together (they'd repel each other), or too far apart. In others, the bonding atoms just wouldn't line up properly.

3) The DNA helix has to twist so that the bases are in the **right alignment** and at the **right distance** apart for the complementary base pairs to form.

When **replicating genetic information**, complementary base pairing makes sure that the **order** of bases is copied **accurately**.

DNA can Copy Itself — Self-Replication

DNA has to be able to **copy itself** before **cell division** can take place, which is essential for growth and reproduction — pretty important stuff. This is how it's done:

1) The hydrogen bonds break and the DNA double helix starts to split into two single strands — a bit like a zip.

2) Bases on **free-floating nucleotides** in the cytoplasm now pair up with the complementary bases on the nucleotides in the DNA. **Complementary base pairing** makes sure the correct nucleotide joins in the correct place.

3) An enzyme called **DNA polymerase** joins the new nucleotides together to form a polynucleotide chain.

4) This happens on each of the strands to make an **exact copy** of what was on the other strand. The result is **two molecules** of DNA **identical** to the **original molecule** of DNA.

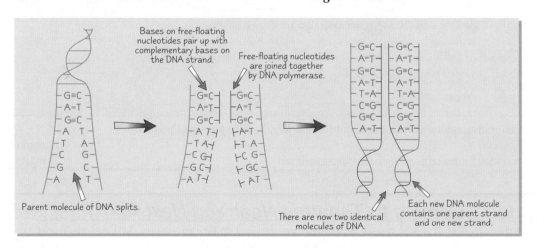

Parent molecule of DNA splits.

Bases on free-floating nucleotides pair up with complementary bases on the DNA strand.

Free-floating nucleotides are joined together by DNA polymerase.

There are now two identical molecules of DNA.

Each new DNA molecule contains one parent strand and one new strand.

The hospital offered a complementary baby pairing facility.

More DNA

Our DNA is Unique and can be Used to Identify Us

Although many parts of the DNA found in human cells are the same, there are sections of the molecule that **vary** from person to person. **Genetic fingerprinting** breaks down DNA and examines the sequences of bases in these sections. The technique is used to **identify people** based on samples of their DNA — which can be collected from a wide variety of fluid or tissue samples.

There is an Ethical Debate About the Use of Human DNA Analysis

Britain set up a **database** to store data collected from human DNA analysis in **1995**. Originally it only held the DNA profiles of **convicted criminals**, but since 2004 **all** DNA data that is collected is **stored**.

1) There are over a million UK citizens who have never been found guilty of any crime, but who have information about their DNA stored in the database.

2) Some people believe this information should be destroyed because it is adding innocent people to a list of criminals.

3) **Civil rights campaigners** argue that people should be able to ask to have their profiles removed — there are concerns about who could **access the information** and what it could be used for.

4) Others believe that the database should include the DNA of everyone who lives in Britain because the information is so **useful** to the police and has helped **solve many crimes**.

Just as soon as he was done analysing Simon's DNA, Harold was going to prove who stole his Take That CD.

Practice Questions

Q1 Name the intermolecular forces between bases on different strands of DNA.

Q3 Why are these forces important in DNA replication?

Q2 What is the name of the enzyme that joins nucleotides together?

Q4 How can our DNA be used to identify us?

Exam Questions

1 One of the vital features of DNA is that it is able to make exact copies of itself. If this were not possible then cells could not reproduce themselves. The process of copying begins with the double helix separating into two strands, which then turn into two identical DNA molecules.
   a) How are the two strands of DNA held together? [2 marks]
   b) When the two strands of the DNA double helix separate, each individual strand joins up with free floating nucleotides. How do these nucleotides join up in the correct order? [2 marks]
   c) If a section of one strand of DNA contains the base sequence ATTGCA, what would the matching sequence on the other strand be? [2 marks]

2 Over the past twenty-five years, the technique of genetic fingerprinting has proved increasingly useful in helping the police with their investigations. There are, however, ethical concerns with the use of human DNA analysis.
   a) What is genetic fingerprinting and why is it useful? [2 marks]
   b) Give one concern about the use of genetic fingerprinting in the UK. [1 mark]

Self-replication — a clever trick by DNA DNA DNA DNA DNA DNA DNA...

This hydrogen bonding lark should be familiar from AS level — if not, it might help if you refresh yourself on the basics. Hydrogen bonding and complementary base pairing are really important when it comes to DNA replication, so make sure you get how they fit together. That's it for DNA folks. Hold onto your hats, it's about to get really exciting...

RNA and Protein Synthesis

You've met DNA, now here comes its partner in crime — that little rascal RNA...

DNA and RNA are Very Similar Molecules

1) RNA is a **polymer of nucleotides**, with a series of bases attached to a sugar-phosphate backbone, just like DNA.

2) But RNA nucleotides have a different sugar. In **DNA** nucleotides it's **deoxyribose** — in **RNA** nucleotides it's **ribose**.

3) The other important difference is that RNA has the base **uracil** instead of **thymine**.

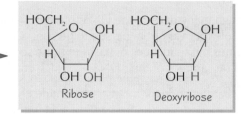

Ribose   Deoxyribose

mRNA, tRNA and rRNA are Different Types of RNA

There are **three types** of RNA and they're all involved in **making proteins**.

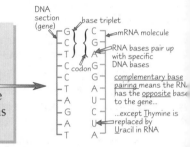

Messenger RNA (mRNA)

1) **mRNA is a single polynucleotide strand**.

2) It's an exact **reverse copy** of a section of DNA — except thymine's replaced by uracil.

3) The three bases in mRNA that pair up with a base triplet on the DNA strand (see page 49) are called a **codon**. Codons are dead important for making proteins. A codon has the **opposite** bases to a base triplet.

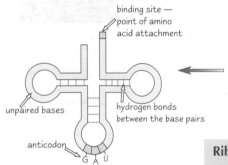

binding site —
point of amino
acid attachment

unpaired bases

hydrogen bonds
between the base pairs

anticodon

Transfer RNA (tRNA)

1) **tRNA is a single polynucleotide strand** that's folded into a **clover shape**.

2) Every tRNA has a **binding site** at one end, where a specific **amino acid** attaches.

3) Each tRNA molecule also has a specific sequence of **three bases**, called an **anticodon**.

Ribosomal RNA (rRNA)

rRNA is made up of polynucleotide strands that are attached to proteins to make things called **ribosomes** (see page 53). It's the largest type of RNA.

mRNA is needed For Protein Synthesis

Messenger RNA (mRNA) is made using DNA as a **template**, in a similar way to DNA replication. The process is called **transcription**.

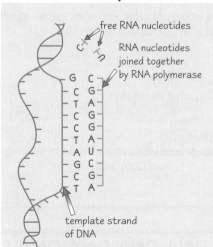

free RNA nucleotides

RNA nucleotides
joined together
by RNA polymerase

template strand
of DNA

1) The DNA double helix unwinds to reveal a **single stranded** portion.

2) The DNA bases attract free **RNA nucleotides** with complementary bases.

3) The RNA nucleotides are joined to each other by the enzyme **RNA polymerase**. This forms a strand of mRNA.

4) The DNA **coils up again**, unaltered.

> Remember the new strand is RNA — so uracil (not thymine) pairs with adenine and the sugar is ribose (not deoxyribose).

The newly made mRNA strand does not wind up with the DNA — it's **released** and is free to **move around** the cell. It's small enough to move outside the cell's nucleus into the cytoplasm, where it's used in the next process you've got to learn about — **translation**.

RNA and Protein Synthesis

Proteins are Made During Translation

In **translation**, amino acids are joined together to make a **polypeptide** chain.

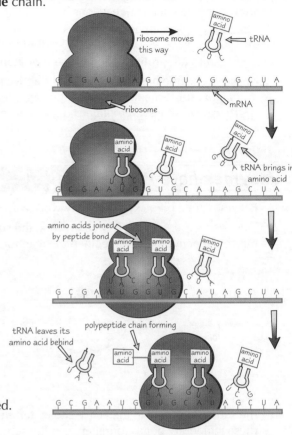

1) **Ribosomes** are large complexes made from rRNA and proteins. A **ribosome** attaches to the **mRNA**, and starts to move along it, looking for a **start codon**.

   Start codons have the base sequence **AUG** and indicate that the code for a new polypeptide chain is beginning. They code for the **first** amino acid in the chain (so this is always the same).

2) Once it's found a start codon, the ribosome temporarily pauses, until a **tRNA** with the correct **anticodon bases** pairs with the AUG codon inside the ribosome. The tRNA has an amino acid attached to it.

3) The ribosome then moves three bases forward, and waits for a different tRNA to bring another amino acid into the ribosome. Now there are two amino acids inside the ribosome and the ribosome joins them together with a **peptide bond**.

4) The ribosome moves forwards again. The first tRNA now **leaves** the ribosome and breaks away from its amino acid. A new tRNA brings in the third amino acid of the chain.

5) The process continues in this way until a **stop codon** is reached. The stop codon **doesn't** code for an amino acid. The ribosome **releases** the polypeptide chain at this point.

Practice Questions

Q1 What's made during transcription?

Q2 What base does RNA have that DNA doesn't?

Exam Questions

1   The sequence of bases in a small portion of mRNA is as follows: –AAGGUGCAUCGA–
    a)   Why couldn't the sequence be from a portion of DNA?   [1 mark]
    b)   How many amino acids does this sequence code for? Explain your answer.   [2 marks]
    c)   Write the sequence of bases for the DNA strand from which the portion of mRNA was transcribed.   [2 marks]

2   DNA contains a sequence of base triplets that represents a sequence of amino acids in a protein molecule.
    The first stage in making a protein is to make a molecule of mRNA from the DNA.
    a)   What is the name of this process and where in the cell does it occur?   [2 marks]
    b)   What is the name of a set of three bases in mRNA, and how are they related to the base triplets in DNA?   [2 marks]
    c)   A protein is made using the bases in mRNA by a process called translation.
         i) What is the name of the protein-RNA complex involved in this process?   [1 mark]
         ii) Why do all proteins made in this way start with the same amino acid (methionine)?   [2 marks]

3   A codon on a section of mRNA has the sequence of bases –GGU–, which corresponds to the amino acid glycine.
    The mRNA codes for a polypeptide which contains 73 amino acids.
    Explain how this glycine molecule is inserted into the polypeptide.   [4 marks]

Help — I need a translation...

When you first go through protein synthesis it might make approximately no sense, but I promise its bark is worse than its bite. All those strange words disguise what is really quite a straightforward process — and the diagrams are dead handy for getting to grips with it. Keep drawing them yourself, 'til you can reproduce them.

Enzymes

Ah enzymes. Where would we be without them? I wouldn't be eating this delicious chocolatey oaty biscuit that's for sure.

Enzymes *are* Biological Catalysts

Enzymes speed up chemical reactions by acting as biological catalysts.

1) They catalyse every **metabolic reaction** in the bodies of living organisms.
2) Enzymes are **proteins**. Some also have **non-protein components**.
3) Every enzyme has an area called its **active site**. This is the part that the **substrate** fits into so that it can interact with the enzyme. The active site is three-dimensional — it's part of the **tertiary structure** of the enzyme protein (see page 47).

> Substrates are the molecules that enzymes act on to speed up reactions.

Enzymes *have* High Specificity

1) Enzymes are a bit picky. They only work with **specific substrates** — usually only one.
2) This is because, for the enzyme to work, the substrate has to **fit** into the **active site**. If the substrate's shape doesn't match the active site's shape, then the reaction won't be catalysed. This is called the '**lock and key**' model.

> The substrate fits into the enzyme the same way a key fits into a lock.

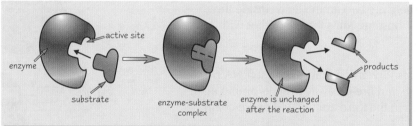

Kevin wondered if he'd ever find the right key.

3) The substrate is held in the active site by **temporary** bonds such as hydrogen bonds and van der Waals forces. These temporary bonds form between the substrate and "R" groups of the enzyme's amino acids.

Enzymes *Only Work Well in a* Narrow Range *of Temperatures and pH*

The graphs below show how the rate of an **enzyme-catalysed reaction** changes at different temperatures and pH values.

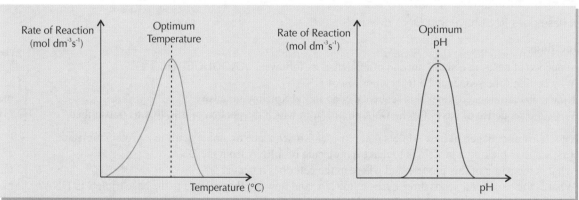

There is an **optimum temperature** and **pH** at which the reaction rate is at a maximum — here the enzyme works best.

1) At **low temperatures**, the reaction is **slow** because the reactant molecules have low kinetic energy.
2) At **higher temperatures**, or at **higher or lower pH values**, the reaction rate drops off dramatically because the enzyme becomes **denatured**. It stops working properly and can no longer effectively catalyse the reaction.

> Enzymes **denature** when they become too hot, or are exposed to too high a concentration of acid or alkali. The bonds that define the **active site** break, changing the **tertiary structure** of the enzyme molecule. The active site is no longer the **correct shape** for the substrate to fit into.

Enzymes

Inhibitors Slow Down the Rate of Reaction

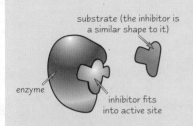

substrate (the inhibitor is a similar shape to it)

enzyme

inhibitor fits into active site

1) **Inhibitors** are molecules with a **similar shape to the substrate**.

2) They compete with the substrate to bond to the active site, but no reaction follows. Instead they **block** the active site, so **no substrate** can **fit** in it.

3) How much inhibition happens depends on the **relative concentrations** of inhibitor and substrate — if there's a lot more of the inhibitor, it'll take up most of the active sites and very little substrate will be able to get to the enzyme. The amount of inhibition is also affected by how **strongly** the inhibitor bonds to the active site.

Enzymes can Reduce the **Environmental Impact** of **Industrial** Reactions

Enzymes are widely used in industry to :

1) Make commercial reactions proceed **quickly** at relatively **low temperatures**.
2) **Increase** the **yields** of reactions and make them more **selective**.

This can help to reduce the **environmental cost** of producing a chemical in several ways:

1) If the reaction is carried out at a lower temperature **less fuel is burned** and **less pollution** is created.
2) Higher yields can often mean **less unreacted waste chemicals** — again reducing pollution.
3) Enzymes can also prevent side-reactions from occurring, **reducing unwanted** and potentially **harmful by-products**.

Practice Questions

Q1 What type of molecule is an enzyme?

Q2 Name the theory that explains why enzymes are very specific.

Q3 What holds substrate molecules to the active site of an enzyme?

Q4 How does an inhibitor prevent an enzyme from catalysing a reaction?

Exam Questions

1 Enzymes are catalysts with a high specificity.
  a) What does it mean to say that enzymes have 'high specificity'. [1 mark]
  b) Explain why enzymes have high specificity. [2 marks]

2 The rate of an enzyme-catalysed reaction is measured at different temperatures. It is found that as the temperature increases the rate of reaction initially increases and then rapidly decreases above about 40 °C.
  a) Explain why:
    i) At low temperatures the reaction is slow. [2 marks]
    ii) At high temperatures the reaction is slow. [2 marks]
  b) What else, apart from temperature, must be at exactly the right value for an enzyme-catalysed reaction to be at its fastest? [1 mark]

3 Sometimes adding a chemical to an enzyme-catalysed reaction can cause the enzyme to stop working properly.
  a) What are chemicals that prevent enzymes from working called? [1 mark]
  b) One way that such a chemical may act to stop an enzyme working is to cause the shape of the active site to change. Explain another way in which a molecule may prevent an enzyme from working. [3 marks]

Substrate keys — they fit, but my gosh, don't they know it...

I don't know what it is with enzymes. They're never bloomin' happy. It's too hot, it's too cold, it's really acidic... You wouldn't catch a non-biological catalyst behaving like that. Still they really do have their uses, so make sure you learn 'em. And make sure you know what makes them tick — the examiners'll love you for it. So will the enzyme, the fickle beast...

Molecular Shapes and Isomerism

Thought you could just draw out a molecule any old way? Think again my friend... Mwahahahah...

Single-Bonded Carbon Atoms Have Their Bonds Arranged Like a Tetrahedron

1) When a carbon atom makes four single bonds (as in alkanes), the atoms around the carbon form **tetrahedral shapes**.

   ~ This is all because electron pairs repel each other ~ and try to get as far apart as possible.

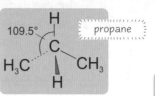

2) This **tetrahedral** shape around each carbon atom means that single-bonded carbon chains containing 3 or more carbon atoms form a 'wiggly line'.

Atoms Round a Double-Bonded Carbon form an Equilateral Triangle

When there's a **double-bond** involved, the situation is different.

1) The C=C double bond and the atoms bonded to these carbons are **planar** (flat).

2) Each double-bonded carbon and the atoms attached to it are **trigonal planar** — the attached atoms are at the corners of an imaginary **equilateral triangle**.

   ~ The bond angles ~ are all 120°.

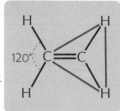

Structural Isomers have Different Structural Arrangements of Atoms

Structural isomers have the same **molecular formula**, but their atoms are **arranged** in different ways.
The molecules below are all structural isomers of each other — they all have the **molecular formula** $C_4H_{10}O$:

butan-1-ol

2-methylpropan-1-ol

butan-2-ol

diethyl ether

Structural isomers can have...   ...different arrangements of the carbon skeleton...   ...different positions of the functional groups...   ...or different functional groups.

Stereoisomers are Arranged Differently in Space

Stereoisomers have the same molecular formula and their atoms are arranged in the same way. The only difference is the **orientation** of the bonds in **space**. There are two types of stereoisomerism — **E/Z** and **optical**.

E/Z Isomerism Happens Because there's no Rotation about the Double Bond

But-2-ene shows E/Z isomerism:

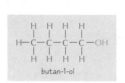

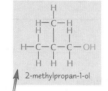

But but-1-ene doesn't:

identical groups

but-1-ene

Z isomers have similar groups on the **same side** of the double bond.

This could also be called '<u>cis</u>-but-2-ene'.

E isomers have similar groups going diagonally across.

It could also be called '<u>trans</u>-but-2-ene'.

~ If there are two identical groups attached to a double bonded carbon, then E/Z isomerism won't happen.

E/Z isomerism is sometimes called **cis-trans isomerism**, where '**cis**' is the **Z-isomer**, and '**trans**' is the **E-isomer**.

The trouble with the cis-trans naming system is that it doesn't work if there are 4 **different** groups involved.

The E/Z system keeps working though because each group linked to the double-bonded carbons is given a **priority**.

If the two carbon atoms have their 'higher priority group' on **opposite** sides, then it's an **E** isomer.

If the two carbon atoms have their 'higher priority group' on the **same** side, then it's a **Z** isomer.

(Thankfully, you don't need to know how to work out the priority of the groups — this is just why the E/Z naming system was developed.)

Molecular Shapes and Isomerism

Optical Isomers are Mirror Images of Each Other

A **chiral** (or **asymmetric**) carbon atom is one that has **four different** groups attached to it. It's possible to arrange the groups in two different ways around the carbon atom so that two different molecules are made — these molecules are called **enantiomers** or **optical isomers**.

The enantiomers are **mirror images** and no matter which way you turn them, they can't be **superimposed**.

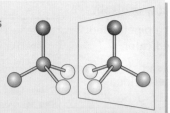

If the molecules can be superimposed, they're achiral — and there's no optical isomerism.

One enantiomer's always labelled **D** and one **L** — luckily you don't have to worry about which is which. Chiral compounds are very common in nature, but you usually only find **one** of the enantiomers — for example, all naturally occurring amino acids are **L–amino acids** (except glycine which isn't chiral).

You have to be able to identify any chiral centres in a molecule and draw optical isomers...

Example

Locating the chiral centre:
Look for the carbon atom with four different groups attached. Here it's the carbon with the four groups H, OH, CHO and CH₃ attached.

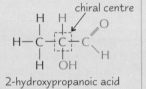

chiral centre

2-hydroxypropanoic acid

Drawing isomers:
Once you know the chiral carbon, draw one enantiomer in a tetrahedral shape. Don't try to draw the full structure of each group — it gets confusing. Then draw a mirror image beside it.

enantiomers of 2-hydroxypropanoic acid

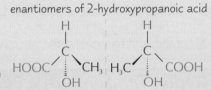

Practice Questions

Q1 State the shapes of methane and ethene. What are the bond angles in each?

Q2 What is the difference between structural isomerism and stereoisomerism?

Q3 Why do alkanes not have E/Z isomers?

Q4 How can you tell whether a carbon atom in a molecule is a chiral centre or not?

Exam Questions

1   There are sixteen possible structural isomers of the compound $C_3H_6O_2$, four of which show stereoisomerism.

   a) Explain the meaning of the term *stereoisomerism*. [2 marks]

   b) Draw a pair of E/Z isomers of $C_3H_6O_2$, with hydroxyl groups. Label them *cis* and *trans*. [3 marks]

   c) i) There are two chiral isomers of $C_3H_6O_2$. Draw the enantiomers of one of the chiral isomers. [2 marks]

   ii) What structural feature in the molecule gives rise to optical isomerism? [1 mark]

2   a) Explain why alkanes cannot have E/Z isomers, but alkenes can. [3 marks]

   b) Do all alkenes have E/Z (or cis/trans) isomers? Explain your answer. [2 marks]

Time for some quiet reflection...

Weelll, this page isn't exactly thrilling. And it takes a while to get your head round all this E/Z, D/L business, but stick with it — you'll get there eventually. If it helps you to visualise stuff then make a few matchstick models (yes I know your mum told you never to play with matches, but you're not setting fire to 'em). Hours of er... fun will follow.

Titrations

Are you sitting comfortably? Then I'll begin — The Steel Story. And it starts a bit mathsy. Sorry.
Just take a deep breath, dive in, and don't bash your head on the bottom.

Acid-Base Titrations — How Much Acid is Needed to **Neutralise** a Base

1) **Titrations** allow you to find out **exactly** how much acid is needed to **neutralise** a quantity of alkali.

2) You measure out some **alkali** using a pipette and put it in a flask, along with some **indicator**, e.g. **phenolphthalein**.

3) First of all, do a rough titration to get an idea where the **end point** is (the point where the alkali is **exactly neutralised** and the indicator changes colour). Add the **acid** to the alkali using a **burette** — giving the flask a regular **swirl**.

4) Now do an **accurate** titration. Run the acid in to within 2 cm³ of the end point, then add the acid **dropwise**. If you don't notice exactly when the solution changed colour you've **overshot** and your result won't be accurate.

5) **Record** the amount of acid used to **neutralise** the alkali. It's best to **repeat** this process a few times, until the volume of the acid recorded is the same (within 0.1 cm³).

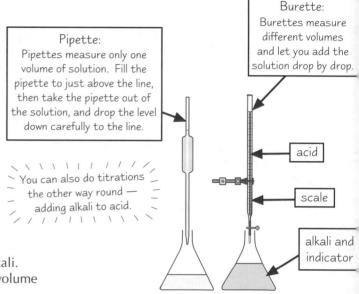

Pipette:
Pipettes measure only one volume of solution. Fill the pipette to just above the line, then take the pipette out of the solution, and drop the level down carefully to the line.

Burette:
Burettes measure different volumes and let you add the solution drop by drop.

acid

scale

alkali and indicator

You can also do titrations the other way round — adding alkali to acid.

Redox Titrations are a Bit Different

Redox titrations let you find out how much **oxidising agent** is needed to **exactly** react with a quantity of **reducing agent**. You need to know the **concentration** of either the oxidising agent or the reducing agent. Then you can use the titration results to work out the concentration of the other.

You need to know about redox titrations in which **manganate(VII) ions** (MnO_4^-) are the oxidising agent.

Choppy seas made it difficult for Captain Blackbird to read the burette accurately. Being 30 miles off the coast didn't help either.

1) First you measure out a quantity of **reducing agent**, e.g. aqueous Fe^{2+} ions, using a pipette, and put it in a conical flask.

2) You then add some **dilute sulfuric acid** to the flask — this is an excess, so you don't have to be too exact (about 20 cm³ should do it).
The acid is added to make sure there are plenty of H⁺ ions to allow the oxidising agent to be reduced — see page 61.

3) Now you add the aqueous MnO_4^- (the **oxidising agent**) to the reducing agent using a **burette**, swirling the conical flask as you do so.

4) You stop when the mixture in the flask **just** becomes tainted with the colour of the MnO_4^- (the **end point**) and record the volume of oxidising agent added. This is the **rough titration**.

5) Now you do some **accurate titrations**. You need to do a few until you get **two or more** readings that are **within 0.10 cm³** of each other.

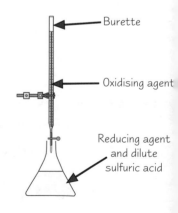

Burette

Oxidising agent

Reducing agent and dilute sulfuric acid

You can also do titrations the **other way round** — adding the reducing agent to the oxidising agent.

There's a **Sharp Colour Change** When the Reaction's **Completed**

1) **Manganate(VII) ions** (MnO_4^-) in **aqueous potassium manganate(VII)** ($KMnO_4$) are **purple**.

2) When they're added to the reducing agent, they start reacting with the reducing agent. The reaction continues until **all** of the reducing agent has reacted. The **very next drop** into the flask will give the mixture the **purple colour of the oxidising agent**. The trick is to spot **exactly** when this happens.

Titrations

You Can Use the **Titration Results** to Find the **Concentration** of a Reagent

Example: 27.5 cm³ of 0.0200 mol dm⁻³ aqueous potassium manganate(VII) reacted with 25.0 cm³ of acidified iron(II) sulfate solution. Calculate the concentration of Fe^{2+} ions in the solution.

$$MnO_{4\ (aq)}^- + 8H^+_{(aq)} + 5Fe^{2+}_{(aq)} \rightarrow Mn^{2+}_{(aq)} + 4H_2O_{(l)} + 5Fe^{3+}_{(aq)}$$

1) Work out the number of **moles of MnO_4^- ions** added to the flask.

Number of moles MnO_4^- added $= \dfrac{\text{concentration} \times \text{volume}}{1000} = \dfrac{0.0200 \times 27.5}{1000} = 5.50 \times 10^{-4}$ moles

2) Look at the balanced equation to find how many moles of **Fe^{2+}** react with **every mole** of MnO_4^-. Then you can work out the **number of moles of Fe^{2+}** in the flask.

5 moles of Fe^{2+} react with 1 mole of MnO_4^-. So moles of $Fe^{2+} = 5.50 \times 10^{-4} \times 5 = 2.75 \times 10^{-3}$ moles.

3) Work out the **number of moles of Fe^{2+}** that would be in 1000 cm³ (1 dm³) of solution — this is the **concentration**.

25.0 cm³ of solution contained 2.75×10^{-3} moles of Fe^{2+}.

1000 cm³ of solution would contain $\dfrac{(2.75 \times 10^{-3}) \times 1000}{25.0} = 0.110$ moles of Fe^{2+}.

So the concentration of Fe^{2+} is **0.110 mol dm⁻³**.

Manganate 007, licensed to oxidise.

Practice Questions

Q1 Name two pieces of equipment you can use to accurately measure the volume of a solution in a titration.
Q2 What is meant by the 'end point' of a titration?
Q3 How do you know when you have reached the end point in an acid-base titration?
Q4 Why don't you need to add an indicator when doing a redox titration with manganate(VII) ions?

Exam Questions

1   Solutions of hydrogen peroxide, H_2O_2, can be analysed by titration with acidified manganate(VII) ions. The equation for the reaction that occurs during the titration is:

$$2MnO_{4\ (aq)}^- + 6H^+_{(aq)} + 5H_2O_{2(aq)} \rightarrow 2Mn^{2+}_{(aq)} + 8H_2O_{(l)} + 5O_{2(g)}$$

A 15.0 cm³ sample of acidified hydrogen peroxide solution exactly reacted with 27.8 cm³ of manganate(VII) solution with a concentration of 0.0100 mol dm⁻³. Calculate the concentration of the hydrogen peroxide solution. Give your answer to a suitable number of significant figures. [5 marks]

2   Describe how the concentration of a sample of hydrochloric acid could be found by titration with a solution of sodium hydroxide that has an accurately known concentration. State clearly the experimental procedure and name any chemicals and equipment used in each stage. [5 marks]

3   The iron content of a sample of steel can be determined using a titration. The steel is first dissolved in sulfuric acid, which converts the iron into Fe^{2+} ions. These can then be oxidised to Fe^{3+} ions in a manganate(VII) titration:

$$MnO_{4\ (aq)}^- + 8H^+_{(aq)} + 5Fe^{2+}_{(aq)} \rightarrow Mn^{2+}_{(aq)} + 5Fe^{3+}_{(aq)} + 4H_2O_{(l)}$$

0.150 g of steel was dissolved in sulfuric acid and required 26.7 cm³ of 0.0200 mol dm⁻³ manganate(VII) solution for complete oxidation.

a)   How many moles of manganate(VII) ions were added to the solution? [1 mark]
b)   How many moles of Fe^{2+} ions were in the solution? [1 mark]
c)   What mass of iron was in the solution? (A_r (Fe) = 55.8) [1 mark]
d)   What was the percentage mass of iron in the steel? [1 mark]

And how many moles does it take to change a light bulb...

*WATCH OUT — those mischievous OCR B examiners might give you **any** calculation you learned at AS in your A2 exams. And I mean **any**. So you'd best go back to your AS notes and check you can still work out molecular formulas, masses of reagents, percentage yields, volumes of gases, volumes and concentration of solutions... go on... you know you should.*

Redox

Redox reactions are all about sharing, caring atoms moving their electrons about.

Redox Reactions Involve Electron Transfer

In a **redox reaction** one chemical is **reduced** and another **oxidised**.
Something is **oxidised** when it **loses electrons** and **reduced** when it **gains electrons**.

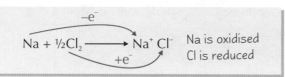

Na is oxidised
Cl is reduced

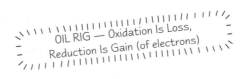

OIL RIG — Oxidation Is Loss,
Reduction Is Gain (of electrons)

I couldn't find a red ox, so you'll have to make do with a multicoloured donkey instead.

1) A **reducing agent donates** some of its electrons to **reduce** something — and gets oxidised itself.
2) The more **powerful** a **reducing agent** is, the more **easily** it can be **oxidised**
3) An **oxidising agent takes** electrons away from something to **oxidise** it — and gets reduced itself.
4) The more **powerful** an **oxidising agent** is, the more **easily** it can be **reduced**.

There are Rules for Assigning Oxidation States

(They're also called oxidation <u>numbers</u>.)

If you see **Roman numerals** in a chemical name, it's an **oxidation number** — it applies to the atom or group immediately before it. Here are the rules for working them out.

1) All atoms are treated as **ions** for this, even if they're covalently bonded.

2) Uncombined **elements** have an oxidation state of **0**.

3) Elements just bonded to **identical atoms**, like O_2 and H_2, also have an oxidation state of **0**.

4) The oxidation state of a simple **monatomic ion**, e.g. Na^+, is the same as its **charge**.

5) In **compounds** or **compound ions**, the **overall oxidation state** is just the ion charge.

SO_4^{2-} — **overall oxidation state = –2**,
oxidation state of O = –2 (total = –8)
so oxidation state of S = +6

Within an ion, the most electronegative element has a negative oxidation state (equal to its ionic charge). Other elements have more positive oxidation states.

6) The sum of the oxidation states for a **neutral compound** is 0.

Fe_2O_3 — **overall oxidation state = 0**, oxidation state of O = –2
(total = –6), so oxidation state of Fe = +3 (total = +6)

7) Combined **oxygen** is nearly always –2, except in peroxides, where it's –1,
...and in the fluorides OF_2, where it's +2, and O_2F_2, where it's +1 (and O_2, where it's zero).

In H_2O, oxidation state of O = –2, but in H_2O_2, oxidation state of H has to be +1
(an H atom can only lose one electron), so oxidation state of O = –1

8) Combined **hydrogen** is +1, except in metal hydrides where it is –1 (and H_2 where it's 0).

In **HF**, oxidation state of H = +1, but in **NaH**, oxidation state of H = –1

E.g. copper has oxidation number **2** in **copper(II) sulfate**, and manganese has oxidation
number **7** in a **manganate(VII) ion** (MnO_4^-).

Redox

You can Separate Redox Reactions into Half-Reactions

1) A redox reaction is made up of an **oxidation half-reaction** and a **reduction half-reaction**.
2) You can write an **ionic half-equation** for each of these **half-reactions**.
3) Then you can **combine** the half-equations to get the equation for the **whole** reaction.

Example: **Zinc metal** displaces **silver ions** from silver nitrate solution to form **zinc nitrate** and a deposit of **silver**.

The zinc atoms are oxidised and each lose 2 electrons $Zn_{(s)} \rightarrow Zn^{2+}_{(aq)} + 2e^-$

The silver ions are reduced and each gain 1 electron $Ag^+_{(aq)} + e^- \rightarrow Ag_{(s)}$

In order to put two half-equations together to make the overall equation, there must be the **same** number of **electrons** in **both**.

Two silver ions are needed to accept the **two electrons** released by each zinc atom. So you need to double the silver half-equation before the two half-equations can be combined:

$$2Ag^+_{(aq)} + 2e^- \rightarrow 2Ag_{(s)}$$

Now the number of electrons lost and gained **balance**, so the half-equations can be combined: $Zn_{(s)} + 2Ag^+_{(aq)} \rightarrow Zn^{2+}_{(aq)} + 2Ag_{(s)}$

Electrons aren't included in the full equation.

H⁺ Ions May be Needed to Reduce Some Oxidising Agents

1) **Manganate(VII) ions**, MnO_4^-, contain Mn with an oxidation number of **+7**. When these ions are **reduced** they gain five electrons to become Mn^{2+} ions, with an oxidation number of **+2**.

2) In a **+2 state**, Mn can exist as simple $Mn^{2+}_{(aq)}$ ions. But in a **+7 state**, Mn has to combine with **oxygen** to form MnO_4^- ions, as $Mn^{7+}_{(aq)}$ ions wouldn't be stable.

3) MnO_4^- ions are good **oxidising agents**. The trouble is, when they get reduced to Mn^{2+} the four O^{2-} ions have to go somewhere. To solve this problem, **H⁺ ions** are added. The $4O^{2-}$ can now react with $8H^+$ to form $4H_2O$. This is why manganate(VII) ions must be **acidified** to work as an oxidising agent.

The half-equation is:
$$MnO_4^-{}_{(aq)} + 8H^+_{(aq)} + 5e^- \rightarrow Mn^{2+}_{(aq)} + 4H_2O_{(l)}$$

Practice Questions

Q1 Is a powerful oxidising agent something that is easily oxidised or easily reduced?
Q2 Define oxidation and reduction in terms of electrons.
Q3 What is the name of an equation that shows only oxidation or only reduction?
Q4 What is the oxidation state of an element always equal to?

Exam Questions

1 Cu_2O reacts with sulfuric acid according to this equation:
$$Cu_2O_{(s)} + H_2SO_{4(aq)} \rightarrow CuSO_{4(aq)} + Cu_{(s)} + H_2O_{(l)}$$
a) What is the oxidation state of copper in:
   i) Cu_2O ii) $CuSO_4$ iii) Cu [3 marks]
b) Name the compounds in a) i) and ii).   [2 marks]
c) The sulfate ion is said to be a 'spectator ion' in this redox reaction. Explain what this means.   [1 mark]

2 The concentration of a solution of manganate(VII) ions can be found by titration with ethanedioate ions, $C_2O_4^{2-}$. The two half-equations for this reaction are:
$$MnO_4^- + 8H^+ + 5e^- \rightarrow Mn^{2+} + 4H_2O$$
$$C_2O_4^{2-} \rightarrow 2CO_2 + 2e^-$$
a) Are the ethanedioate ions being oxidised or reduced? Explain your answer.   [2 marks]
b) What are the oxidation states of carbon in $C_2O_4^{2-}$ and CO_2?   [2 marks]
c) Use the two half-equations to form a correctly balanced overall equation.   [3 marks]

They tried to make me study redox, but I said no, no, no...

*The words oxidation and reduction are tossed about a lot in chemistry — so they're important. Don't forget, oxidation is really about electrons being lost, **not** oxygen being gained, but you'll hopefully remember that from AS. Fortunately OIL RIG was invented to help out...*

OIL RIG
- **O**xidation **I**s **L**oss
- **R**eduction **I**s **G**ain
(of electrons)

Electrode Potentials

On these pages there are electrons toing and froing in redox reactions. And when electrons move, you get electricity.

Electrochemical Cells *Make* Electricity

Electrochemical cells can be made from **two different metals** dipped in salt solutions of their **own ions** and connected by a wire (the **external circuit**).

There are always **two** reactions within an electrochemical cell — one's an oxidation and one's a reduction — so it's a **redox process** (see page 60).

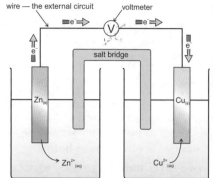

Here's what happens in the **zinc/copper** electrochemical cell on the right:

1) Zinc **loses electrons** more easily than copper. So in the half-cell on the left, zinc (from the zinc electrode) is **OXIDISED** to form $Zn^{2+}_{(aq)}$ ions.
$$Zn_{(s)} \rightarrow Zn^{2+}_{(aq)} + 2e^-$$
This releases electrons into the external circuit.

2) In the other half-cell, the **same number of electrons** are taken from the external circuit, **REDUCING** the Cu^{2+} ions to copper atoms.
$$Cu^{2+}_{(aq)} + 2e^- \rightarrow Cu_{(s)}$$

The solutions are connected by a **salt bridge** made from filter paper soaked in $KNO_{3(aq)}$. The K^+ and NO_3^- ions flow through the salt bridge and balance out the charges in the beakers.

So **electrons** flow through the wire from the most reactive metal to the least.

A voltmeter in the external circuit shows the **voltage** between the two half-cells. This is the **cell potential** or **emf**, E_{cell}.

The boys tested the strength of the bridge, whilst the girls just stood and watched.

You can also have half-cells involving **solutions of two aqueous ions of the same element**, such as $Fe^{2+}_{(aq)}/Fe^{3+}_{(aq)}$.

The conversion from Fe^{2+} to Fe^{3+}, or vice versa, happens on the surface of the **electrode**.

$$Fe^{2+}_{(aq)} \rightarrow Fe^{3+}_{(aq)} + e^-$$
$$Fe^{3+}_{(aq)} + e^- \rightarrow Fe^{2+}_{(aq)}$$

Because neither the reactants nor the products are solids, you need something else for the **electrode**.
It needs to **conduct electricity** and be very **inert**, so that it won't react with anything in the half-cell. **Platinum** is an excellent choice, but is very **expensive**, so **graphite** is often used instead.

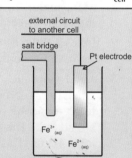

The *Standard Electrode Potential* Tells You Which *Metal* is Oxidised

All electrode potentials are measured against a **standard hydrogen electrode**.

The **standard electrode potential** $E^\ominus$ of a half-cell is the **voltage measured** under **standard conditions** when the **half-cell** is connected to a **standard hydrogen electrode**.

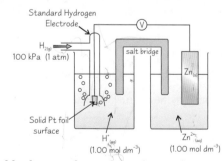

The ⊖ symbol means standard conditions, which are:
1) Any solution must have a concentration of 1.00 mol dm^{-3}
2) The temperature must be 298 K (25 °C)
3) The pressure must be 100 kPa

1) The **standard hydrogen electrode** is always shown on the **left** — it doesn't matter whether or not the other half-cell has a more positive value. The standard hydrogen electrode half-cell has a value of **0.00 V**.

2) The whole cell potential = $E^\ominus_{\text{right-hand side}} - E^\ominus_{\text{left-hand side}}$.

$E^\ominus_{\text{left-hand side}} = 0.00$ V, so the **voltage reading** will be equal to $E^\ominus_{\text{right-hand side}}$.
This reading could be **positive** or **negative**, depending which way the **electrons flow**.

3) In an electrochemical cell, the half-cell with the **most negative** standard electrode potential is the one in which **oxidation** happens.

Electrode Potentials

Work Out E_{cell} From Standard Electrode Potentials

You can **calculate** the **cell potential**, E_{cell}, by doing the calculation: $E^{\circ}_{cell} = \left(E^{\circ}_{more\ positive} - E^{\circ}_{more\ negative} \right)$

The cell potential will always be a **positive voltage**, because the more
negative E° value is being subtracted from the more positive E° value.

So for a Zn/Cu cell, E_{cell} = +0.34 – (–0.76) = **+1.10 V**

Half-cell	E° (V)
$Zn^{2+}_{(aq)}/Zn_{(s)}$	–0.76
$Cu^{2+}_{(aq)}/Cu_{(s)}$	+0.34

Standard Electrode Potentials Tell you if a Reaction is Feasible

You can **work out** if a reaction is **possible** by looking at the **standard electrode potentials**.
If the standard electrode potential for what is being **reduced** is **greater** (more positive) than the
electrode potential for whatever is being oxidised then the reaction could take place.

> For example zinc will react with copper(II) sulfate. $Zn + CuSO_4 \rightarrow ZnSO_4 + Cu$
>
> In this reaction copper(II) ions are being **reduced** and zinc oxidised. The standard electrode potential
> for Cu^{2+}/Cu (+0.34) is **more positive** than the one for Zn^{2+}/Zn (–0.76). This reaction **could happen**.
> The **reverse reaction**, where copper reduces zinc ions, could **not happen**.

1) A reaction can be **feasible** but you may not see anything happen, or be able to collect
   any product from the reaction.

2) The electrode potential values tell you **nothing** about the **rate of reaction**.

3) The rate can be so slow that effectively the reaction doesn't happen.
   '**Feasible**' only means '**possible**' — it **doesn't** mean a reaction will definitely **happen**.

Practice Questions

Q1 Draw a diagram of the half-cell used for determining the standard electrode potential for the Fe^{3+}/Fe^{2+} system.

Q2 List the three standard conditions used when measuring standard electrode potentials.

Q3 $Fe^{3+} + e^- \rightleftharpoons Fe^{2+}$, E° = +0.77 V $Mn^{3+} + e^- \rightleftharpoons Mn^{2+}$, E° = +1.48 V
   Show that the cell potential for the above system is +0.71 V.

Exam Questions

1   An electrochemical cell containing a zinc half-cell and a silver half-cell was set up using a potassium nitrate salt bridge.
   The cell potential at 25 °C was measured to be 1.40 V.

$$Zn^{2+}_{(aq)} + 2e^- \rightleftharpoons Zn_{(s)} \qquad E^{\circ} = -0.76\ V$$
$$Ag^+_{(aq)} + e^- \rightleftharpoons Ag_{(s)} \qquad E^{\circ} = +0.80\ V$$

   a) Draw a labelled diagram of this cell. [3 marks]
   b) Use the standard electrode potentials given to calculate the standard cell potential for a zinc-silver cell. [1 mark]
   c) Suggest why the actual cell potential was different from the value calculated in part (b). [1 mark]
   d) Write an equation for the overall cell reaction. [1 mark]
   e) Which half-cell released the electrons into the circuit? Why is this? [1 mark]

2   Use the E° values given below to determine the outcome of mixing the following substances. If there is a reaction,
   determine the E° value and write the equation. If there isn't a reaction, state this and explain why.

$$Ni^{2+}_{(aq)} + 2e^- \rightleftharpoons Ni_{(s)} \qquad E^{\circ} = -0.25\ V$$
$$Fe^{3+}_{(aq)} + e^- \rightleftharpoons Fe^{2+}_{(aq)} \qquad E^{\circ} = +0.77\ V \quad \text{(See Q1 for zinc and silver.)}$$

   a) Zinc metal and a solution of Ni^{2+} ions. [2 marks]
   b) A solution of Ag^+ ions and a solution of Fe^{2+} ions. [2 marks]

Go with the flow...

*You've just got to think long and hard about this stuff. The metal on the left-hand electrode disappears off into the solution,
leaving its electrons behind. This makes the left-hand electrode the negative one. So the right-hand electrode's got to be
the positive one. It makes sense if you think about it. This electrode gives up electrons to turn the positive ions into atoms.*

Iron — Rusting, Recycling and Extraction

I saw a film about an iron man. He stopped the baddies and saved the world. If only the bad guys had read this page. They could have stopped him in no time. Ahh well...

Rusting is All Down to Electrochemical Processes

If iron's exposed to **oxygen** and **water**, it'll turn into crumbly, flaky stuff called **rust**. Here's how:

1) There are two half-equations involved:

$$Fe_{(s)} \rightleftharpoons Fe^{2+}_{(aq)} + 2e^- \qquad E^\circ = +0.44\ V$$

$$2H_2O_{(l)} + O_{2(g)} + 4e^- \rightleftharpoons 4OH^-_{(aq)} \qquad E^\circ = +1.23\ V$$

Double the first half-equation to keep the e⁻ balanced.

So the overall reaction is: $\quad 2H_2O_{(l)} + O_{2(g)} + 2Fe_{(s)} \rightarrow 2Fe^{2+}_{(aq)} + 4OH^-_{(aq)} \qquad E^\circ = +1.67\ V$

2) The $Fe^{2+}_{(aq)}$ and $OH^-_{(aq)}$ ions produced combine to form a precipitate of iron(II) hydroxide, $Fe(OH)_2$. $\qquad Fe^{2+}_{(aq)} + 2OH^-_{(aq)} \rightarrow Fe(OH)_{2(s)}$

3) The $Fe(OH)_2$ is further oxidised to $Fe(OH)_3$ by oxygen and water. $\quad 2H_2O_{(l)} + O_{2(g)} + 4Fe(OH)_{2(s)} \rightarrow 4Fe(OH)_{3(s)}$

4) Iron(III) hydroxide gradually turns into hydrated iron(III) oxide, $\mathbf{Fe_2O_3.xH_2O}$ — this is **rust**.

There are Two Main Ways to Prevent Rusting

1) The obvious way to prevent rusting is to coat the iron with a **barrier** to keep out either the oxygen, the water or both.

Barrier methods include:

Painting/Coating with a polymer — ideal for big and small structures alike. It can be decorative too.

Oiling/Greasing — this has to be used when moving parts are involved, like on bike chains.

2) The other way is the **sacrificial method**. This involves placing a **more reactive metal** with the iron. The water and oxygen then react with this **sacrificial metal** instead of with the iron.

Zinc is often used as a sacrificial metal.
The Zn/Zn²⁺ system has a **more negative** E° value than the Fe/Fe²⁺ system.
This means the **zinc** will be **oxidised** to Zn²⁺ ions in preference to the iron.
A coating of **zinc** can be sprayed onto the object — this is known as **galvanising**.
Alternatively, **blocks of zinc** can be bolted to the iron. This is used on the hulls of ships, or on underground iron pipes.

$$Zn^{2+}_{(aq)} + 2e^- \rightleftharpoons Zn_{(s)} \qquad E^\circ = -0.76\ V$$
$$Fe^{2+}_{(aq)} + 2e^- \rightleftharpoons Fe_{(s)} \qquad E^\circ = -0.44\ V$$

Almost all Iron and Steel Packaging Can be Recycled

Recycling iron and its alloys, such as steel, is really important — digging and extracting new ore takes **a lot of energy** and generates a lot of **pollution**. And the disposal of it in landfill also takes up **space**.

Fortunately, **almost** all iron and steel packaging (e.g. food and drinks cans) can be recycled. Aerosol cans are more of a problem — they can be **dangerous** if they aren't completely empty and need **special facilities** to empty them before they can be recycled.

The first step is to **separate** the iron and steel from other stuff e.g. aluminium, paper and plastics. This is made easy because iron is **magnetic**. The mixture of materials is passed under a giant magnet and... bish bash bosh all the iron and steel stick to it and are separated out.

Gary combined his love of steel recycling with his flair for fashion.

Next, the iron needs to be **cleaned**. To do this the iron is **melted** in a **furnace** and then **oxygen** is blown through it to **burn off** the impurities e.g. carbon. Since the burning is an exothermic reaction (gives energy out), the **temperature** will **rise** as the impurities are removed. To stop it getting too hot **more** solid **iron** and **steel** is added to be recycled.

After the impurities have been removed, **carbon** and **other elements** such as nickel, chromium or manganese may need to be added in carefully **controlled amounts** to obtain steel with exactly the **desired properties**.

Iron — Rusting, Recycling and Extraction

Metals Are Extracted From Their Ores By Reduction

Most metals occur in the Earth's crust **combined** with **oxygen** (as an oxide), **sulfur** (as a sulfide) or with **silicon and oxygen** (as a silicate). To extract the metal it needs to be **reduced** (gain electrons). Here are three ways of doing this...

Heating with carbon

The **carbon** is **oxidised** to carbon monoxide and then to carbon dioxide. At each step the carbon **loses electrons** and reduces the metal. This is a **cheap** method because there are lots of cheap sources of carbon — but it **doesn't work** with **reactive metals** because carbon isn't a strong enough reducing agent.

Reduction by a more reactive metal

Very reactive metals (e.g. sodium) are **powerful reducing agents**. They're used in the extraction of metals like titanium. In order to get pure titanium, the compound $TiCl_4$ is heated with sodium or magnesium. It's an **expensive** process because of the high cost of sodium metal.

Electrolysis

Metals can be extracted from their ores by passing an **electric current** through the **molten ore**. Aluminium is extracted like this. It's an **expensive** process because **high temperatures** are needed to melt the ore and **a lot** of **electricity** is used.

Metals can also be **refined** (purified) by electrolysis. Copper is usually extracted from its ore by other processes, e.g. reduction by carbon, but then electrolysis is used to purify it (see diagram).

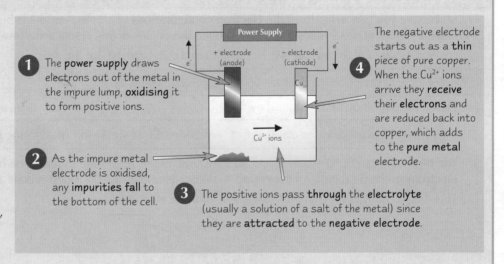

1. The **power supply** draws electrons out of the metal in the impure lump, **oxidising** it to form positive ions.

2. As the impure metal electrode is oxidised, any **impurities fall** to the bottom of the cell.

3. The positive ions pass **through** the **electrolyte** (usually a solution of a salt of the metal) since they are **attracted** to the **negative electrode**.

4. The negative electrode starts out as a **thin** piece of pure copper. When the Cu^{2+} ions arrive they **receive** their **electrons** and are reduced back into copper, which adds to the **pure metal** electrode.

Practice Questions

Q1 State the two substances that react with iron to produce rust.

Q2 Describe four ways of preventing rust forming.

Q3 Why are aerosol cans not recycled in the same way as other steel containers such as food and drink cans?

Q4 What are the main three processes used to extract metals from their ores?

Exam Questions

1 Use the data in the table to answer the following questions
   a) 'Tin' cans are mainly made of steel with a very thin coating of tin to
      prevent the steel from rusting. Explain why the tin is acting only as a
      barrier and is not a sacrificial protector. [2 marks]
   b) 'Galvanising' is a method of protecting steel that involves coating
      the steel object with a layer of zinc. Is this a barrier or sacrificial method
      of protection? Explain your answer. [3 marks]

Half-cell	E° (V)
$Zn^{2+}_{(aq)}/Zn_{(s)}$	–0.76
$Fe^{2+}_{(aq)}/Fe_{(s)}$	–0.44
$Sn^{2+}_{(aq)}/Sn_{(s)}$	–0.14

2 Explain how electrolysis can be used to remove impurities from a sample of crude copper metal.
   Your explanation should describe how the electrochemical cell is set up and include details of
   the reactions at the anode and at the cathode, with relevant half-equations. [6 marks]

I'm watching a film about galvanising taps — it's a kitchen-zinc drama...

OK, I didn't write the gag and I admit I had to look up what a kitchen sink drama was. Apparently it's a style from the 1950s and 1960s about working class Britons in domestic scenes. I didn't laugh either, so I'm off find the writer and poke them with a fork until they squeal. You make sure you can answer all the practice questions and I'll see you on the next page...

Transition Metals

Get ready to make the transition to the next two pages...

Transition Elements are Found in the d-Block

The **d-block** is the block of elements in the middle of the periodic table.

Most of the elements in the d-block are **transition elements**, also known as **transition metals**.

You only need to know about the transition elements in the first row of the d-block.

These include the elements from **titanium to copper** but not scandium or zinc (see below).

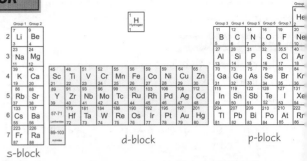

The Electron Configurations of Transition Metals Cause Their Properties

1) Make sure you can write down the **electron configurations** of all the Period 4 d-block elements in subshell notation. Have a look at your AS notes if you've forgotten the details of this. Here are a few examples:

$$V = 1s^2\ 2s^2\ 2p^6\ 3s^2\ 3p^6\ 3d^3\ 4s^2 \qquad Co = 1s^2\ 2s^2\ 2p^6\ 3s^2\ 3p^6\ 3d^7\ 4s^2$$

The 4s electrons fill up before the 3d electrons. But chromium and copper are a trifle odd — see below

2) Here's the definition of a transition metal:

> A **transition metal** is a metal that can form **at least one stable ion** with an **incomplete d-subshell**.

3) The d-orbitals can fit **10** electrons in. So transition metals must form **at least one ion** that has **between 1 and 9 electrons** in the d-orbital. All the Period 4 d-block elements are transition metals apart from **scandium** and **zinc**. This diagram shows the 3d and 4s subshells of these elements:

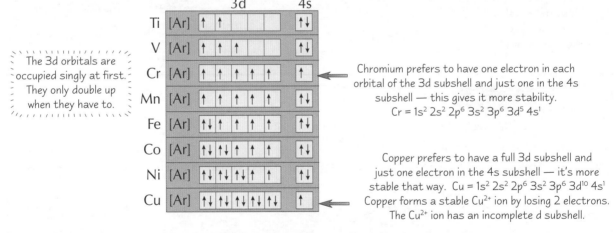

The 3d orbitals are occupied singly at first. They only double up when they have to.

Chromium prefers to have one electron in each orbital of the 3d subshell and just one in the 4s subshell — this gives it more stability.
$$Cr = 1s^2\ 2s^2\ 2p^6\ 3s^2\ 3p^6\ 3d^5\ 4s^1$$

Copper prefers to have a full 3d subshell and just one electron in the 4s subshell — it's more stable that way. $Cu = 1s^2\ 2s^2\ 2p^6\ 3s^2\ 3p^6\ 3d^{10}\ 4s^1$
Copper forms a stable Cu^{2+} ion by losing 2 electrons. The Cu^{2+} ion has an incomplete d subshell.

It's the incomplete d-subshell that causes the **special chemical properties** of transition metals on the next page.

When Ions are Formed, the s Electrons are Removed First

When the atoms form **positive** ions, the **s electrons** are removed **first**, **then** d electrons.

For example, iron forms Fe^{2+} ions and Fe^{3+} ions.

When it forms 2+ ions, it loses **both its 4s electrons**. $Fe = 1s^2\ 2s^2\ 2p^6\ 3s^2\ 3p^6\ 3d^6\ 4s^2 \rightarrow Fe^{2+} = 1s^2\ 2s^2\ 2p^6\ 3s^2\ 3p^6\ 3d^6$

Only once the 4s electrons are removed can a **3d electron** be removed.

E.g. $Fe^{2+} = 1s^2\ 2s^2\ 2p^6\ 3s^2\ 3p^6\ 3d^6 \rightarrow Fe^{3+} = 1s^2\ 2s^2\ 2p^6\ 3s^2\ 3p^6 3d^5$

Sc and Zn Aren't Transition Metals

Scandium only forms one ion, Sc^{3+}, which has an **empty d-subshell**. Scandium has the electron configuration $1s^2\ 2s^2\ 2p^6\ 3s^2\ 3p^6\ 3d^1\ 4s^2$. It loses three electrons to form Sc^{3+}, which has the electron configuration $1s^2\ 2s^2\ 2p^6\ 3s^2\ 3p^6$.

Zinc only forms one ion, Zn^{2+}, which has a **full d-subshell**. Zinc has the electron configuration $1s^2\ 2s^2\ 2p^6\ 3s^2\ 3p^6\ 3d^{10}\ 4$
When it forms Zn^{2+} it loses 2 electrons, both from the 4s subshell. This means it keeps its full 3d subshell.

Transition Metals

Transition Elements have **Special Chemical Properties**

1) They can form **complex ions** — see pages 68-69. E.g. iron forms a **complex ion with water** — $[Fe(H_2O)_6]^{2+}$.

2) They can exist in **variable oxidation states**.

> E.g. iron can exist in the +2 oxidation state as Fe^{2+} ions and in the +3 oxidation state as Fe^{3+} ions.
>
> 1) To make Fe^{2+}, two 4s electrons are removed.
> 2) To make Fe^{3+}, two 4s electrons and one 3d electron are removed.
> 3) The **4s orbital** and the five **3d orbitals** are all at very **similar energy levels**, so there isn't much difference in energy between making an Fe^{2+} or Fe^{3+} ion.
> 4) **No single** electronic configuration is the most stable, and so **several** can exist – each corresponding to a different **oxidation state**.

3) They form **coloured ions**. E.g. Fe^{2+} ions are **pale green** and Fe^{3+} ions are **yellow**.

4) Transition metals and their compounds make **good catalysts** because they can **change oxidation states** by gaining or losing electrons within their **d orbitals**. This means they can **transfer electrons** to **speed up** reactions.

> For example:
> 1) **Iron** is the catalyst used in the **Haber process**, to produce ammonia (see page 71).
> 2) **Vanadium(V) oxide**, V_2O_5, is the catalyst used in the **Contact process** to make sulfuric acid.
> 3) **Nickel** is the catalyst used to **harden margarine**.

Copper Ions Show **Two** Oxidation States — **+1** and **+2**

Oxidation state	Formula	Electronic configuration	Colour of aqueous ions
0	Cu	$1s^2\ 2s^2\ 2p^6\ 3s^2\ 3p^6\ 3d^{10}\ 4s^1$	
+1	Cu^+	$1s^2\ 2s^2\ 2p^6\ 3s^2\ 3p^6\ 3d^{10}$	Cu^+ ions are unstable and disproportionate in aqueous solution: $2Cu^+_{(aq)} \rightarrow Cu^{2+}_{(aq)} + Cu_{(s)}$
+2	Cu^{2+}	$1s^2\ 2s^2\ 2p^6\ 3s^2\ 3p^6\ 3d^9$	Pale blue in aqueous solution

Disproportionate means to be simultaneously oxidised and reduced.

Practice Questions

Q1 Which two d-block elements from Period 4 aren't transition elements?

Q2 Give the electron configuration of: (a) a vanadium atom, (b) a V^{2+} ion.

Q3 State four chemical properties which are characteristic of transition elements.

Q4 Write down the common oxidation states of iron and copper and the colours of their aqueous ions.

Exam Questions

1 When solid copper(I) sulfate is added to water, a pale blue solution forms with a red-brown precipitate of copper metal.
   a) Give the electron configuration of copper(I) ions. [1 mark]
   b) Does the formation of copper(I) ions show copper acting as a transition metal? Explain your answer. [2 marks]
   c) Identify the pale blue solution. [1 mark]

2 Many of the properties of transition metals are caused by their electronic structures.
   a) Give the electronic configuration of :
      i) Zn (atomic number 30) ii) Zn^{2+}
      iii) Cr (atomic number 24) iv) Cr^{3+} [4 marks]
   b) What is the definition of a transition metal? Use this definition to explain why
      Cu (atomic number 29) **is** a transition metal, but Zn is **not**. [4 marks]

That copper's gone mad — he's 1 electron short of a full 4s-orbital...

Definitely have a quick read of the electronic configuration stuff in your AS notes if it's been pushed to a little corner of your mind labelled, "Well, I won't be needing that again in a hurry". It should come flooding back pretty quickly. This page is just an overview of transition metal properties. Don't worry — they're all looked at in lots more detail in the coming pages...

Complex Ions

Transition metals are always forming complex ions. These aren't as complicated as they sound, though. Honest.

Complex Ions are Metal Ions Surrounded by Ligands

A **complex ion** is a **metal ion** surrounded by **coordinately bonded ligands.**

1) A **ligand** is any **ion** or **molecule** that forms a **coordinate bond** with a metal ion.

2) A **coordinate bond** (or dative covalent bond) is a covalent bond in which **both electrons** in the shared pair come from the **same atom.**

3) The **coordination number** is the **number** of **coordinate bonds** that are formed with the central metal ion.

4) The usual coordination numbers are **6** and **4.**
If the ligands are **small**, like H_2O, CN^- or NH_3, **6** can fit around the central metal ion.
But if the ligands are **larger**, like Cl^-, **only 4** can fit around the central metal ion.

Blake's complex coordination skills weren't much use in his chemistry exam.

6 COORDINATE BONDS MEAN AN OCTAHEDRAL SHAPE

Here are a few examples:

The different types of bond arrow show that the complex is 3-D. The wedge-shaped arrows represent bonds coming towards you and the dashed arrows represent bonds sticking out behind the molecule.

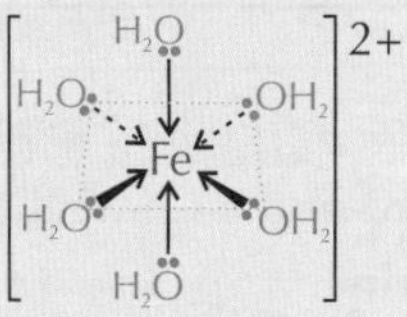

$[Fe(H_2O)_6]^{2+}_{(aq)}$

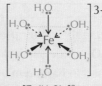

$[Fe(H_2O)_6]^{3+}_{(aq)}$

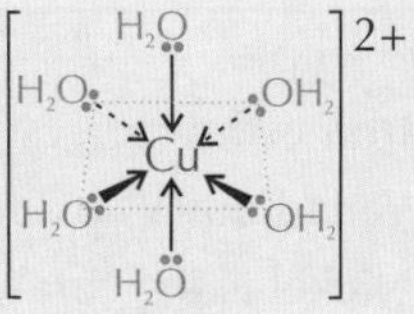

$[Cu(H_2O)_6]^{2+}_{(aq)}$

4 COORDINATE BONDS USUALLY MEAN A TETRAHEDRAL SHAPE...

E.g. $[CuCl_4]^{2-}$, which is yellow.

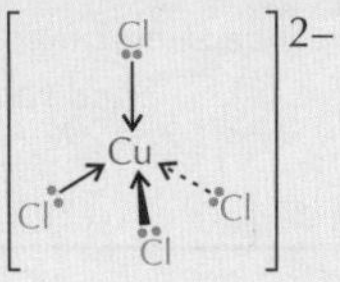

...BUT NOT ALWAYS

In a **few** complexes, **4 coordinate bonds** form a **square planar** shape.

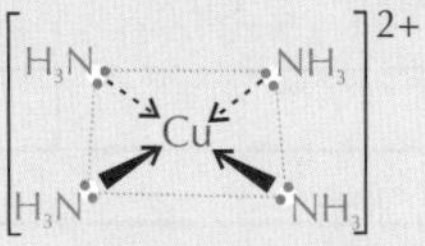

$[Cu(NH_3)_4]^{2+}$

Ligands Form Bonds Using Lone Pairs of Electrons

A ligand must have **at least one lone pair of electrons**, or it won't have anything to form a **coordinate bond** with.

Ligands with **one lone pair** are called **monodentate** (or **unidentate**) — e.g. $H_2\ddot{O}$, $\ddot{N}H_3$, $\ddot{C}l^-$, $\ddot{C}N^-$.

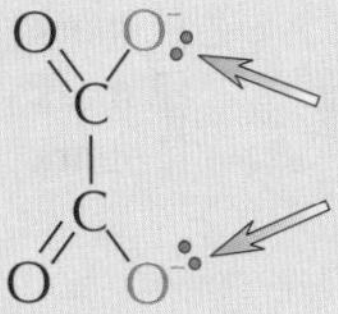

In ethanedioate both these pairs of electrons interact with the same metal ion

Ethanedioate

Ligands with **two lone pairs** are called **bidentate** — e.g. ethanedioate. Bidentate ligands can each form **two coordinate bonds** with a metal ion.

Ligands with **more than two lone pairs** are called **polydentate** — e.g. $EDTA^{4-}$ has six lone pairs (so it's **hexadentate**, to be precise). It can form **six coordinate bonds** with a metal ion.
Haemoglobin contains a molecule with **four nitrogens** that each form a coordinate bond with Fe^{2+} — so this is a polydentate ligand too.

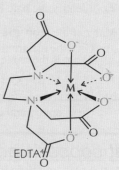

$EDTA^{4-}$

Complex Ions

Ligands can Exchange Places with One Another

One ligand can be **swapped** for another ligand — this is **ligand substitution**.
It pretty much always causes a **colour change**.

1) If the ligands are of **similar size**, e.g. H_2O and NH_3, then the **coordination number** of the complex ion **doesn't** change, and neither does the **shape**.

$[Co(H_2O)_6]^{2+}{}_{(aq)} + 6NH_{3(aq)} \rightarrow [Co(NH_3)_6]^{2+}{}_{(aq)} + 6H_2O_{(l)}$
octahedral   octahedral
pink   pale brown

$[Cr(H_2O)_6]^{3+}{}_{(aq)} + 6OH^-{}_{(aq)} \rightarrow [Cr(OH)_6]^{3-}{}_{(aq)} + 6H_2O_{(l)}$
octahedral   octahedral
violet   pale green

2) If the ligands are **different sizes**, e.g. H_2O and Cl^-, there's a **change of coordination number** and a **change of shape**.

$[Cu(H_2O)_6]^{2+}{}_{(aq)} + 4Cl^-{}_{(aq)} \rightleftharpoons [CuCl_4]^{2-}{}_{(aq)} + 6H_2O_{(l)}$
octahedral   tetrahedral
pale blue   yellow

$[Co(H_2O)_6]^{2+}{}_{(aq)} + 4Cl^-{}_{(aq)} \rightleftharpoons [CoCl_4]^{2-}{}_{(aq)} + 6H_2O_{(l)}$
octahedral   tetrahedral
pink   blue

The forward reaction is endothermic, so the equilibrium can be shifted to the right-hand side by heating. The equilibrium will also shift to the right if you add more concentrated hydrochloric acid. Adding water to this equilibrium shifts it back to the left.

3) Sometimes the substitution is only **partial**.

$[Fe(H_2O)_6]^{3+}{}_{(aq)} + SCN^-{}_{(aq)} \rightarrow [Fe(H_2O)_5SCN]^{2+}{}_{(aq)} + 4H_2O_{(l)}$
octahedral   distorted octahedral
pale violet when pure   **blood red**

but this usually looks yellow

Practice Questions

Q1 What type of bonding exists between metal ions and ligands in complex ions?

Q2 Why do ligands such as Cl^- ions form complexes with lower coordination numbers than ligands such as H_2O?

Q3 What is the shape of a complex ion with 6 ligands?

Q4 What would you usually observe happening during a ligand substitution reaction?

Exam Questions

1 Solution A is aqueous copper(II) sulfate and is pale blue in colour.
When concentrated hydrochloric acid is added, solution B forms. Solution B is yellow in colour.
a) Identify the formula of the complex ion causing the colour of each solution. [2 marks]
b) Write an equation to show the conversion of solution A to solution B. [1 mark]
c) Draw and name the shapes of the complex ions in solutions A and B. [4 marks]

2 Look at the two reactions below:
Reaction A: $[Co(H_2O)_6]^{3+} + Cl^- \rightarrow [Co(H_2O)_5Cl]^{2+} + H_2O$
Reaction B: $[Co(H_2O)_6]^{2+} + 4Cl^- \rightarrow [CoCl_4]^{2-} + 6H_2O$

a) What is the name for these types of reaction? [1 mark]
b) What do H_2O and Cl^- have in common that allows them to act as ligands? [1 mark]
c) Which of the reactions – A, B, or both – involves a change in shape? [1 mark]
d) State all the shape changes involved in your answer to c) and explain why there is a change of shape. [4 marks]

Ligands with pasta for lone pairs are called aldentate...

fancy pasta for tea tonight. OK, so it's only gonna be a tin of tomatoes with some mixed herbs that have been on the shelf in the kitchen since I moved in, but we can't all be master chefs. Anyway, whilst I go and cook you make sure that you can remember all those examples of ligand complexes. It might not be fun, but you're not far off the end of the section...

More on Transition Metals

More on transition metals — now in glorious colour...

Mixing **NaOH** and **Transition Metal** Ions gives Coloured **Precipitates**

Transition metal ions in aqueous solutions form **complex ions** (see p68-69)
e.g. iron(II) ions in water form $[Fe(H_2O)_6]^{2+}$ complex ions.

Adding **hydroxide ions removes H⁺** from the water ligands, taking positive charge away.

When enough H⁺ ions have been removed, the complex ion becomes **neutral**, and forms a **precipitate**.

You need to know the **equations** and the **colours** for these examples.

Iron(II) ions	$[Fe(H_2O)_6]^{2+} + 2OH^- \rightarrow$ **Green solution**	$[Fe(H_2O)_4(OH)_2] + 2H_2O$ **Green precipitate**
Iron(III) ions	$[Fe(H_2O)_6]^{3+} + 3OH^- \rightarrow$ **Orange/brown solution**	$[Fe(H_2O)_3(OH)_3] + 3H_2O$ **Rust-brown precipitate**
Copper(II) ions	$[Cu(H_2O)_6]^{2+} + 2OH^- \rightarrow$ **Pale blue solution**	$[Cu(H_2O)_4(OH)_2] + 2H_2O$ **Blue precipitate**

Ammonia Reacts With Transition Metal Ion Solutions In **Two** Ways

1st reaction – a little NH₃

$[Cu(H_2O)_6]^{2+} + 2NH_3 \rightarrow [Cu(H_2O)_4(OH)_2] + 2NH_4^+$
Pale blue solution **Blue precipitate**

2nd reaction – a lot of NH₃

$[Cu(H_2O)_6]^{2+} + 4NH_3 \rightarrow [Cu(NH_3)_4]^{2+} + 6H_2O$
Pale blue solution **Intense blue solution**

Adding a **little** ammonia solution to an aqueous solution of copper(II) ions, causes the **same reaction** as **hydroxide ions** do — it removes H⁺ ions and forms a **blue** neutral complex **precipitate**.

If you **keep adding** ammonia solution, a **second** reaction will happen. The precipitate will dissolve and form an **intense blue solution**. This is because the NH₃ molecules can also act as **ligands**.

Transition Metal Compounds are Good **Homogeneous Catalysts**

1) A **homogeneous catalyst** is one that is in the **same phase** as the reactant chemicals — usually in solution.

2) Transition metal compounds are good at catalysing reactions because they can **change oxidation state** easily.

3) This means that they can **take electrons** from one chemical and **give them** to another — they can both **oxidise** and **reduce** things easily.

Example: Peroxodisulfate ions oxidising iodide ions.

This reaction is extremely **slow** because it is difficult for two negative ions to meet since their **charges repel**. This gives the reaction a **high activation energy**. But...

$$S_2O_8^{2-} + 2I^- \rightarrow 2SO_4^{2-} + I_2$$

... the reaction becomes much **faster** if iron(III) ions are added because they can **take** electrons from the I⁻ and **give** them to the $S_2O_8^{2-}$ ion:

Fe³⁺ **takes electrons** from I⁻ to become Fe²⁺...

$$2Fe^{3+} + 2I^- \rightarrow 2Fe^{2+} + I_2$$

... the Fe²⁺ **gives electrons** to $S_2O_8^{2-}$, returning to Fe³⁺.

$$2Fe^{2+} + S_2O_8^{2-} \rightarrow 2Fe^{3+} + 2SO_4^{2-}$$

Although the Fe³⁺ appears to be getting used up in the first reaction, it is all **reformed** in the second. Fe²⁺ can also be used to catalyse this reaction — the two steps would just happen the other way round.

More on Transition Metals

Transition Metals and Their Compounds are also **Heterogeneous Catalysts**

A **heterogeneous catalyst** is in a **different phase** from the reactants. Usually the reactants are gases or in solution and the catalyst is a solid. Transition metals make good heterogeneous catalysts because they can use their **s- and d-orbitals** for **bonding** to the reactant molecules. The reaction works in three stages:

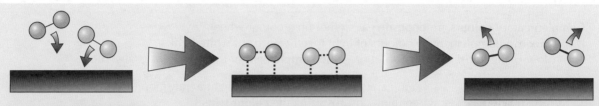

1) The **reactant** molecules are **attracted** to the surface of the catalyst and stick to it — this is called **adsorption**.

2) The surface of the catalyst **activates** the molecules so they react more easily. E.g. interaction with the catalyst **weakens** the bonds in the molecule making them **easier** to **break** and reform as the products.

3) The **product** molecules **leave** the surface of the catalyst making way for fresh reactants to take their place. This is called **desorption**.

For something to be a **good** heterogeneous catalyst, it must —

1) **Attract reactant** molecules strongly enough so that they are held to the surface long enough to react.

2) **Not attract** the **product** molecules so strongly they won't be able to desorb and block the catalyst from fresh reactants.

> **Example**: Iron catalyses the reaction of nitrogen with hydrogen to make ammonia in the Haber process.
>
> **Both** N_2 and H_2 are **adsorbed** on to the surface of the iron. This has the effect of **weakening the bonds** in the molecules, which allows the N_2 and H_2 molecules to **split** into N and H atoms more easily. The N and H atoms are then able to bond together to form NH_3, which **desorbs from the iron**.

Practice Questions

Q1 What would you see if you added sodium hydroxide solution to solutions of Fe^{2+}, Fe^{3+}, and Cu^{2+} ions?

Q2 What would you see if you added a little ammonia solution to a solution of Cu^{2+} ions? What would happen if you added more ammonia solution?

Q3 What is the difference between a heterogeneous and a homogeneous catalyst?

Q4 What feature of transition metals makes them good homogeneous catalysts?

Exam Questions

1   Hydroxide ions react with transition metal ions in solution to form coloured precipitates.
   a)   Describe what you would see if a solution of sodium hydroxide was added to a solution of:
        i) $[Fe(H_2O)_6]^{2+}$ ions   ii) $[Fe(H_2O)_6]^{3+}$ ions   [2 marks]
   b)   Write ionic equations for both of the above reactions.   [4 marks]

2   Solutions of ammonia and sodium hydroxide both react with solutions of copper(II) compounds.
   a)   Describe one similarity and one difference in what you would observe as increasing amounts of $NaOH$ or NH_3 were added.   [2 marks]
   b)   Write an equation to show what happens when a solution of a copper(II) compound reacts with:
        i)   a small amount of ammonia solution,
        ii) excess ammonia solution.   [4 marks]

3   Transition metal compounds are used as both heterogeneous and homogeneous catalysts.
   a)   Explain the meaning of the terms 'heterogeneous' and 'homogeneous'.   [2 marks]
   b)   How does the fact that a transition metal has partially filled d-orbitals help it act as a **heterogeneous** catalyst?   [1 mark]
   c)   How does the fact that transition metals have variable oxidation states allow them to act as **homogeneous** catalysts?   [2 marks]

Bagpuss, Sylvester, Tom — the top three on my catalyst...

Transition metals are able to do so many different things. And it's all down to those d-orbital electron thingies. Unfortunately that means there's a lot for you to remember. But hey, what can you do... Well, you could shut the book and make sure you can write out the reactions for iron(II), iron(III) and copper(II) with NaOH. And don't forget the colours.

Transition Metal Ion Colour

Transition metal complex ions have distinctive colours, which is handy when it comes to identifying them.

The **Colours** You See are the **Complements** of Those That are **Absorbed**

When **white light** hits a transition metal ion one frequency of the light is **absorbed**.

The rest of the frequencies are **transmitted** and it's the **transmitted frequencies** that correspond to the **colour** that you see.

Complementary colours are **opposite** each other on a colour wheel.
If you **mix** two complementary colours of light together you get **white light**.
The colour of the transition metal solution is the **complement** of the colour that's absorbed.

You can guess what frequency of light a transition metal solution absorbs using the **colour wheel**.

For example $[Cu(H_2O)_6]^{2+}$ ions appear cyan blue.
So they must absorb in the red part of the spectrum.

The colour that a transition metal absorbs depends on:
1) The oxidation state of the ion.
2) The type of ligand.
3) The coordination number/shape of the complex.

A **Colorimeter** Measures the **Absorbance** of a Solution

A **colorimeter** really is what it sounds like. A meter to measure colour. It is used to **measure** the **absorbance** of a solution. You can use it to work out the concentration of transition metal ions in a solution because as their **concentration increases** so will the **absorbance**.

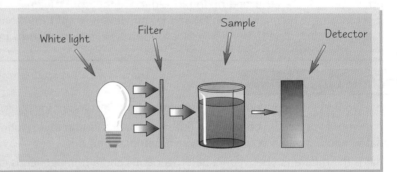

A colorimeter works by **filtering** a source of **white light**, which contains all the frequencies of visible light, into **monochromatic** light which only has one frequency.

You need to pick a **filter** that produces a **colour** that's **absorbed** by the transition metal you want to look at. Otherwise it won't be absorbed and you can't measure any change.

Before you can measure any samples in the colorimeter you need to **set it to zero**. To do this you measure the absorbance of a **blank sample**. This is a **sample** of the **solvent** your metal ions are dissolved in — usually it's just water. The blank tells the colorimeter what zero is, so that it is **only measuring** the **absorbance** of the metal ions and not the solvent too.

Anwar's absorbency experiment was on a roll.

After passing through the filter the light goes through the **sample** where some of it is **absorbed**. The samples are placed in a **cuvette**, which is a container that's designed not to absorb any of the light. The remaining light travels to the **detector**, which **compares** the absorbance of the **sample** to the **blank**.

A **high absorbance** reading means a lot of light has been absorbed and the sample is **very concentrated**.

Transition Metal Ion Colour

Colorimeters can be used to Find Concentrations of Transition Metal Ions

To work out the concentration of an unknown transition metal solution you will need a **calibration graph**. This is made by **measuring** the absorbance of samples with a **known concentration**.

Standard samples of increasing concentration.

These standard samples can be made by **dissolving** different amounts of the metal ion in a **fixed** volume of water or by making **consecutive dilutions** of a single concentrated solution. They must contain the **same metal ion** as the unknown sample and be in the **same solution** or **solvent**.

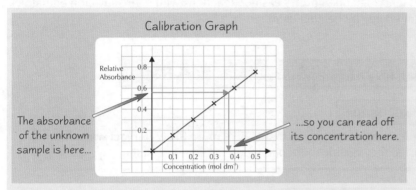

Calibration Graph

Relative Absorbance

0.8
0.6
0.4
0.2

0.1 0.2 0.3 0.4 0.5
Concentration (mol dm⁻³)

The absorbance of the unknown sample is here...

...so you can read off its concentration here.

You **plot** the **absorbance** of each of these samples against their **concentration** to get a **calibration graph**.

Now when you **measure** the absorbance of the **unknown** sample you can use the standard curve to **read off** its **concentration**. Lovely.

Practice Questions

Q1 State three factors that affect the colour of a transition metal compound.

Q2 How does colorimetry measure the concentration of a solution?

Q3 Why is it important to choose the right filter when using a colorimeter?

Q4 What is the purpose of a calibration graph?

Exam Questions

1   Colorimetry can be used to find the concentration of coloured solutions such as those of transition metal compounds. Potassium manganate(VII) is an intense purple colour. Describe the steps you would take to find the concentration of an aqueous solution of potassium manganate(VII) using colorimetry.   [5 marks]

2   A student wishes to find the concentration of a solution of a nickel(II) compound. She first makes up four standard solutions of the same compound. Next she fills a cuvette with each of the solutions and one with pure water.
   a) Solutions of nickel(II) compounds are green. What coloured filter should the student use?
       Explain your choice.   [2 marks]
   b) What is the purpose of the cuvette of pure water?   [1 mark]
   c) Explain what the student will do with the four standard solutions of different concentrations, and how this will enable her to work out the unknown concentration.   [3 marks]

3   Four standard solutions of compound X were prepared and their absorbances measured.
    The results are shown in the table.
   a) Plot a calibration graph using the data in the table.   [6 marks]
   b) A solution of compound X had an absorbance of 0.780.
       What was its concentration?   [2 marks]

Concentration (mol dm⁻³)	Absorbance
0.0102	0.209
0.0212	0.426
0.0489	0.998
0.0635	1.275

The End — of the Steel Story...

.. and they all lived happily ever after. Will they make a sequel? Not in this syllabus. So if you still haven't got enough of electrode potentials, rusting, transition metals and all their talents you will just have to wait for the movie to come out. Which is bound to be a critical success and rush straight to number 1 in the box office charts. Maybe...

Rates and Equilibria

Now you've already covered rates of reaction and equilibria at AS level — as I'm sure you remember vividly — but at A2 you've got to know how it's all put to use by engineers in the chemical industry. I bet you can't wait to find out. First though, a quick recap...

Particles Must **Collide** to **React**

1) Particles in liquids and gases are **always moving** and **colliding** with **each other**.
   But a reaction **won't** take place between two particles **unless** they have enough kinetic energy.

2) Particles need kinetic energy to **break the bonds** holding them together — then the broken up bits from the different particles can react with each other and form new bonds. The **minimum amount of kinetic energy** particles need to react is called the **activation enthalpy**.

3) Reactions with **low activation enthalpies** tend to happen **pretty easily**. Reactions with high activation enthalpies don't. You need to give the particles extra energy by heating them.

Temperature, *Pressure* and *Catalysts* All Affect *Reaction Rate*

Increasing Temperature Speeds Up Reactions

Increasing the temperature gives the particles **more energy**, so that they're **more likely to react** when they collide. And because they're moving faster, they collide more often too. It's win-win all the way.

Increasing Pressure Speeds Up Reactions

Increasing the **pressure** of a gas means that particles are **closer together** on average. So they **collide more often**, and have **more chances** to react.

Catalysts Can Speed Up Reactions

Catalysts are really useful. They **lower the activation enthalpy** by providing a **different way** for the bonds to be broken and remade. If the activation enthalpy's **lower**, more particles will have **enough energy** to react.

Faster, pussycatalyst! Lower that activation enthalpy!

Lots of *Chemical Reactions* are *Reversible* — They Can Go *Both Ways*

1) A reversible reaction can go in either direction — i.e. from **reactants to products** (forwards) or **products to reactants** (backwards). To show a reaction is reversible, you stick in a $\rightleftharpoons$.

2) As the **reactants** get used up, the **forward** reaction **slows down**. As more **product** is formed, the **reverse** reaction **speeds up**.

3) After a while, the forward reaction will be going at exactly the **same rate** as the backward reaction. The amounts of reactants and products **won't be changing** any more — this is called a **dynamic equilibrium**.

E.g. If **hydrogen gas** and **iodine gas** are mixed together in a closed flask, **hydrogen iodide** is formed.

$$H_{2(g)} + I_{2(g)} \rightleftharpoons 2HI_{(g)}$$

A dynamic equilibrium can only happen in a closed system at a constant temperature.

When equilibrium is reached, no matter how long you leave the gases at this temperature, the amounts **never change**. It's all a matter of the forward and backward rates **being equal**.

Rates and Equilibria

Le Chatelier's Principle Predicts what will happen if Conditions are Changed

Le Chatelier's principle tells you how the position of equilibrium will change if a condition changes:

> If there's a change in pressure or temperature, the equilibrium will move to help counteract the change.

Basically, if you change the pressure or temperature of a reversible reaction, you're going to alter the position of equilibrium. If the position of equilibrium moves to the left, you'll get more reactants. If the position of equilibrium moves to the right, you'll get more products — i.e. the yield of the reaction will have increased.

TEMPERATURE
1) Increasing the temperature means adding heat. The equilibrium shifts in the endothermic (positive ΔH) direction to absorb this heat.
2) Decreasing the temperature removes heat. The equilibrium shifts in the exothermic (negative ΔH) direction to try to replace the heat.
3) If the forward reaction's endothermic, the reverse reaction will be exothermic, and vice versa.

This reaction is exothermic in the forward direction. If you increase the temperature, the equilibrium shifts to the left to absorb the extra heat. The amount of product will decrease.

Exothermic $\Longrightarrow$
$$2SO_{2(g)} + O_{2(g)} \rightleftharpoons 2SO_{3(g)} \quad \Delta H = -197 \text{ kJ mol}^{-1}$$
$\Longleftarrow$ Endothermic

PRESSURE (changing this only affects equilibria involving gases)
1) Increasing the pressure shifts the equilibrium to the side with fewer gas molecules. This reduces the pressure.
2) Decreasing the pressure shifts the equilibrium to the side with more gas molecules. This raises the pressure again.

There are 3 moles on the left, but only 2 on the right. So, an increase in pressure shifts the equilibrium to the right. $\Longrightarrow$ $2SO_{2(g)} + O_{2(g)} \rightleftharpoons 2SO_{3(g)}$ The amount of product increases.

> Catalysts have NO EFFECT on the position of equilibrium. They can't increase yield — but they do mean equilibrium is reached faster.

The Conditions of an Industrial Reaction are Carefully Chosen

1) There's a lot to consider when designing an industrial process — rate of reaction, product yield and cost all need to be balanced against each other to come up with the right reaction conditions. This means conditions usually end up as a compromise between several different factors.
2) When designing an industrial process, chemical engineers are trying to make as much product as they can, as cheaply and as quickly as possible. This will make the company a bigger profit when they sell their product.

TEMPERATURE High temperatures make reactions more expensive to carry out because of the cost of fuel. But, reactions go faster at higher temperatures, meaning more product will be made.

PRESSURE
1) Higher pressures make gaseous reactions go faster.
2) To create a high pressure, gas must be pumped into the reaction vessel. Running powerful pumps uses a lot of energy and is expensive.
3) High pressures can also be very dangerous. This means that reaction vessels must be made out of a strong material like thick steel, and incorporate safety systems. Again, this is very expensive.

CATALYSTS
1) Industrial catalysts can also be expensive, but if the right one is used it can make a reaction go quickly at relatively low temperatures — in some cases, no heat is needed at all. This saves money on fuel.
2) Catalysts are a good investment because they don't get used up.

Rates and Equilibria

The **Position of Equilibrium** Affects How **Economical** a Reaction Is

For a **reversible reaction**, chemical engineers need to look at how much **product** will be made — this is the **yield** of the reaction. If the equilibrium gives a very **low yield** under the chosen conditions, it will not be **economically viable**. Again, a **compromise** to find the best conditions needs to be reached.

The classic example of this is the **Haber process** for producing **ammonia**...

Scalpel... cheese-grater... wooden spoon...

$$N_{2(g)} + 3H_{2(g)} \rightleftharpoons 2NH_{3(g)} \qquad \Delta H = -92 \text{ kJ mol}^{-1}$$

1) This reaction is usually carried out at **400 °C** and **200 atmospheres** of pressure.

2) **High pressure** favours the **forward reaction**, **increasing** the yield of ammonia. This is because the equilibrium moves to the side with **fewer molecules** — in this case the **product** side. High pressure also **speeds up** the reaction.

Dr Mullins liked his operating conditions to be as economical as possible.

3) **High temperature** makes the reaction go **faster** too — it increases the kinetic energy of the reactant molecules. **BUT**, it also **lowers the product yield**. This is because the forward reaction is **exothermic** — high temperatures shift the position of equilibrium to the left, to absorb the extra heat.

4) A reaction temperature of 400 °C is a **compromise**. A **greater yield** could be achieved at **lower** temperatures, but the reaction would be **too slow** to be **economical** — there's no point waiting years to get your product, even if you eventually make loads. At **higher temperatures** the reaction would go **faster**, but the **yield** would become **too low** to produce ammonia efficiently.

Practice Questions

Q1 What's the name for the minimum amount of kinetic energy needed for two colliding particles to react?

Q2 State two reasons why increasing the temperature causes reactions to go faster.

Q3 When a dynamic equilibrium is reached, what is the relationship between the forward and reverse reactions?

Q4 Will increasing the temperature of an exothermic reaction increase or decrease the amount of product formed?

Q5 What are the main concerns for chemical engineers designing an industrial process?

Exam Questions

1 Nitrogen dioxide is a brown gas that can react with itself to form the colourless gas dinitrogen tetroxide:

$$2NO_{2(g)} \rightleftharpoons N_2O_{4(g)}$$

a) If some nitrogen dioxide is sealed in a gas syringe, it reacts as shown above and reaches a state of dynamic equilibrium. What does the term 'dynamic equilibrium' mean? [2 marks]

b) If the plunger of the syringe is pushed in, the brown colour of the gas mixture becomes fainter. Explain why this is the case. [4 marks]

2 Methanol is produced industrially by reacting carbon monoxide with hydrogen.

$$CO_{(g)} + 2H_{2(g)} \rightleftharpoons CH_3OH_{(g)} \qquad \Delta H = -91 \text{ kJ mol}^{-1}$$

State, with a reason, the effect that increasing the temperature of this reaction would have on:

a) The rate. [2 marks]

b) The position of equilibrium. [2 marks]

Equilibrium — it's all swings and roundabouts. And see-saws...

The take home message here is that the big chemical companies want to make lots of product quickly and cheaply so they can sell it all at a nice tidy profit. To do that, they need their reactions to be as economical as possible — this means that sometimes reaction conditions are a compromise, balancing factors like rate of reaction, product yield, safety and cost.

Equilibrium Constants

Ladies and gentlemen, we are about to encounter some maths. Please stay calm and remain in your seats. Thank you.

K_c is an **Equilibrium Constant**

If you know the **molar concentration** of each substance at equilibrium, you can work out the **equilibrium constant**, K_c. Your value of K_c will only be true for that particular **temperature**.

Before you can calculate K_c, you have to write an **expression** for it. Here's how:

For the general reaction $aA + bB \rightleftharpoons dD + eE,$ $K_c = \dfrac{[D]^d [E]^e}{[A]^a [B]^b}$

The products go on the top line. The square brackets, [ ], mean concentration in mol dm^{-3}.

The lower-case letters a, b, d and e are the number of moles of each substance.

So for the reaction $H_{2(g)} + I_{2(g)} \rightleftharpoons 2HI_{(g)}$, $K_c = \dfrac{[HI]^2}{[H_2]^1 [I_2]^1}$. This simplifies to $K_c = \dfrac{[HI]^2}{[H_2][I_2]}$.

Calculate K_c by **Sticking Numbers** into the Expression

If you know the **equilibrium concentrations**, just bung them in your expression. Then with a bit of help from the old calculator, you can work out the **value** of K_c. The **units** are a bit trickier though — they **vary**, so you have to work them out after each calculation.

Example: If the volume of the closed flask in the hydrogen iodide example on page 74 is 2.0 dm^3, what is the equilibrium constant, K_c, for the reaction at 640 K?
The equilibrium concentrations are: [HI] = 0.8 mol dm^{-3}, [H$_2$] = 0.1 mol dm^{-3} and [I$_2$] = 0.1 mol dm^{-3}.

Just stick the concentrations into the **expression** for K_c: $K_c = \dfrac{[HI]^2}{[H_2][I_2]} = \dfrac{0.8^2}{0.1 \times 0.1} = 64$ ← This is the value of K_c.

To work out the **units** of K_c put the units in the expression instead of the numbers:

$K_c = \dfrac{(\text{mol dm}^{-3})^2}{(\text{mol dm}^{-3})(\text{mol dm}^{-3})} = 0$, so there are **no units** for K_c because the concentration units cancel.

So K_c is just **64**.

You Might Need to **Work Out** the **Equilibrium Concentrations**

You might have to figure out some of the **equilibrium concentrations** before you can find K_c:

Example: 0.20 moles of phosphorus(V) chloride decomposes at 600 K in a vessel of 5.00 dm^3. The equilibrium mixture is found to contain 0.08 moles of chlorine. Write the expression for K_c and calculate its value, including units.

$$PCl_{5(g)} \rightleftharpoons PCl_{3(g)} + Cl_{2(g)}$$

First find out how many moles of PCl$_5$ and PCl$_3$ there are at equilibrium:

The **equation** tells you that when **1 mole of PCl$_5$** decomposes, **1 mole of PCl$_3$** and **1 mole of Cl$_2$** are formed. So if 0.08 moles of chlorine are produced at equilibrium, there will be **0.08 moles** of PCl$_3$ as well. 0.08 mol of PCl$_5$ must have decomposed, so there will be **0.12 moles** left (0.2 − 0.08).

Divide each number of moles by the volume of the flask to give the molar concentrations:

[PCl$_3$] = [Cl$_2$] = 0.08 ÷ 5.00 = **0.016 mol dm^{-3}**   [PCl$_5$] = 0.12 ÷ 5.00 = **0.024 mol dm^{-3}**

Put the concentrations in the expression for K_c and calculate it: $K_c = \dfrac{[PCl_3][Cl_2]}{[PCl_5]} = \dfrac{[0.016][0.016]}{[0.024]} = \mathbf{0.011}$

Now find the units of K_c: $K_c = \dfrac{(\text{mol dm}^{-3})(\text{mol dm}^{-3})}{\text{mol dm}^{-3}} = \textbf{mol dm}^{-3}$ So K_c = **0.011 mol dm^{-3}**

Equilibrium Constants

K_c can be used to Find **Concentrations** in an **Equilibrium Mixture**

Example: When ethanoic acid was allowed to reach equilibrium with ethanol at 25 °C, it was found that the equilibrium mixture contained 2.0 mol dm^{-3} ethanoic acid and 3.5 mol dm^{-3} ethanol. The K_c of the equilibrium is 4.0 at 25 °C. What are the concentrations of the other components?

$$CH_3COOH_{(l)} + C_2H_5OH_{(l)} \rightleftharpoons CH_3COOC_2H_{5\,(l)} + H_2O_{(l)}$$

Put all the values you know in the K_c expression:
$$K_c = \frac{[CH_3COOC_2H_5][H_2O]}{[CH_3COOH][C_2H_5OH]} \Rightarrow 4.0 = \frac{[CH_3COOC_2H_5][H_2O]}{2.0 \times 3.5}$$

Rearranging this gives:
$$[CH_3COOC_2H_5][H_2O] = 4.0 \times 2.0 \times 3.5 = 28.0$$

From the equation, you know that $[CH_3COOC_2H_5] = [H_2O]$, so:
$$[CH_3COOC_2H_5] = [H_2O] = \sqrt{28} = 5.3 \text{ mol dm}^{-3}$$

The concentration of $CH_3COOC_2H_5$ and H_2O is 5.3 mol dm^{-3}

With **Gases**, You Can Use **Partial Pressures** Instead of **Concentration**

In a mixture of gases, each gas exerts its own pressure — this is called its **partial pressure**.

The **total pressure** of a gas mixture is the **sum** of all the **partial pressures** of the individual gases.

When dealing with **gas-phase equilibria** it can be easier to use partial pressures rather than concentrations. The **partial pressure of one gas** in a **mixture of gases** is calculated like this:

$$\text{Partial pressure of A, } p(A) = \frac{\text{number of moles of A}}{\text{total number of moles of gas}} \times \text{total pressure of the mixture}$$

So if the number of moles of a gas increases, so does its partial pressure.

The **Equilibrium Constant K_p** Is Calculated Using **Partial Pressures**

The expression for **K_p** is written in the same way as for **K_c** but using partial pressure instead of concentration.

For the equilibrium $aA_{(g)} + bB_{(g)} \rightleftharpoons dD_{(g)} + eE_{(g)}$:
$$K_p = \frac{p(D)^d\, p(E)^e}{p(A)^a\, p(B)^b}$$

There are no square brackets because they're partial pressures, not molar concentrations.

To **calculate K_p**, it's just a matter of sticking the partial pressures in the expression. You have to work out the **units** each time though, just like for K_c.

Example: When 3.0 moles of PCl_5 gas is heated, it decomposes into PCl_3 and Cl_2.

$$PCl_{5(g)} \rightleftharpoons PCl_{3(g)} + Cl_{2(g)}$$

Calculate K_p for the decomposition of PCl_5 gas at 500 K.
The partial pressures of each gas are: $p(PCl_5) = 186$ kPa, $p(PCl_3) = 264$ kPa and $p(Cl_2) = 264$ kPa.

$$K_p = \frac{p(PCl_3)\,p(Cl_2)}{p(PCl_5)} = \frac{264 \times 264}{186} = 375$$

The units for K_p are worked out by putting the units into the expression instead of the numbers, and cancelling (like for K_c): $K_p = \frac{kPa \times kPa}{kPa} = kPa$ So, **$K_p = 375$ kPa**

Equilibrium Constants

Temperature Changes Alter K_c and K_p — Pressure Changes and Catalysts Don't

This is a really **key** bit to remember:

> Only changes in **temperature** cause the **equilibrium constants** (K_c and K_p) to change.

PRESSURE

1) If you change the **pressure** of a reaction system, the position of equilibrium will move to help **counteract** that change.

2) No matter what you do to the pressure though, the values of K_c and K_p **remain the same**.

1) If you increase the total pressure of this reaction system, you will increase the partial pressures of both the products and the reactants.

$$2SO_{2(g)} + O_{2(g)} \rightleftharpoons 2SO_{3(g)} \qquad K_p = \frac{p(SO_3)^2}{p(SO_2)^2 p(O_2)} \quad \Longleftarrow \quad$$

2) This has a bigger affect on the **bottom** half of the K_p equation.

3) So why doesn't K_p change? Well, the position of equilibrium shifts to the right to counteract the increase in pressure. This means more SO_3 and a further increase to the **top** of the fraction — keeping the value of K_p the same.

TEMPERATURE

1) A change in **temperature** also causes the position of equilibrium to move. But, this change **will** alter the value of the equilibrium constants.

2) If the temperature change means that **more product** is formed, K_c and K_p will **rise**. If it means **less product** is formed, K_c and K_p will **decrease**.

The reaction below is exothermic in the forward direction. If you increase the temperature, the equilibrium shifts to the left to absorb the extra heat. This means that less product is formed.

$$\text{Exothermic} \Longrightarrow$$
$$2SO_{2(g)} + O_{2(g)} \rightleftharpoons 2SO_{3(g)} \quad \Delta H = -197 \text{ kJ mol}^{-1} \qquad K_p = \frac{p(SO_3)^2}{p(SO_2)^2 p(O_2)} \quad \Longleftarrow$$
$$\Longleftarrow \text{Endothermic}$$

There's less product, so K_p decreases.

CATALYST

Adding a **catalyst** doesn't have any effect on the equilibrium constants. This is because catalysts affect both the forward and reverse reactions equally, so there is **no overall change** to the equilibrium.

Practice Questions

Q1 What do the square brackets mean in a K_c expression?

Q2 What quantities would you need to know to calculate K_p?

Q3 When a system is at equilibrium, which conditions affect the value of the equilibrium constant?

Exam Questions

1 0.1 moles of dichromate(VI) ions and 0.1 moles of water were mixed together in a non-aqueous solvent and allowed to reach equilibrium at a fixed temperature: $Cr_2O_7{}^{2-}{}_{(aq)} + H_2O_{(l)} \rightleftharpoons 2CrO_4{}^{2-}{}_{(aq)} + 2H^+{}_{(aq)}$
   a) Write an expression for K_c for this reaction. [2 marks]
   b) At equilibrium there were 0.03 moles of $Cr_2O_7{}^{2-}$ ions. If the total volume of the solution was 100 cm³, calculate the equilibrium concentrations of:
   i) H_2O ii) $CrO_4{}^{2-}$ iii) H^+ [4 marks]
   c) Calculate a value for K_c at this temperature. [2 marks]

2 When nitric oxide and oxygen were mixed in a 2:1 mole ratio, an equilibrium was set up at a constant temperature in a sealed flask, according to the equation: $2NO_{(g)} + O_{2(g)} \rightleftharpoons 2NO_{2(g)}$.
   The partial pressure of the nitric oxide (NO) at equilibrium was 36 kPa and the total pressure in the flask was 99 kPa.
   a) Deduce the partial pressure of oxygen in the equilibrium mixture. [2 marks]
   b) Calculate the partial pressure of nitrogen dioxide in the equilibrium mixture. [2 marks]
   c) Write an expression for the equilibrium constant, K_p, for this reaction and calculate its value at this temperature. State its units. [4 marks]

Much like an equilibrium, I've always been opposed to change...

Well there you have it. The complicated world of equilibrium constants. If you're currently feeling like you've been hit over the head with half a pound of frozen mince, don't worry. Take a deep breath. Have a biscuit (this is possibly time for two). And then go over it all again until you've got it. Remember: only temperature makes the equilibrium constants change...

Nitrogen Chemistry

Ah nitrogen — my favourite element... After cobalt obviously... Not forgetting boron... Lithium's pretty nifty too...

Nitrogen Occurs Naturally as a Diatomic Molecule

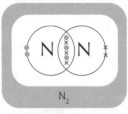

N_2

1) Nitrogen is found at the top of **Group 5** in the periodic table. It has the electronic configuration $1s^2 2s^2 2p^3$. This means that there are **5 electrons** in its **valence** or **outer shell**.

2) To get a full outer shell of **8 electrons**, nitrogen atoms pair up. They form **diatomic molecules**, N_2, sharing **3 pairs of electrons** between the 2 atoms. This makes a **triple bond**.

3) A triple bond is very difficult to break, so N_2 is very unreactive.

Nitrogen and Hydrogen Form Ammonia and Ammonium Ions

1) **Ammonia, NH_3,** is formed from the reaction between N_2 and H_2. The N atom forms **covalent bonds** by sharing 1 of its valence electrons with each of the **3 H atoms** — this leaves 2 electrons as a **lone pair** on the N atom.

2) Ammonia can form **hydrogen bonds** between molecules, which makes it **very soluble** in water.

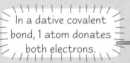
In a dative covalent bond, 1 atom donates both electrons.

3) The lone pair of electrons on the N atom means that ammonia can form **dative covalent bonds**. This allows it to act as a **ligand**, forming complex ions with transition metals. See page 68.

4) The lone pair is also responsible for ammonia behaving as a base — the molecule forms dative covalent bonds with protons to form the **ammonium ion, NH_4^+** : $NH_3 + H^+ \rightleftharpoons NH_4^+$

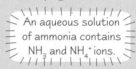
An aqueous solution of ammonia contains NH_3 and NH_4^+ ions.

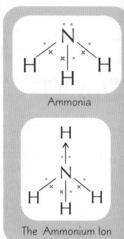

Ammonia

The Ammonium Ion

Nitrogen Also Forms Several Oxides

There are lots of different oxides of nitrogen, but here are the ones you need to know about:

1) **NO** is called **nitrogen monoxide, nitric oxide** or **nitrogen(II) oxide**. It is a colourless gas.

2) **N_2O** is called **dinitrogen monoxide, nitrous oxide** or **nitrogen(I) oxide** (you might've heard of it as 'laughing gas'). It has a sweet smell and is also colourless.

3) **NO_2** is called **nitrogen dioxide** or **nitrogen(IV) oxide**. Also a gas, it is brown, has a sharp odour and is toxic.

Nitrogen Has Lots of Different Oxidation States

Plants and animals need **nitrogen** to make **proteins**, but they can't absorb it from the air. This is what the **nitrogen cycle** on the next page is for — to convert nitrogen into more **accessible** forms. The cycle converts nitrogen through its different **oxidation states**.

Form of nitrogen	Formula	Oxidation state	What produces this form of nitrogen
Nitrogen in the air	$N_{2(g)}$	0	Denitrifying bacteria
Ammonium ions in the soil	$NH_{4\ (aq)}^+$	−3	Bacteria and micro-organisms in the soil
Nitrate(V) ions in the soil	$NO_{3\ (aq)}^-$	+5	Nitrifying bacteria in the soil, bacteria in root nodules
Nitrate(III) ions in the soil	$NO_{2\ (aq)}^-$	+3	Nitrifying bacteria in the soil, bacteria in root nodules
Nitrogen(II) oxide	$NO_{(g)}$	+2	Thunderstorms, car engines, denitrifying bacteria in the soil
Nitrogen(IV) oxide	$NO_{2(g)}$	+4	Oxidation of NO in the atmosphere
Nitrogen(I) oxide	$N_2O_{(g)}$	+1	Denitrifying bacteria in the soil

Here's a couple of handy tips for calculating oxidation states:

1) Remember that the **roman numeral** in brackets (e.g. nitrogen(**IV**) oxide) is telling you the **oxidation state for N** (e.g. **+4**).

2) If you have to **calculate** the oxidation state for nitrogen, remember that — **when combined with N**, O has an oxidation state of **−2** and H has an oxidation state of **+1**. The oxidation states should add up to the **overall charge** of the compound (i.e. O) or ion.

Nitrogen Chemistry

The Nitrogen Cycle Involves Many Redox Reactions

Redox reactions involve the **transfer of electrons** — nitrogen, the little devil, gets involved in loads of 'em as part of the nitrogen cycle. It can **donate electrons** and be **oxidised**, or **accept electrons** and be **reduced**. You need to know the major redox reactions involving nitrogen and be able to write equations and half-equations for them. Lucky you.

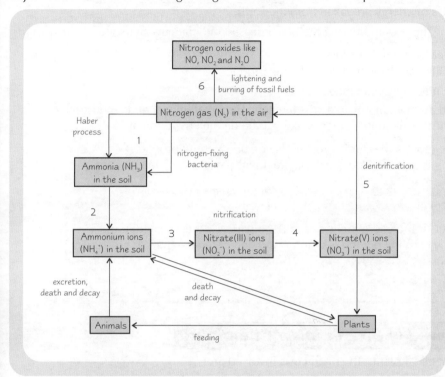

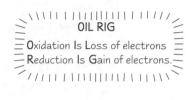

OIL RIG

Oxidation **I**s **L**oss of electrons
Reduction **I**s **G**ain of electrons.

1) $N_2 + 3H_2 \rightarrow 2NH_3$
   $N_2 + 6e^- \rightarrow 2N^{3-}$
   $3H_2 \rightarrow 6H^+ + 6e^-$

2) $NH_3 + H^+ \rightarrow NH_4^+$

3) $NH_4^+ + O_2 \rightarrow NO_2^- + 4H^+ + 2e^-$

4) $NO_2^- + H_2O \rightarrow NO_3^- + 2H^+ + 2e^-$

5) $2NO_3^- + 10e^- + 12H^+ \rightarrow N_2 + 6H_2O$

6) $N_2 + O_2 \rightarrow 2NO$

There are lots of **different ways** that compounds in the nitrogen cycle can **inter-convert** and **not** all of them are listed here — ammonium ions can be oxidised directly to nitrate(V) ions for example. You need to feel comfortable with writing equations **from scratch** rather than learning them by rote.

Practice Questions

Q1 Explain why ammonia can act as a base.

Q2 What is the oxidation state of nitrogen in nitrogen dioxide?

Q3 What is the definition of oxidation and reduction in terms of electrons?

Exam Questions

1   Aqueous solutions of ammonium ions, NH_4^+, can be converted to nitrate ions, NO_3^-.

   a)   What is the oxidation state of N in:
   i) NH_4^+
   ii) NO_3^- [2 marks]

   b)   Is nitrogen being oxidised or reduced when NH_4^+ ions turn into NO_3^- ions? Explain your answer.   [1 mark]

   c)   Write a half-equation for the reaction of NH_4^+ in the presence of water to form NO_3^-.   [3 marks]

2   During lightening storms, nitrogen and oxygen in the air can react to form nitrogen monoxide.

   a)   Write an equation for this reaction.   [2 marks]

   b)   In N_2, nitrogen has an oxidation state of 0. What is its oxidation state in nitrogen monoxide?   [1 mark]

   c)   Nitrogen monoxide reacts further with oxygen to form nitrogen dioxide.
        What would you see during this reaction?   [1 mark]

The nitrogen cycle — enough to make you soil yourself...

Redox reactions were a major topic at AS and like a good 90's boy band they're back for another crack at the top spot. Well, the exam anyway... Excuse me if my analogies don't always go to plan... If you're unsure about all this oxidation is loss / reduction is gain malarkey, I'd suggest dusting off the AS notes and brushing up on your equation writing technique. Fabulous.

The Chemical Industry and Food

This may seem like a series of random, unrelated topics, but let me assure you nothing could be further from the truth. It's all about chemicals and... erm, industry... and food... and stuff.

The **Environmental Impact** of Reactions Has to be Considered

Industrial chemical production **impacts on the environment** in two ways:

> 1) **Raw materials** and **sources of energy** are taken from the Earth.
>
> 2) **Waste products** (including those from burning fuel) are released into the environment.

Less efficient reactions tend to have a **greater** impact because:

- They require **more raw materials** (including fuel) to make the product.
- They produce **more waste** per unit of product made.

You can look at the **percentage yield** and **atom economy** to assess the environmental impact of an industrial reaction. The **higher** these figures are, the less the impact there's likely to be on the environment.

1) **Atom economy** tells you what proportion of the starting materials end up in useful products
— basically, how wasteful a reaction is in itself. You can't change it without changing the reaction.

$$\% \text{ atom economy} = \frac{\text{mass of desired product}}{\text{total mass of all products}} \times 100$$

You can use masses in grams, or relative molecular masses.

2) **Percentage yield** tells you how efficient the entire process is under a particular set of conditions.
You may be able change this, e.g. by carrying out the reaction at a different temperature or pressure.

$$\% \text{ yield} = \frac{\text{actual product yield}}{\text{theoretical yield}} \times 100$$

There are Many **Costs** Involved in **Producing a Chemical**

It's generally quite **expensive** to run a chemical plant. The main costs involved are:

1) **Raw Materials**
The plant needs to buy chemicals for the reaction — cheap, widely available ones are best.

2) **Fuel/Energy**
Reactions needing high temperature or pressure will use up a lot of energy. Energy is also used in transporting chemicals to, from and around a plant, mixing them and purifying products.

3) **Overheads/Fixed costs**
No matter how much fuel or raw material a company uses, there are certain costs that need to be met regularly. These include staff wages, rent of equipment or space, taxes, insurance, telephone bills, etc.

4) **Disposal Costs**
Any unwanted by-products will have to be disposed of safely — this is subject to government regulations and can be very expensive.

Again, reactions with **high atom economies** and **high percentage yields** tend to be best because they use fewer raw materials and have fewer waste products. This **saves money** for a company.

There are Both **Benefits** and **Risks** Involved in Producing a Chemical

Large-scale production of chemicals like **medicines**, **fertilisers**, **cleaning products** and **dyes**, as well as new materials like **plastics**, has revolutionised our lives. Where would we be without aspirin, household bleach and blue denim? In a pretty pickle, I tell you. But chemical production is not without **risks**...

1) Some chemicals, especially gases, are highly flammable and carry the risk of explosion e.g. propane, pressurised hydrogen. They must be stored and handled correctly to minimise this risk.

2) Some chemicals are harmful to our health if we come into contact with them or their vapours. Chlorine, for example, is toxic if inhaled and can irritate the eyes and lungs. Workers in the chemical industry are most at risk, but an accident or fire at a chemical plant, or a spill during transportation, could also expose the public to hazardous material.

3) Some chemicals can also damage the environment. Sulfur dioxide is a by-product of sulfuric acid production. It is an acidic gas and a contributor to acid rain.

The Chemical Industry and Food

Chemicals Can Improve Food Production

In 1960 there were just over 3 billion people on the planet. By 2000 there were twice as many, and it's just going to keep rising. Feeding so many people is a **huge challenge**. There are three main ways the **chemical industry** can help:

1) FERTILISING THE SOIL

This provides crops with **nutrients** — improving plant growth and **increasing crop yield**.
'Great news' I hear you cry, but **overuse** of artificial fertilisers has its **problems**.

- Rain can wash them from the soil into **lakes** and **rivers** where they cause **excessive algae growth** — this **reduces** the amount of **light** available for plants that are needed to oxygenate the water. The lack of light causes the plants to die and the decomposing plant matter is a source of nutrients for **bacteria** — as their numbers increase they **further deplete** the water of oxygen.
- **Nitrate(V) ions** from fertilisers can get into **drinking water**. There are concerns about the **health risks** of this, especially to young children.

2) ACID NEUTRALISATION

Each crop has a **soil pH** at which it grows best. Too much acid in the soil can lead to poor plant growth. Chemicals such as **limestone** (calcium carbonate) or **lime** (calcium hydroxide) can be added to soils to neutralise acid and **improve** the overall **growth** of a crop.

3) KILLING PESTS

Pesticides are chemicals that kill **insects**, **weeds** or **moulds**, all of which can **reduce crop yield** and **quality**. But the use of pesticides has **downsides** too, of course:

- They often end up killing non-pest organisms — some of which are actually **beneficial** to the crop.
- Some pesticides **don't break down** easily, this means that they can **accumulate** in the food chain and reach levels harmful to the health of much larger bird and animal species.
- As with fertilisers, they can be washed from the soil and end up in **drinking water**.

Practice Questions

Q1 State two ways in which the industrial production of chemicals impacts upon the environment.

Q2 Why do reactions with higher atom economies and percentage yields tend to be less harmful to the environment?

Q3 Give three examples of the fixed costs that a chemical company has to meet.

Q4 How do artificial fertilisers allow farmers to get a greater yield of crop?

Exam Questions

1   Bromomethane is reacted with sodium hydroxide to make methanol:

$$CH_3Br + NaOH \rightarrow CH_3OH + NaBr$$

Calculate the atom economy for this reaction using the relative atomic masses of each of the elements.   [4 marks]

2   Agrochemicals are chemical products used by farmers to improve the quantity or quality of the food that they produce.

a)   Describe three different ways that agrochemicals are used in farming.   [3 marks]

b)   Explain two problems associated with the use of agrochemicals.   [4 marks]

've got a chemical plant — it's a chemis-tree

know it seems like there's a lot to learn on these two pages, but it's mostly pretty straightforward. Make sure you're happy ith calculating atom economy and percentage yield though — that's pretty important. In the grand scheme of things, robably not as important as war, or widespread famine... but, you know... useful for the exam and all that.

Benzene

Yes, it's the 'Colour by Design' section and yet we're about to cover seemingly-unrelated stuff like benzene and fats and oils. The Universe works in mysterious ways. We'll get onto the colour bit later — just think of this as building the suspense...

Aromatic Compounds are Derived from Benzene

Arenes or **aromatic compounds** contain a **benzene ring**. Benzene can be represented in two ways...

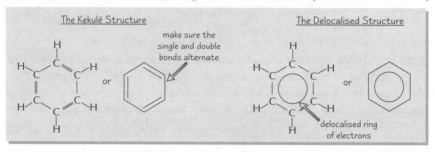

Benzene has the formula C_6H_6. For a while, benzene's structure was a bit of a puzzle — it couldn't be a simple carbon chain because there aren't enough hydrogens. The scientist **Kekulé** was the first to solve this problem, proposing that the carbons were arranged in a **planar ring** as above.

Kekulé also suggested that the single and double bonds continuously **flipped** between the carbons, as shown.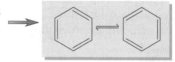

If Kekulé's structure is correct, there should always be three bonds with the length of a C–C bond and three bonds with the length of a C=C bond. But **X-ray diffraction studies** have shown that all the carbon-carbon bonds in benzene are the same length — between the length of a single bond and a double bond. So Kekulé's structure **wasn't quite right** — even so, it's still used a lot today as a useful representation of benzene.

The **delocalised model** was developed later to better explain benzene's properties. The carbons are still arranged in a ring, but there are no alternating single and double bonds. Instead, each carbon donates an electron from its **p-orbital**. which combine to form a ring of **delocalised electrons**.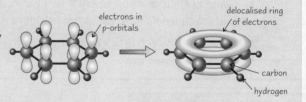

The Delocalised Structure Explains Why Benzene Reacts Via Substitution

1) If you add a few drops of **bromine** to an **alkene**, the reaction is very quick — you can see the **orange colour** of bromine **disappear**. This is an example of **electrophilic addition** and just **one product** is formed — a dibromoalkane

$$H_2C=CH_2 + Br-Br \longrightarrow H_2BrC-CBrH_2$$

     ethene   bromine   1,2,-dibromoethane

> Bromine is the **electrophile** — it attacks the region of **high electron density** in the alkene double bond.

2) If you add bromine to benzene **nothing happens** — the orange colour remains.

3) If you use a **catalyst** you can get benzene and bromine to react, but it's very **slow** and they react by electrophilic **substitution** rather than addition (it's covered on p88).

4) The **Kekulé structure** isn't much good at explaining this — it represents benzene as though it had C=C bonds just like an alkene. So based on **this**, you'd expect benzene to react **like alkenes do**.

5) The **delocalised model** is better at explaining what's going on...

> – The electrons in the delocalised ring have **more room** than if they were squeezed into localised double bonds. They can get further away from each other, **spreading out** the **negative charge**, so the molecule is **more stable**.
>
> – An addition reaction would need to take electrons from the stable delocalised ring to form **new bonds**. Substitution reactions **don't** do this — a hydrogen atom just gets swapped for something else and the **stability** of the delocalised electrons is **preserved**. Which makes benzene a happy bunny...

Fats and Oils

Now this next stuff is a bit random, but hey — you've got to know it, so here it is...

Fatty Acids are **Carboxylic Acids**

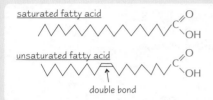

Fatty acids have a long hydrocarbon chain with a **carboxylic acid** group at the end. If the hydrocarbon chain contains **no double bonds** then the fatty acid is **saturated**, but if it contains one or more double bonds then it's **unsaturated**.

Fatty acids can also be written like this $\longrightarrow$ where 'R' is a hydrocarbon chain.

Triglycerides are *Triesters* of *Glycerol* and *Fatty Acids*

1) The **animal** and **vegetable fats** and **oils** we eat are mainly **triglycerides**.

2) Triglycerides contain the ester functional group $-COO-$ three times — they are **triglyceryl esters**. They're made by reacting **glycerol (propane-1,2,3-triol)** with **fatty acids**.

3) The **three -OH groups** on the glycerol molecules link up to **fatty acids** to produce triglyceride molecules. Water is eliminated, so it's a type of **condensation** reaction.

A condensation reaction involves the elimination of a small molecule, typically water (although it doesn't have to be).

Practice Questions

Q1 Draw out the two representations of the benzene molecule.

Q2 How did X-ray diffraction studies show that the Kekulé structure of benzene was incorrect?

Q3 Why does benzene tend to react via substitution not addition reactions?

Q4 Draw a diagram to show how glycerol and fatty acids combine to form fats and oils.

Exam Questions

1   When cyclohexene reacts with hydrogen, one mole of H_2 adds across the double bond in one mole of cyclohexene. 120 kJ of energy is released.

$\bigcirc + H_2 \rightarrow \bigcirc$ $\Delta H = -120 \text{ kJmol}^{-1}$

   a) Look at the structure of cyclohexa-1,3-diene below.
       i) Predict the number of moles of H_2 that one mole of cyclohexa-1,3-diene will react with.
       ii) Predict how much energy will be released during this reaction. [2 marks]

   $\bigcirc$ Cyclohexa-1,3-diene $\bigcirc$ Benzene (Kekulé structure)

   b) Look at the Kekulé structure for benzene.
       i) Predict the number of moles of H_2 that one mole of benzene will react with.
       ii) Predict how much energy will be released during this reaction. [2 marks]

   c) One mole of benzene actually releases 208 kJ of energy when it reacts with hydrogen. Suggest how the delocalised model of benzene explains the difference between this number and the one that you predicted in part b). [2 marks]

2   Outline some of the reasons why the delocalised structure is generally accepted as a better representation of benzene than the Kekulé structure. You should refer to the shape of the molecule and to its chemical properties. [4 marks]

Everyone needs a bit of stability in their life...

So here's a handy tip — if you're asked why benzene reacts the way it does, it's bound to be to do with the ring of delocalised electrons. Remember there's a hydrogen at every point on the benzene ring — it's easy to forget they're there. Don't forget to learn all the fats and oils stuff on this page. I know it's a bit random, but so is life sometimes. Potato!

Reactions of Aromatic Compounds

*On the last double page you learned that benzene prefers to react by electrophilic substitution — this is so that the stabilit
of its delocalised electron ring is preserved. Now you're gonna take a closer look at some of those reactions. Yippee...*

Arenes Undergo **Electrophilic Substitution** Reactions...

...with **Nitronium Ions** as the Electrophile

When you warm **benzene** with **concentrated nitric** and **sulfuric acids**, you get **nitrobenzene**.
Sulfuric acid's a **catalyst** — it helps to make the nitronium ion, NO_2^+, which is the electrophile.

$$HNO_3 + H_2SO_4 \rightarrow H_2NO_3^+ + HSO_4^- \Longrightarrow H_2NO_3^+ \rightarrow NO_2^+ + H_2O$$

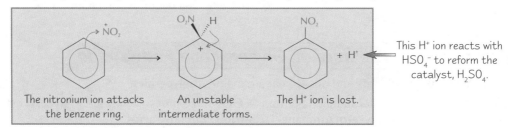

The nitronium ion attacks
the benzene ring.

An unstable
intermediate forms.

The H⁺ ion is lost.

This H⁺ ion reacts with
HSO_4^- to reform the
catalyst, H_2SO_4.

If you only want one NO_2 group added (**mononitration**), you need to keep the
temperature **below 55 °C**. Above this temperature you'll get lots of substitutions.

...and with **Sulfur Trioxide Molecules** as the Electrophile

If you wanted to make **benzenesulfonic acid** (and you never know, one day you might...), you could either:

> 1) Boil benzene under reflux with **concentrated sulfuric acid** for several hours, or...
> 2) ...warm benzene to 40 °C with **fuming sulfuric acid** for half an hour.

The electrophile in the reaction is **sulfur trioxide**, SO_3...

– Conc. sulfuric acid contains SO_3 because it breaks up like this... $H_2SO_4 \rightarrow H_2O + SO_3$

– Fuming sulfuric acid is basically a lot of SO_3 molecules dissolved in sulfuric acid. It's much richer
in SO_3 than conc. sulfuric acid which is why the reaction is quicker and needs less heating.

The mechanism is similar to the one with the NO_2^+ electrophile.

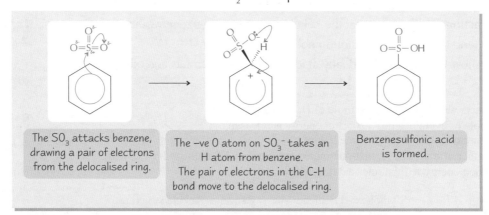

The SO_3 attacks benzene,
drawing a pair of electrons
from the delocalised ring.

The –ve O atom on SO_3^- takes an
H atom from benzene.
The pair of electrons in the C-H
bond move to the delocalised ring.

Benzenesulfonic acid
is formed.

Escaping from prison is a
breeze with the patented
CGP electro-file.

Halogen Carriers Help to Make Good Electrophiles

An electrophile has to have a pretty strong **positive charge** to be able
to attack the stable benzene ring. Most compounds just **aren't
polarised enough** — but some can be made into **stronger
electrophiles** using a catalyst called a **halogen carrier**.

A halogen carrier accepts a **lone pair of electrons** from a polar molecule
containing a halogen — the electrophile. As the lone pair of electrons is
pulled away, the **polarisation** in the electrophile **increases** and sometimes
a **carbocation** forms. This makes the electrophile loads stronger.
Halogen carriers include **aluminium halides**, **iron halides** and **iron**.

> A carbocation is an organic
> ion with a positively charged
> carbon atom.

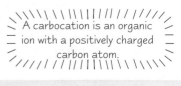

haloalkane   halogen
carrier

carbocation

Although R⁺ gets shown as a free ion, it probably
remains associated with $AlCl_4^-$ — this doesn't
affect how R⁺ reacts though.

Reactions of Aromatic Compounds

Halogen Carriers Can be Used to Put an Alkyl Group on Benzene

1) **Alkyl groups** have one fewer H atoms than alkane molecules, e.g. CH_3 is a 'methyl group'
— when it's bonded to a benzene ring the molecule is called 'methyl benzene'.

2) Alkyl groups can be substituted for H atoms on benzene rings by refluxing a **chloroalkane** and **benzene** with a **halogen carrier** such as $AlCl_3$. This is how methylbenzene can be made:

'Reflux' means boiling reactants in a flask fitted with a condenser to stop them boiling away.

The **carbocation** is formed from the chloroalkane and $AlCl_3$: $CH_3Cl + AlCl_3 \rightarrow CH_3^+ + AlCl_4^-$

The carbocation then reacts with benzene via **electrophilic substitution**:

The carbocation is the electrophile. It is attracted to the electrons in the delocalised ring.

An unstable intermediate forms.

Methylbenzene is made and the H^+ ion is lost.

The halogen carrier gets regenerated when $AlCl_4^-$ reacts with the H^+ ion that comes off the benzene ring:

$$AlCl_4^- + H^+ \rightarrow AlCl_3 + HCl$$

3) This method can be used to put **any alkyl group** onto a benzene ring and is called **Friedel-Crafts alkylation**. Since the halogen carriers don't get used up, they're sometimes called **Friedel-Crafts catalysts**. This general reaction can be represented by the equation:

'R' just means any alkyl group

$$C_6H_6 + RCl \xrightarrow[\text{Reflux}]{AlCl_3} C_6H_5R + HCl$$

Halogen Carriers Can Also Put an Acyl Group on Benzene

1) **Acyl groups** contain a **C=O** double bond. They can be substituted for H atoms on benzene using the **Friedel-Crafts** technique — this time by refluxing benzene with an **acyl chloride** instead of a chloroalkane. This produces **phenylketones** (unless R = H, in which case an aldehyde called benzenecarbaldehyde, or benzaldehyde, is formed).

An acyl group. In an acyl chloride, R^1 = Cl.

2) There's a different electrophile, but the mechanism is the same as in alkylation:

An **acylium ion** is formed from the acyl chloride and $AlCl_3$: $CH_3COCl + AlCl_3 \rightarrow CH_3CO^+ + AlCl_4^-$

The acylium ion acts as the **electrophile** and goes on to react with benzene:

Phenylethanone.

As in the reaction above, $AlCl_3$ then gets regenerated.

Reactions of Aromatic Compounds

Halogen Carriers Help **Halogens Substitute** into the Benzene Ring

Halogen carriers polarise halogen dimers, such as Br_2 or Cl_2. The **positively charged** end of the halogen molecule then acts as an **electrophile** and reacts with the benzene ring in the usual **electrophilic substitution** reaction.

benzene → → bromobenzene + HBr + AlCl₃

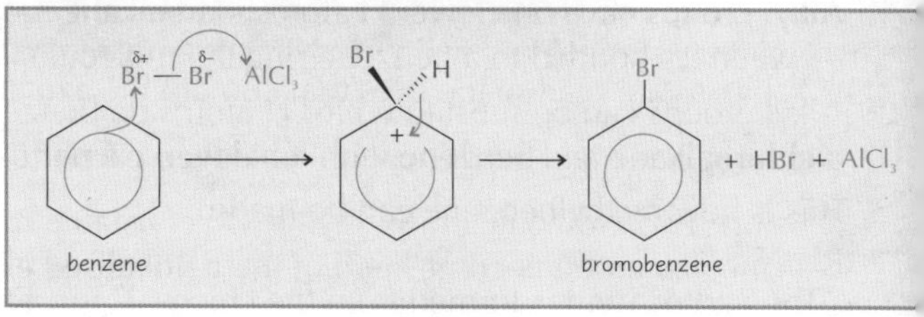

Ionic Liquids Can Be Used as an **Alternative** to **Traditional Solvents**

Ionic liquids are ionic compounds with relatively **low melting points** — usually less than 100 °C. Sometimes, their melting point is so low, they're liquid at **room temperature**. Recently a lot of research has been done on using ionic liquids instead of **organic solvents** in industrial reactions because they have many **environmental advantages**:

- They are **less volatile** and so release **less vapour**.
- They are **less flammable** and often **less toxic**.
- They are easier to re-use and so **reduce waste**.

Friedel-Crafts reactions can be performed with ionic liquids called dialkylimidazolium chlorides (don't worry, you don't need to remember this name). $AlCl_3$ is added to it to form a catalyst-solvent system, which allows reactions to be performed at **lower temperatures** than using traditional solvents, **saving fuel** as well as reducing **pollution**.

Practice Questions

Q1 Name the electrophile formed when concentrated sulfuric and nitric acids are mixed.

Q2 What catalysts are used in Friedel-Crafts reactions?

Q3 What could you react benzene with to form methylbenzene?

Q4 Why do compounds such as $AlCl_3$ and $FeBr_3$ help benzene to react with halogens?

Exam Questions

1 Two electrophilic substitution reactions of benzene are summarised in the diagram:

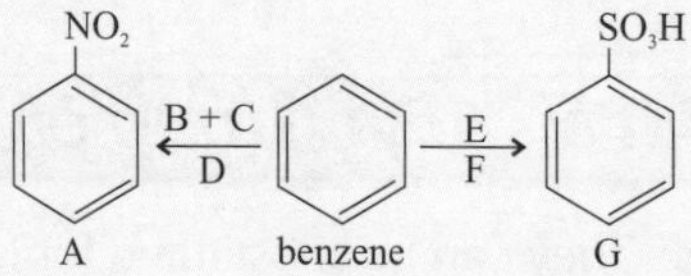

a) i) Name the product A, and the reagents B and C, and give the conditions D. [4 marks]

   ii) Outline a mechanism for this reaction. [3 marks]

   iii) Write equations to show the formation of the electrophile. [2 marks]

b) i) Name the product G, and the reagent E, and give the conditions F. [3 marks]

   ii) What is the electrophile in this reaction? [1 mark]

2 Friedel-Crafts reactions that produce methylbenzene from benzene can be performed with ionic liquid solvents.

a) Explain what is mean by the term 'ionic liquid'. [1 mark]

b) Give three reasons why producing methyl benzene using an ionic liquid solvent is better for the environment than using a traditional organic solvent. [3 marks]

Sniff, sniff — is that the sweet smell of exam success?

Ok, lots of reactions here. Sugar-coating it never helped anyone (except perhaps the almond) so I'm just gonna give it to you straight — you do need to know 'em. Fortunately the mechanisms are pretty much along the same lines. I'd make sure you your head around all that Friedel-Crafts malarkey especially. And be nice to your mum. Two tips for a trouble-free life there.

Dyes

I'm sure you've been dying to get this far... ha ha haa. Ah dear. At least I amuse myself.

Aromatic Amines are Used to Make Azo Dyes

1) Azo dyes are man-made dyes that contain the **azo group**, –N=N–.

2) In most azo dyes, the azo group links **two aromatic groups** .

3) Having two aromatic groups creates a very **stable molecule**
   — the azo group becomes part of the **delocalised electron system**.

4) The **colours** are the result of **light absorption** by the delocalised
   electron system. Different **colours** are made by combining
   different phenols and amines (see below).

Phenols were covered on p12.

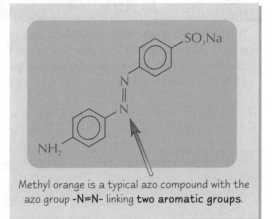

Methyl orange is a typical azo compound with the
azo group -N=N- linking **two aromatic groups**.

Azo Dyes can be made in a Coupling Reaction

The first step in creating an azo dye is to make a **diazonium salt** — diazonium compounds contain the group $-\overset{+}{N}\equiv N-$.
The **azo dye** is then made by **coupling** the diazonium salt with an **aromatic** compound that is susceptible to
electrophilic attack — like a **phenol**.

Here's the method for creating a yellow-orange azo dye:

React Phenylamine with Nitrous Acid to make a Diazonium Salt

1) **Nitrous acid (HNO$_2$)** is **unstable**, so it has
   to be made *in situ* from sodium nitrite and
   hydrochloric acid.

   'in situ' means 'in the reaction'

   $$NaNO_2 + HCl \rightarrow HNO_2 + NaCl$$

2) **Nitrous acid** reacts with **phenylamine** and **hydrochloric acid** to form **benzenediazonium
   chloride**. The temperature **must** be below **10 °C** to prevent a phenol forming instead.

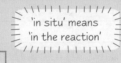

I wish you hadn't put my white robe in with the coloured washing, darling.

Gasp! He hates me...

True love never dyes.

Make the Azo Dye by Coupling the Diazonium Salt with a Phenol

1) First, the **phenol** has to be dissolved in **sodium hydroxide** solution
   to make **sodium phenoxide** solution.

2) It's then stood in **ice**, and chilled **benzenediazonium chloride** is added.

3) Here's the overall equation for the reaction:

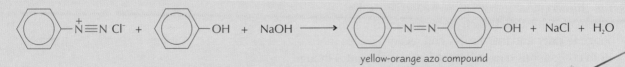

yellow-orange azo compound

4) The azo dye **precipitates** out of the solution immediately.

5) Phenol is a **coupling agent**. The lone pairs on its oxygen increase
   the **electron density** of the benzene ring, especially around carbons
   2, 4 and 6. This gives the diazonium ion (a **weak electrophile**)
   something to attack.

Remember — electrophile means 'electron lover'.

Dyes

I think I'll dye... another page... I'm gonna dye... another page...

Dyes have to **Attach** Themselves to Fibres

A good dye has got to be **colourfast** — it can't **wash out** too easily or **fade** in the light.
Colourfastness depends on the strength of the **bonding** between the **dye** and **fibre** molecules.
Dye molecules can have **functional groups** added to them that help them bind to a material.
Often a dye that binds well to one type of material **won't bind** as strongly to others.

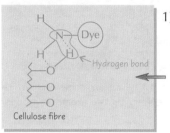

Cellulose fibre

Di's attachment to fibre was getting out of hand.

1) Some functional groups, like the **amine group** ($-NH_2$) enable dye molecules to form **hydrogen bonds** with fibre molecules. This works well with **cellulose fibres** like cotton, rayon and linen because they contain loads of **–OH groups**.

   These dyes aren't particularly colourfast because the hydrogen bonds just aren't strong enough.

2) Acidic groups like **carboxylic acid** (–COOH) or **sulfonic acid** ($-SO_3H$) help dyes bind to alkaline **–NH– links** in fibres — these links are found in wool, silk and nylon. **H^+ ions** move from dye to fibre molecule, and **ionic interactions** then hold them together. These give better colourfastness than hydrogen bonding.

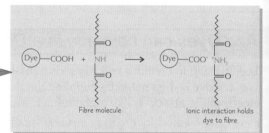

Fibre molecule

Ionic interaction holds dye to fibre

> **Fibre reactive dyes** are the most permanent type of dye. They have a functional group that will **react** with the **–OH** or **–NH– group** in the fibre, forming strong **covalent bonds**.

The **Colour** of Dyes Comes from **Chromophores**

1) The structures in molecules that give them their colour are called **chromophores**.

2) When **light** hits a chromophore, certain wavelengths are **absorbed** by electrons in the chromophore (see pages 92 and 93). **Visible wavelengths** not absorbed will be seen as a particular **colour**.

3) Chromophores tend to contain **double or triple bonds** (like C=C or N=N), **lone pairs** of electrons, or **benzene rings**. Usually, these components form part of a **delocalised electron system** across a large section of the molecule.

4) **Modifying** the chromophore will change the **frequency** of light that it absorbs, and so change the **colour** of the molecule.

5) Functional groups containing **O** or **N** atoms with **lone pairs of electrons** can be added to a chromophore to adjust the colour of a dye molecule. They do this because the lone pair of electrons becomes **part of** the delocalised system responsible for **absorbing light**.

The structures of the azo dyes **methyl red** (in acidic conditions) and **aniline yellow** are shown below. In the form shown, methyl red appears, err... **red** and aniline yellow is, well... **yellow**.

1) The chromophore in both these molecules is the system of **delocalised electrons** that spans the two benzene rings and the –N=N– connection.

2) Both compounds have **different functional groups** though and that's what makes them appear **different colours**.

3) The N and O atoms in these groups have **lone pairs of electrons** that become **part of** the **delocalised system** of the chromophore. This changes the **frequency of light** it absorbs and so the colour of the molecule. Different groups change the chromophore by **different amounts**.

Dyes

Many Dyes Need to be *Water Soluble*

The process of dyeing usually involves soaking material in a solution of the dye compound. This is a problem if the dye doesn't **dissolve**.

Ideally the dye will dissolve easily in **water** since it's cheap, readily available and non-toxic.

To make it more soluble in water, **solubilising functional groups** can be incorporated into a dye molecule. These are often **ionic groups**, such as the **sulfate ion** (usually in the form of its **sodium salt**) shown on the right. Water dissolves ionic substances because of its **polar nature**.

Strictly speaking, if a coloured compound is insoluble it's a pigment rather than a dye.

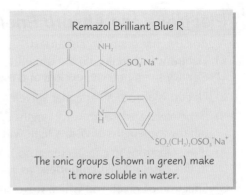

Remazol Brilliant Blue R

The ionic groups (shown in green) make it more soluble in water.

Practice Questions

Q1 Why do diazonium ions attack phenols?
Q2 What functional group could be added to a dye to make it bind to a protein such as wool?
Q3 What's a chromophore? What happens when you change it?
Q4 What functional groups can be added to a dye molecule to make it more soluble?

Exam Questions

1   Consider this synthesis pathway:

NH_2 → Step 1 → $N_2^+ Cl^-$ → [with $N(CH_3)_2$ ring] → Compound Y + HCl

a) i) One of the reagents needed for Step 1 is $HCl_{(aq)}$. Give the other reagent needed for Step 1. Write an equation to show its generation in situ from sodium nitrite and hydrochloric acid.   [2 marks]
    ii) Give the conditions for Step 1.   [1 mark]

b) Compound Y is a yellow solid.
    i) Draw a possible structure for Compound Y.   [1 mark]
    ii) What feature(s) are responsible for its yellow colour?   [3 marks]
    iii) Suggest a use for Compound Y.   [1 mark]

2   The compound shown is the dye 'Acid Orange 6'.

HO— [ring with OH] —N=N— [ring] —$SO_3^- Na^+$

a) Which molecular feature(s) may:
    i) be chromophores?   [3 marks]
    ii) make the dye more soluble?   [1 mark]

b) Explain how Acid Orange 6 would bond to silk proteins.   [3 marks]

c) Acid Orange 6 is made by a coupling reaction. Draw the structures of the reactants involved.   [2 marks]

...asked Van Gogh if he wanted a drink — He said, "Nah, I've got one ear"...

They really need to find a better red dye — like one that doesn't turn everything pink if you accidentally wash a red sock with your white clothes. Anyway, I hope you're pleased that we've finally made it onto the colour content of the colour section. And at the risk of losing your respect forever, I have to say... all this chromophoromalarkey is actually quite... cool.

Colour

Ever wondered why roses appear red and vanadium(IV) oxide looks blue? Well read on my friend...

Electrons can Absorb Energy and Become Excited to Higher Energy Levels

1) Electrons in a molecule are usually at their **lowest possible energy levels**. But if the molecule **absorbs energy**, electrons can become **excited** and move up to a **higher energy level**. This is an **electronic transition**.

2) Electrons absorb a particular wavelength of light to move to a higher energy level.

3) If the electrons absorb wavelengths of light from the **visible region** of the spectrum, only the other wavelengths of visible light will be **transmitted**, making the compound look **coloured**.

4) If the electrons in a molecule absorb **UV light** instead, **all** wavelengths of visible light will be transmitted. In this case, it looks **colourless**, as our eyes can't detect UV light. This is where **spectrometers** come in.

5) Spectrometers tell you which wavelengths of visible light **and** UV light have been absorbed. A **colorimeter** is a special type of spectrometer (see page 72).

The 3d Subshells of Transition Element Ions Split into Two Energy Levels

1) Transition elements form ions with incomplete d subshells. In the transition element ions that you need to worry about, it's the 3d subshell that's incomplete.

2) Normally the 3d orbitals of transition element ions **all** have the **same energy**. But when **ligands** come along and bond to the ions, some of the orbitals are given more energy than others. This splits the 3d orbitals into **two different energy levels**.

3) Electrons tend to **occupy the lower orbitals** — to jump up to the higher orbitals they need **energy** equal to the energy gap, ΔE. They get this energy from **visible light**.

> You can read more about transition metals, d subshells and ligands on pages 66-69.

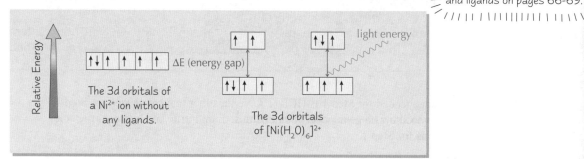

4) The amount of energy needed to make electrons jump corresponds to a **particular wavelength** of light. The rest of the wavelengths are transmitted, giving the colour you see.

5) This energy depends on the **central metal ion**, the **ligands** and the **coordination number**, as these affect the **size of the energy gap**.

Electrons Can be Excited to Higher Energy Levels in Organic Molecules Too

1) 3d-orbitals in transition metals are examples of **atomic orbitals**.

2) When a **covalent bond** forms, atomic orbitals **link up** to form **molecular orbitals**.

3) Just like atomic orbitals, some molecular orbitals contain electrons and some are empty. The **lowest energy** molecular orbitals usually fill up first.

4) By absorbing **exactly** the right amount of **energy**, electrons can move from a filled molecular orbital to an empty one — forming an **excited state**. This energy can be in the form of **UV** or **visible light**.

5) If the energy gap between filled and empty molecular orbitals corresponds to frequencies of **visible light**, then the molecule appears **coloured**.

Stuggling with colour? This picture should provide a few tips.

Colour

Delocalisation Affects the Energy Needed to Excite Electrons

1) A single covalent bond forms when **two atomic orbitals**, each holding one electron, come together to form **two molecular orbitals**. Since each molecular orbital can hold two electrons, **only one** is filled. The **energy gap** between these orbitals is **very large**. **High-frequency UV** needs to be absorbed to excite the electrons.

2) A **double bond** contains **four molecular orbitals**. There is a smaller **energy gap** between the **highest filled** molecular orbital and the **lowest empty** molecular orbital than in a single bond. It requires **lower frequency UV** to excite the electrons in a double bond.

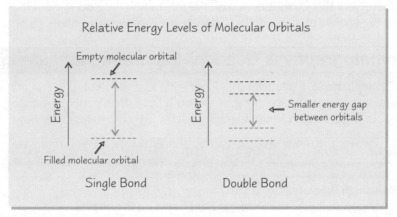

3) In a **delocalised system** — like benzene — many molecular orbitals are formed. These orbitals are even **closer in energy** than in a double bond. The electrons in them absorb very low frequency UV and **visible light** when they become excited.

4) As delocalisation **increases** more molecular orbitals form and are closer in energy. **Less energy** is needed to excite electrons and the **frequency of light** absorbed **drops**. This is why functional groups that **extend the delocalisation** in chromophores cause the colour to change (see page 90).

5) Not all delocalised systems involve benzene rings. When C=C double and C–C single bonds **alternate**, like in buta-1,3-diene ($CH_2=CH–CH=CH_2$), electrons become **delocalised** — this is known as **conjugation**.

Practice Questions

Q1 Explain what happens when an electron becomes excited.

Q2 3d orbitals normally have the same energy. What causes them to split into two different energy levels?

Q3 State three factors that affect the frequency of light absorbed by a transition metal ion.

Q4 What effect does delocalisation have on energy levels in a compound? How does increasing delocalisation change the colour of a molecule?

Exam Question

1 Cobalt chloride is used to test for the presence of water. When it is dry it is blue, but if water is added it turns pink. The pink colour is caused by the complex ion $[Co(H_2O)_6]^{2+}$.

a) Explain how the addition of water ligands results in a colour change.   [3 marks]

b) Benzene is a liquid that absorbs only UV light.

   i) What colour is benzene?   [1 mark]
   ii) What machine could be used to confirm that benzene only absorbs UV light?   [1 mark]

c) Benzene contains a ring of delocalised electrons which often form part of a chromophore in organic molecules.

   i) Explain how delocalised systems can produce coloured organic molecules.   [2 marks]
   ii) Explain how adding functional groups to the chromophores of organic molecules changes their colour.   [2 marks]

Take it to the next level...

lectrons, eh? I'm telling ya, the world would be a very dull place without those little blighters getting all excited and zipping bout between orbitals. Fireworks wouldn't be the same for one thing. Remember though, electrons can't just do what hey like — they have to absorb a set amount of energy to move between orbitals and only certain movements are allowed.

Identifying Materials Used in a Painting

Ok. I won't lie to you, you're about to be bombarded with analytical techniques. It's a lot to learn. But you can do this...

There are a Few Techniques for **Identifying the Chemicals** in a Painting

1) Paint is usually a **coloured compound** — called a **pigment** — dispersed in a liquid **binding medium** such as **oil** or **water**. The liquid holds the dry pigment together and determines the properties of the paint.

2) There are a variety of techniques to **identify** the pigments used in a **painting**. This helps to date a picture and is useful in restoration because you can make sure you're using **exactly** the right colour. It's also helpful if you can identify the binding medium used by the artist, as it tends to affect the paint's texture and appearance.

3) Chemists can only remove very **tiny quantities** of material for study — you don't want to go ruining a valuable work of art by scraping big chunks of paint off it. Luckily some very **sensitive** methods of analysis are available.

Gas-Liquid Chromatography is Good for **Separating** and **Identifying** Things

Chromatography is used to **separate** stuff in a mixture — once it's separated out, you can often **identify** the components. There are quite a few different types of chromatography — you'll have done paper chromatography before — but the one you need to know about is **gas-liquid chromatography** (GLC). All chromatography has two phases:

1) A **mobile phase** — where the molecules can move. This is always a liquid or a gas.

2) A **stationary phase** — where the molecules can't move. This must be a solid, or a liquid on a solid support.

The mobile phase **moves through** the stationary phase.
As this happens, the components in the mixture **separate out** between the phases.
Gas-liquid chromatograms are great for showing the **proportion of esters** in oils used as binding mediums in **paint**. This helps to **identify** the oil present. Only a very small sample of paint is needed.

1) In **gas-liquid chromatography** (GLC) the stationary phase is a **viscous liquid**, such as an oil, or a **solid**, which coats the inside of a long tube. The tube's **coiled** to save space, and built into an oven.

2) The mobile phase is an **unreactive carrier gas** such as nitrogen or helium.

3) The **sample** to be analysed is **injected** into the stream of carrier gas, which carries it through the **tube** and over the stationary phase.

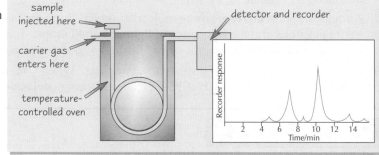

4) The components of the mixture constantly **dissolve in the stationary phase**, **evaporate** into the mobile phase and then **redissolve** as they travel through the tube.

5) The **solubility** of each component of the mixture determines **how long** it spends **dissolved in the stationary phase** and how long it spends **moving along** the tube in the **mobile phase**. A substance with a high solubility will spend more time dissolved, so will take longer to travel through the tube to the detector than one with a lower solubility.

GLC Chromatograms Show the **Proportions** of the Components in a Mixture

A **gas-liquid chromatogram** shows a **series of peaks** at the times when the **detector** senses something other than the carrier gas **leaving the tube**. They can be used to **identify the substances** within a sample and their **relative proportions**.

1) The time taken to reach the detector is called the **retention time**.
Each **peak** on a chromatogram corresponds to a substance with a particular **retention time**.

2) **Retention times** are measured from **zero** to the **centre** of each peak, and can be looked up in a **reference table** to **identify** the **substances** present. You have to be careful though — **similar compounds** often have **similar retention times**, so they're difficult to identify **accurately**.

3) The **area** under each peak is proportional to the relative **amount of each substance** in the original mixture. Remember, it's **area**, not height, that's important — the **tallest** peak on the chromatogram **won't always** represent the **most abundant substance**.

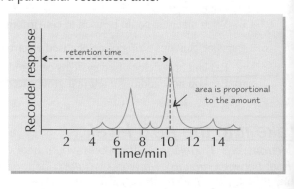

Identifying Materials Used in a Painting

Mass Spectroscopy can be Combined with Gas-Liquid Chromatography

Gas-liquid chromatography is very good at **separating** a mixture into its individual components, but not so good at identifying those components. **Mass spectroscopy**, on the other hand, (see pages 23–25) is great at **identifying** unknown compounds, but would give confusing results from a mixture of substances.

If you put these **two techniques together**, you get an **extremely useful** analytical tool.

> **Gas-liquid chromatography-mass spectroscopy** (GLC-MS) **combines the benefits** of gas-liquid chromatography and mass spectrometry to make a super analysis tool.
>
> The sample is **separated** using **gas-liquid chromatography**, but instead of going to a detector, the separated components are fed into a **mass spectrometer**.
>
> The spectrometer produces a **mass spectrum** for each **component**, which can be used to **identify** each one and show what the original **sample** consisted of.

Visible Spectroscopy Can Help Identify a Pigment

There are two variations of this technique — **visible absorption** and **visible reflection** spectroscopy. Both techniques use beams of **monochromatic light** — light of a **single wavelength** or **colour**.

White light is a **mixture** of all the different wavelengths of visible light. It can be split into monochromatic beams using a **filter**.

VISIBLE ABSORPTION SPECTROSCOPY

1) The beam of monochromatic light is passed through a **dilute solution** of the pigment. A detector measures the **intensity of light** before and after it's passed through the solution. From this you can calculate **absorbance** — a measure of how much light the pigment has absorbed.

2) Different frequencies of light are passed through the solution to produce a **visible absorption spectrum** (a graph of frequency or **wavelength** against absorbance). The **peaks** in the graph tell you which colours of light the pigment absorbs most **strongly**.

3) Every pigment has a unique colour, so produces a **unique** visible **absorption spectrum**. This allows it to be **identified**.

FOR EXAMPLE This is the visible **absorption** spectrum of **carotene**, the pigment in carrots:

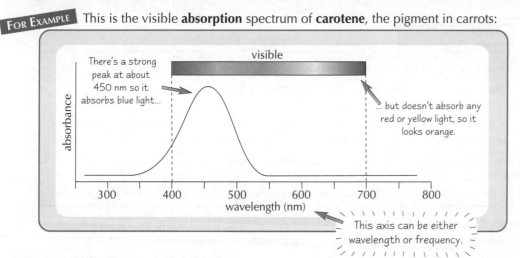

There's a strong peak at about 450 nm so it absorbs blue light...

... but doesn't absorb any red or yellow light, so it looks orange.

This axis can be either wavelength or frequency.

Claude's painting materials were: 6% canvas, 5% paint and 100% pure genius.

VISIBLE REFLECTION SPECTROSCOPY

1) It's not always possible to make a solution of a pigment — it might not dissolve easily, or you may not want to remove it from the painting. In this case **visible reflection spectroscopy** can help.

2) A beam of monochromatic light is shone onto the **surface of a solid**. The intensity of the beam before and after reflection from this surface is measured and the **reflectance** is calculated.

3) Reflectance is a measure of what **percentage** of the light falling on the solid is **reflected back**. **Low values** of reflectance mean that **lots** of light is being **absorbed**. By changing the frequency of the light and calculating reflectance values a **visible reflectance spectrum** is produced.

Identifying Materials Used in a Painting

Atomic Emission Spectroscopy Can Identify the Elements in a Pigment...

Atomic emission spectroscopy is used to analyse the **individual elements** present in the pigment.
This is how it works:

1) You already know that when an electron absorbs the right amount of energy, it becomes **excited** and jumps to a **higher energy orbital**. But it doesn't remain in this **excited state**. When it falls back down to the lower energy level — its **ground state** — the electron **emits** its excess energy as **UV, visible,** or **infra-red light**.

2) Each energy level is **discrete** — it has a certain **fixed** energy. Electrons must absorb and emit a fixed amount of energy to move between levels. The frequency of the light emitted depends on the **energy gap** between the excited and ground states.

3) There's **more than one** energy level that an electron in an atom can be excited to — as a result, **different frequencies** (or wavelengths) of light will be emitted by electrons returning to their ground states.

4) The energy levels in every element are different, so **each element** will emit its own **unique** set of frequencies. This produces an **atomic emission spectrum** which can be used to identify the element. If you carry out atomic emission spectroscopy on an **unknown compound** — such as a pigment — you can use the spectrum produced to identify the elements **within it**.

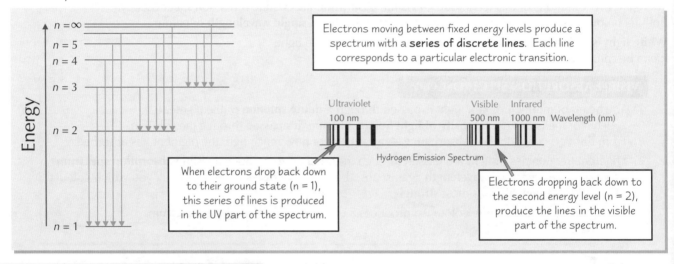

Electrons moving between fixed energy levels produce a spectrum with a **series of discrete** lines. Each line corresponds to a particular electronic transition.

When electrons drop back down to their ground state (n = 1), this series of lines is produced in the UV part of the spectrum.

Electrons dropping back down to the second energy level (n = 2), produce the lines in the visible part of the spectrum.

...and this is How You Do It...

1) A high-energy pulse of laser light is focused onto a **tiny sample** of paint, which **vaporises** the pigment.

2) The vapour is then passed between **two electrodes** — the energy from the electric current **excites** the electrons in the pigment atoms.

3) When the electrons return to their ground state they **emit light** with a particular set of frequencies. A **spectrometer** is used **separate out** all the frequencies into an **emission spectrum**.

4) The atoms present in the pigment are identified by **comparing** the spectrum produced to those from **known elements**. It's also possible to find out the **relative quantities** of each element by measuring the **intensities** of certain frequencies of light.

So, if you wanted to see whether **element X** was present in your compound, you'd **compare** the atomic emission spectrum for X, with the emission spectrum produced by your **pigment**.

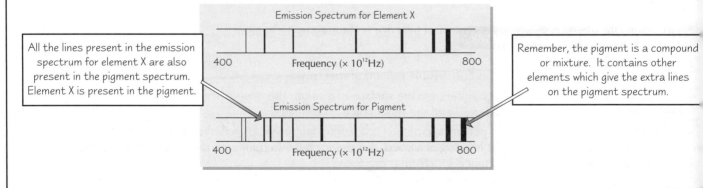

All the lines present in the emission spectrum for element X are also present in the pigment spectrum. Element X is present in the pigment.

Remember, the pigment is a compound or mixture. It contains other elements which give the extra lines on the pigment spectrum.

Identifying Materials Used in a Painting

Practice Questions

Q1 Explain the terms 'stationary phase' and 'mobile phase' in the context of chromatography.

Q2 Describe how you would find the retention time of a particular substance from a gas-liquid chromatogram.

Q3 What is monochromatic light? How can it be produced?

Q4 What technique could be used to identify a pigment in a painting without removing it?

Q5 What technique could be used to find out the elemental composition of a pigment?

Exam Questions

1   A scientist has a mixture of several organic chemicals. He wants to know if it contains any hexene.
    He runs a sample of pure hexene through a GLC machine and finds that its retention time is 5 minutes.
    Then he runs a sample of his mixture through the same machine, under the same conditions,
    and produces the chromatogram shown on the right.

    a) Describe what happens to the mixture in the apparatus.   [4 marks]

    b) What feature of the chromatogram suggests that the sample contains hexene? [1 mark]

    c) Give a reason why the researcher may still not be certain that his
        mixture contains hexene. What could he do to confirm his findings?   [2 marks]

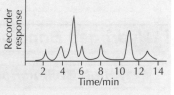

2   The diagram below shows the atomic emission spectra for three different elements — A, B and C.
    Below this is the spectrum of a pigment thought to contain these elements.

    a) Explain what happens in an atom to produce a spectrum
        like this.   [2 marks]

    b) Explain why different elements produce spectra consisting
        of emissions of different frequencies of light.   [3 marks]

    c) Which of the elements, A to C, do you think are present
        in the pigment? Explain how you can tell this.   [3 marks]

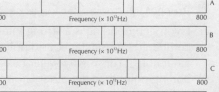

3   a) Explain how a visible absorption spectrum of a coloured solution can be produced.
        You should include what is measured and plotted to produce the spectrum.   [3 marks]

    b) Suggest an alternative method of producing a visible spectrum of a pigment without dissolving it to make a solution.
                                                                                              [1 mark]

4   The diagram below shows a visible reflectance spectrum recorded from a particular spot of pigment on a painting.

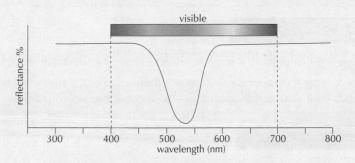

    a) Using the spectrum shown, state a colour of light that is absorbed by the pigment.   [1 mark]

    b) Suggest why measuring reflectance rather than absorbance would be preferred in this case.   [2 marks]

    c) How could the reflectance spectrum be used to help identify the exact chemical in the spot of pigment? [1 mark]

Rolf's spectroscopy club — can you tell what it is yet?

urrah! You've made it through the last few pages without running for the hills (or if you have, you've taken a few deep
eaths, admired the scenery and made your way back again). Better yet, next time you're presented with an original Van Gogh
u'll have no probs identifying the pigments, restoring it back to its original glory and selling it for millions. Double hurrah.

Water and Dissolving

The oceans might sound like a broad subject area but actually the topics in this section are all quite Pacific*.

Water forms **Hydrogen Bonds**

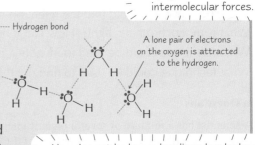

1) Water molecules form bonds between each other called **hydrogen bonds**. In a hydrogen bond, an H atom is attracted to a lone electron pair on an O atom (see diagram).

2) It works because water molecules are **polar** — the electronegative O atoms draw bonding electrons **away** from the H atoms, creating $\delta+$ charges on the Hs.

3) Hydrogen bonds are strong for **intermolecular forces**, compared to, for example, instantaneous dipole-induced dipole attractions, but very weak compared to the likes of ionic or covalent bonds.

See page 27 for more about intermolecular forces.

A lone pair of electrons on the oxygen is attracted to the hydrogen.

You also get hydrogen bonding when hydrogen is covalently bonded to other electronegative atoms like fluorine or nitrogen (e.g. in ammonia).

Hydrogen Bonding Explains Water's **Unusual** Physical Properties Like...

1) High Boiling Point

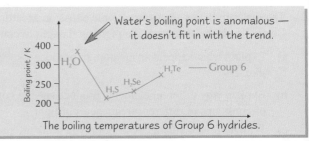

1) To **boil** a liquid, you need to **overcome** the intermolecular forces, so that the molecules can **escape**. Liquids with stronger intermolecular forces have **higher boiling points**.

2) Hydrogen bonding is a **strong** intermolecular force, compared to instantaneous dipole-induced dipole attractions. This is why water has a much higher boiling point than the other Group 6 hydrides.

Water's boiling point is anomalous — it doesn't fit in with the trend.

The boiling temperatures of Group 6 hydrides.

2) High Specific Heat Capacity

1) **Different substances** that absorb the **same** amount of energy don't change **temperature** by the same amount. **Specific heat capacity** measures how easy it is to raise the temperature of something — it's the energy needed to raise the temperature of a unit mass of a substance by 1 °C. It depends on a substance's **internal structure**.

2) Water's got a **high** specific heat capacity — that's why the sea heats up (and cools down) a lot slower than land.

3) The Earth's **oceans** can absorb and store huge amounts of heat energy from the Sun. **Ocean currents** transport this heat energy around the world, e.g. by carrying energy absorbed at the equator to colder regions of the world.

3) High Enthalpy of Vaporisation

1) **Enthalpy of vaporisation** is the amount of energy needed to change a substance from its standard state to a **vapour**.

2) Water needs a lot more energy to **evaporate** than most other liquids. If it's on your skin, it takes loads of energy (in the form of heat) from your skin as it evaporates — so it cools you down quickly.

4) Ice is Less Dense than Water

1) Normally, density **increases** as temperature falls — think gas, liquid, solid.

2) But as water freezes into ice, the density actually **decreases**. Water is actually at its most dense at about 4 °C.

3) It's to do with the way hydrogen bonds affect the structure of ice. As water freezes, all the hydrogen bonds that could form, do form — this forms a lattice structure with lots of wasted space, making it **less dense**.

4) As ice **melts**, some hydrogen bonds **break** and the lattice **breaks down**, allowing water molecules to 'fill in' the gaps, increasing the density.

Hydrogen bonds were responsible for sinking the Titanic... (kind of)

WARNING: This introduction contains a dodgy pun. It may disturb those of a sensitive disposition.

Water and Dissolving

Solutes *Dissolve* Best in Solvents with *Similar Intermolecular Forces*

When something dissolves, bonds within the **solvent** and **solute break** and new bonds **between** the solvent and solute are **made**. Generally speaking substances **won't** dissolve if the bonds to be **broken** are **stronger** than those that will be **formed**.

There are **two** main types of solvent — **polar** (such as water) and **non-polar** (such as hexane).

Ionic substances **won't** dissolve in **non-polar** solvents.
Non-polar molecules **don't** interact strongly enough with ions to **pull them away** from the ionic lattice. The **electrostatic forces** between the ions are way **stronger** than any bonds that could form between the ions and the solvent molecules.

Most **covalent** substances **only** dissolve in **non-polar** solvents.
The bonds **between** covalent molecules tend to be **pretty weak**. They **can be** broken by non-polar solvent molecules. Covalent substances **don't** tend to dissolve in **polar solvents** though. For example, **iodine** doesn't dissolve much in water — the **hydrogen bonds** between water molecules are **stronger** than the bonds that would form between water molecules and iodine molecules.

Ionic Solids Dissolve in *Polar Solvents*

Ionic compounds can be dissolved by **polar solvents** like water. It's the polar H–O bonds in water that make it work...

1) The $\delta+$ on the H atoms are attracted to the **negative ions** and the $\delta-$ on the O atoms are attracted to the **positive ions**.

2) The ions **separate** from the ionic lattice and become **surrounded** by water molecules.

3) Although the water-ion bonds are a lot weaker, the **total attraction** from all the water molecules is enough to **overcome** the strong ionic attraction in the lattice. This is all explained in more detail on the next page in terms of energy changes.

4) The process of the ions being surrounded by water molecules is called **hydration**. If the solvent isn't water, it's called **solvation**.

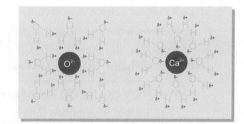

Practice Questions

Q1 Explain how hydrogen bonds form.

Q2 Give three unusual properties of water that are caused by hydrogen bonding.

Q3 Explain briefly how polar solvents are able to dissolve ionic solids.

Exam Questions

1 The diagram on the right shows some water molecules in liquid water. Explain, in terms of bonding, what happens when water boils and why it is said to have an 'anomalous' boiling point. [3 marks]

2 An experiment was carried out to compare the solubility of sodium chloride in two different solvents at 25 °C. The results are shown in the table. Explain why sodium chloride will dissolve in water but not in hexane. [6 marks]

Solvent	Solubility (g of NaCl per 100g solvent)
Water – H_2O	35.92
Hexane – C_6H_{12}	0.000

3 Capsaicin is a non-polar molecule that causes chillies to taste 'hot' when ingested. Using your knowledge of dissolving, suggest why water is not a suitable drink to reduce the burning sensation. [3 marks]

Now, I never knew water was so interesting...

*Read over these pages, while imagining the sound of the ocean lapping against your brain and before you know it you'll...
be... zzzz.... zzzzzzzzzzzz..... zzz... z...zzz Sorry — nodded off. Actually hydrogen bonding isn't that boring. I mean it's quite amazing that something like water is actually really weird, chemically speaking. Don't you think? No? Just me then.*

Enthalpies and Dissolving

On this page, we're going to look a bit more at dissolving and other equally exciting stuff. This time, we're focusing on the energy changes going on. There's also some definitions to learn, just to add to the fun.

Lattice Enthalpy is a Measure of Ionic Bond Strength

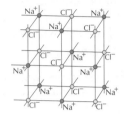

1) **Ionic solids** exist as **giant ionic lattices** with the positive and negative ions held together by **electrostatic attraction** (ionic bonds).

2) **Lattice enthalpy** tells you the enthalpy change when an ionic lattice is formed.

> The **standard lattice enthalpy**, $\Delta H_{latt}^{\ominus}$, is the enthalpy change when **1 mole** of a **solid ionic compound** is formed from its **gaseous ions** under standard conditions.

E.g.
$$Na^+_{(g)} + Cl^-_{(g)} \rightarrow NaCl_{(s)} \quad \Delta H_{latt}^{\ominus} = -780 \text{ kJ mol}^{-1}$$
$$Mg^{2+}_{(g)} + O^{2-}_{(g)} \rightarrow MgO_{(s)} \quad \Delta H_{latt}^{\ominus} = -3791 \text{ kJ mol}^{-1}$$

3) Lattice enthalpy is always **negative** because energy is **released**.

4) The **more negative** the lattice enthalpy, the **stronger** the bonding. So out of NaCl and MgO, **MgO** has stronger bonding.

> If ΔH is negative, energy is given out — it's exothermic.
> If ΔH is positive, energy is taken in — it's endothermic.
> The symbol $\ominus$ in $\Delta H^{\ominus}$ means <u>under standard conditions</u>.

Dissolving Involves Enthalpy Changes

When a solid **ionic lattice** dissolves in water, **two** things happen:

1) Bonds between the ions **break** — this is **endothermic** and the enthalpy change is the **opposite** of the **lattice enthalpy**

2) Bonds between the ions and the water are **made** (hydration — see previous page). This is the **enthalpy change of hydration** (or **enthalpy change of solvation**) and it's always **exothermic**...

> The **enthalpy change of hydration**, ΔH_{hyd}, is the enthalpy change when **1 mole** of **aqueous ions** is formed from **gaseous ions**, e.g. $Na^+_{(g)} \rightarrow Na^+_{(aq)}$

3) The **enthalpy change of solution** is the overall effect on the enthalpy when something dissolves. It's the net effect of the two enthalpy changes above (lattice enthapy and the enthalpy change of hydration/solvation)

> The **enthalpy change of solution**, $\Delta H_{solution}$, is the enthalpy change when **1 mole** of **solute** is dissolved in **sufficient solvent** that no further enthalpy change occurs on further dilution, e.g. $NaCl_{(s)} \rightarrow NaCl_{(aq)}$

Use an Enthalpy Cycle to find the Enthalpy Change of Solution

Enthalpy cycles are handy little tools for finding an unknown enthalpy change from ones you do know. Here's how to use one for finding the enthalpy change of solution:

1 Put the ionic lattice and the dissolved ions on the top — connect them by the enthalpy change of solution. This is the direct route.

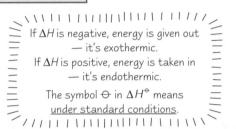

2 Connect the ionic lattice to the gaseous ions by the reverse of the lattice enthalpy.
– (lattice enthalpy)
–(–780 kJ mol⁻¹)
The breakdown of the lattice has the opposite enthalpy change to the formation of the lattice.

$$NaCl_{(s)} \xrightarrow{\text{Enthalpy change of solution}} Na^+_{(aq)} + Cl^-_{(aq)}$$
$$\Delta H3$$
$$\Delta H1 \qquad \Delta H2$$
$$Na^+_{(g)} + Cl^-_{(g)}$$

Enthalpy of hydration of $Na^+_{(g)}$ (–406 kJ mol⁻¹)
Enthalpy of hydration of $Cl^-_{(g)}$ (–364 kJ mol⁻¹)

3 Connect the gaseous ions to the dissolved ions by the hydration enthalpies of **each** ion. This completes the indirect route.

From Hess's law: $\Delta H3 = \Delta H1 + \Delta H2 = +780 + (-406 + -364) = +10 \text{ kJ mol}^{-1}$

> Hess's law says that the total enthalpy change of a reaction is always the same, no matter which route is taken.

Enthalpies and Dissolving

The fun isn't quite over. There are still some more enthalpy definitions to learn.

Ionisation Enthalpy is the Enthalpy Change when Electrons are Removed

The **first ionisation enthalpy** is the enthalpy change when 1 electron is removed from **each atom** in **1 mole** of **gaseous** atoms to form 1 mole of gaseous 1+ ions.

e.g. $O_{(g)} \rightarrow O^+_{(g)} + e^-$

The **second ionisation enthalpy** is the enthalpy change when 1 electron is removed from **each ion** in **1 mole** of **gaseous** 1+ ions to form 1 mole of gaseous 2+ ions.

e.g. $O^+_{(g)} \rightarrow O^{2+}_{(g)} + e^-$

Three main things affect the size of ionisation enthalpies:

1) **Atomic radius** — the further the outer shell electrons are from the positive nucleus, the less they'll be attracted towards the nucleus. So, the ionisation enthalpy will be **lower**.

2) **Nuclear charge** — the **more protons** there are in the nucleus, the more it'll attract the outer electrons — it'll be harder to remove the electrons, so the ionisation enthalpy will be **higher**.

3) **Electron shielding** — the inner electron shells **shield** the outer shell electrons from the attractive force of the nucleus. Because more inner shells mean more shielding, the ionisation enthalpy will be **lower**.

First Ionisation Enthalpies Decrease Down a Group...

This is because there's **less attraction** between the nucleus and outer electrons.
- The outer electrons are in shells **further** from the nucleus.
- There's more **shielding** from inner shells.

...And Generally Increase Across a Period

*I say 'generally' because there are **small drops** between Groups 2 and 3, and Groups 5 and 6.*

1) This is because the number of protons is increasing, which means a stronger **nuclear attraction**.

2) And since all the outer-shell electrons are at **roughly the same** energy level — there's generally little **extra shielding** effect or **extra distance** to lessen the attraction from the nucleus.

Practice Questions

Q1 Define the terms: a) lattice enthalpy, b) enthalpy change of hydration, c) enthalpy change of solution.

Q2 What three things affect the size of ionisation enthalpies?

Exam Questions

1 The ionic compound KBr dissolves easily in water.
   a) The following equations represent processes involved in the dissolution of KBr in water.
      For each one give the name of the enthalpy change associated with the process that it represents.
      i) $K^+_{(g)} + Br^-_{(g)} \rightarrow KBr_{(s)}$
      ii) $K^+_{(g)} \rightarrow K^+_{(aq)}$ [2 marks]
   b) Write balanced equations to represent the following processes:
      i) The hydration of 1 mole of bromide ions.
      ii) The dissolution of 1 mole of potassium bromide in water. [2 marks]

2 The diagram shows an incomplete enthalpy cycle for the dissolution of calcium chloride. Fill in the missing formulae in the box at the bottom, and give the names of the enthalpy changes represented by arrows 1, 2 and 3. [5 marks]

$CaCl_{2(s)} \xrightarrow{1} Ca^{2+}_{(aq)} + 2Cl^-_{(aq)}$

3 a) Draw an enthalpy cycle for the enthalpy change of solution of $SrF_{2(s)}$. Label each enthalpy change. [5 marks]
   b) Calculate the enthalpy change of solution for SrF_2 from the following data:
      $\Delta H^\ominus_{latt} [SrF_{2(s)}] = -2492$ kJ mol^{-1}, $\Delta H^\ominus_{hyd} [Sr^{2+}_{(g)}] = -1480$ kJ mol^{-1}, $\Delta H^\ominus_{hyd} [F^-_{(g)}] = -506$ kJ mol^{-1} [2 marks]

So the Wicked Witch of the West must have been ionic then...

These enthalpy diagrams are a lot easier than they look. You've got to make sure the definitions are firmly fixed in your mind though. Speaking of which, (no pun intended this time) there are no less than five definitions that you need to learn on these pages. So make sure you know them before you move on. Cover them up and write them out until you do.

Entropy

"What's entropy got to do with the oceans?" I hear you cry. Well, oceans can be disordered — oecasn, canoes, enosac...

Entropy *Tells you How Much* Disorder *there is*

Entropy is a measure of the **number of ways** that **particles** can be **arranged** and the **number of ways** that the **energy** can be shared out between the particles.

Substances really **like** disorder, they're actually more **energetically stable** when there's more disorder. So the particles move to try to **increase the entropy**.

There are a few things that affect entropy:

Physical State affects Entropy

You have to go back to the good old **solid-liquid-gas** particle explanation thingy to understand this.

Solid particles just wobble about a fixed point — there's **hardly any** randomness, so they have the **lowest entropy**.

Gas particles whizz around wherever they like. They've got the most **random arrangements** of particles, so they have the **highest entropy**.

Dissolving a solid also increases its entropy — dissolved particles can **move freely** as they're no longer held in one place.

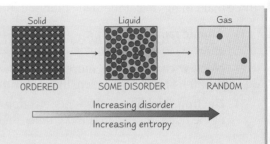

Solid — ORDERED   Liquid — SOME DISORDER   Gas — RANDOM

Increasing disorder → / Increasing entropy →

The Amount of Energy a Substance has affects Entropy too

Energy can be measured in **quanta** — these are fixed '**packages**' of energy. The more energy quanta a substance has, the **more ways** they can be arranged and the greater the **entropy**.

More Particles means More Entropy

It makes sense — the more particles you've got, the **more ways** they and their energy can be **arranged** — so in a reaction like $N_2O_{4(g)} \rightarrow 2NO_{2(g)}$, entropy increases because the **number of moles** increases.

You can Calculate the Total Entropy Change

During a reaction, there's an entropy change between the **reactants and products** — the entropy change of the **system**. The entropy of the **surroundings** changes too (because **energy** is transferred to or from the system). The **TOTAL entropy change** is the sum of the entropy changes of the **system** and the **surroundings**.

The units of entropy are J K^{-1} mol^{-1}

$$\Delta S_{total} = \Delta S_{system} + \Delta S_{surroundings}$$

This equation isn't much use unless you know ΔS_{system} and $\Delta S_{surroundings}$. Luckily, there are formulas for them too:

This is just the difference between the entropies of the reactants and products. →

$$\Delta S_{system} = S_{products} - S_{reactants}$$

and

$$\Delta S_{surroundings} = -\frac{\Delta H}{T}$$

← ΔH = enthalpy change (in J mol^{-1}) / T = temperature (in K)

> **Example:** Calculate the total entropy change for the reaction of ammonia and hydrogen chloride under standard conditions.
> $$NH_{3(g)} + HCl_{(g)} \rightarrow NH_4Cl_{(s)} \qquad \Delta H^{\ominus} = -315 \text{ kJ mol}^{-1} \text{ (at 298K)}$$
> $S^{\ominus}[NH_{3(g)}] = 192.3 \text{ J K}^{-1}\text{mol}^{-1}$, $S^{\ominus}[HCl_{(g)}] = 186.8 \text{ J K}^{-1}\text{mol}^{-1}$, $S^{\ominus}[NH_4Cl_{(s)}] = 94.6 \text{ J K}^{-1}\text{mol}^{-1}$
>
> First find the entropy change of the **system**:
> $$\Delta S^{\ominus}_{system} = S^{\ominus}_{products} - S^{\ominus}_{reactants} = 94.6 - (192.3 + 186.8) = \mathbf{-284.5 \text{ J K}^{-1}\text{mol}^{-1}}$$
> ← This shows a negative change in entropy. It's not surprising as 2 moles of gas have combined to form 1 mole of solid.
>
> Now find the entropy change of the **surroundings**:
> $$\Delta H^{\ominus} = -315 \text{ kJ mol}^{-1} = -3.15 \times 10^5 \text{ J mol}^{-1}$$
> ← Put $\Delta H^{\ominus}$ in the right units.
> $$\Delta S^{\ominus}_{surroundings} = -\frac{\Delta H^{\ominus}}{T} = \frac{-(-3.15 \times 10^5)}{298} = \mathbf{+1057 \text{ J K}^{-1}\text{mol}^{-1}}$$
>
> Finally you can find the **total** entropy
> $$\Delta S^{\ominus}_{total} = \Delta S^{\ominus}_{system} + \Delta S^{\ominus}_{surroundings} = -284.5 + (+1057) = \mathbf{+772.5 \text{ J K}^{-1}\text{mol}^{-1}}$$
> The total entropy has **increased**. The entropy increase in the surroundings was big enough to make up for the entropy decrease in the system.

Entropy

Reactions *Won't* Happen Unless the *Total Entropy Change* is *Positive*

A spontaneous (or feasible) change is one that'll **just happen** by itself — you don't need to give it energy.

For a reaction to be spontaneous or feasible, the total entropy change must be **positive**.

If the entropy change in the **system** is **negative**, there must be a **positive** change in the **surroundings** for the reaction to still be spontaneous.

Reactions where ΔS_{total} is **negative** are **never** spontaneous.

Entropy Increase May Explain Spontaneous Endothermic Reactions

Some **endothermic** reactions are **spontaneous** — which is a bit weird. You'd normally have to supply **energy** to make an endothermic reaction happen, but if the **entropy** increases enough, the reaction will happen by itself.

The reaction of sodium hydrogencarbonate with hydrochloric acid is a **spontaneous endothermic reaction**.

$$NaHCO_{3(s)} + H^+_{(aq)} \rightarrow Na^+_{(aq)} + CO_{2(g)} + H_2O_{(l)}$$

1 mole solid   1 mole aqueous ions   1 mole aqueous ions   1 mole gas   1 mole liquid

It happens because of the large **increase in entropy** — the product has more particles and also the particles are in higher entropy states overall (gas and liquid, rather than solid).

Another simple example is water evaporating at room temperature. This change needs **energy** to break the bonds between the molecules — but it happens because the **changing of state** (from liquid to gas) increases the entropy.

Practice Questions

Q1 What does the term 'entropy' mean?

Q2 In each of the following pairs, choose the one with the greater entropy value.
a) 1 mole of $NaCl_{(aq)}$ and 1 mole of $NaCl_{(s)}$ b) 1 mole of $Br_{2(l)}$ and 1 mole of $Br_{2(g)}$
c) 1 mole of $Br_{2(g)}$ and 2 moles of $Br_{2(g)}$

Q3 Write down the formulas for the following:
a) total entropy change,   b) entropy change of the surroundings,   c) entropy change of the system.

Exam Questions

1 a) Based on just the equation, predict whether the reaction below is likely to be spontaneous. Give a reason for your answer.
$$Mg_{(s)} + \tfrac{1}{2}O_{2(g)} \rightarrow MgO_{(s)}$$
[2 marks]

b) Use the data on the right to calculate the entropy change for the system above. [3 marks]

Substance	Entropy — standard conditions ($J\ K^{-1}\ mol^{-1}$)
$Mg_{(s)}$	32.7
$\tfrac{1}{2}O_{2(g)}$	102.5
$MgO_{(s)}$	26.9

c) Does the result of the calculation indicate than the reaction will be spontaneous? Give a reason for your answer. [2 marks]

2   $S^{\ominus}[H_2O_{(l)}] = 70\ J\ K^{-1}\ mol^{-1}$, $S^{\ominus}[H_2O_{(s)}] = 48\ J\ K^{-1}\ mol^{-1}$, $\Delta H = 6\ kJ\ mol^{-1}$

For the reaction $H_2O_{(l)} \rightarrow H_2O_{(s)}$:
a) Calculate the total entropy change at:
i) 250 K
ii) 300 K [5 marks]
b) Will this reaction be spontaneous at 250 K or 300 K? Explain your answer. [2 marks]

Being neat and tidy is against the laws of nature...

There's a couple of formulas to get to grips with on these pages. They aren't too hard to use, but watch out for your units. Make sure the temperature's in kelvin — if you're given one in °C, you need to add 273 to it to get it in kelvin. And check that all your enthalpy and entropy values involve joules, not kilojoules (so J mol⁻¹, not kJ mol⁻¹, etc.).

Acids and Bases

Remember this stuff? Well, it's all down to Brønsted and Lowry — they've got a lot to answer for.

An Acid **Releases** Protons — a Base **Accepts** Protons

Brønsted-Lowry acids are **proton donors** — they release **hydrogen ions** (H^+) when they're mixed with water. You never get H^+ ions by themselves in water though — they're always combined with H_2O to form **hydroxonium ions**, H_3O^+.

HA is just any old acid. $\Longrightarrow$ $$HA_{(aq)} + H_2O_{(l)} \rightarrow H_3O^+_{(aq)} + A^-_{(aq)}$$

Brønsted-Lowry bases do the opposite — they're **proton acceptors**. When they're in solution, they grab **hydrogen ions** from water molecules.

B is just a random base. $\Longrightarrow$ $$B_{(aq)} + H_2O_{(l)} \rightarrow BH^+_{(aq)} + OH^-_{(aq)}$$

Acids and Bases can be **Strong** or **Weak**

These are really all reversible reactions, but the equilibrium lies extremely far to the right.

1) **Strong acids ionise almost completely** in water — **nearly all** the H^+ ions will be released. **Hydrochloric acid** is a strong acid — $HCl_{(g)}$ + water $\rightarrow H^+_{(aq)} + Cl^-_{(aq)}$.
   Strong bases (like sodium hydroxide) **ionise almost completely** in water too. E.g. $NaOH_{(s)}$ + water $\rightarrow Na^+_{(aq)} + OH^-_{(aq)}$

2) **Weak acids** (e.g. ethanoic or citric) ionise only very **slightly** in water — so only small numbers of H^+ ions are formed. An **equilibrium** is set up which lies well over to the **left**. E.g. $CH_3COOH_{(aq)} \rightleftharpoons CH_3COO^-_{(aq)} + H^+_{(aq)}$.
   Weak bases (such as ammonia) **only slightly ionise** in water too. E.g. $NH_{3(aq)} + H_2O_{(l)} \rightleftharpoons NH_4^+_{(aq)} + OH^-_{(aq)}$.
   Just like with weak acids, the equilibrium lies well over to the **left**.

Protons are **Transferred** when **Acids** and **Bases** React

Acids **can't** just throw away their protons — they can only get rid of them if there's a **base** to accept them. In this reaction the **acid**, HA, **transfers** a proton to the **base**, B:

$$HA_{(aq)} + B_{(aq)} \rightleftharpoons BH^+_{(aq)} + A^-_{(aq)}$$

It's an **equilibrium**, so if you add more **HA** or **B**, the position of equilibrium moves to the **right**. But if you add more **BH⁺** or **A⁻**, the equilibrium moves to the **left**. This is all down to **Le Chatelier's principle** (see page 75).

When an acid is added to **water**, water acts as the **base** and accepts the proton:

$$HA_{(aq)} + H_2O_{(l)} \rightleftharpoons H_3O^+_{(aq)} + A^-_{(aq)}$$

The equilibrium's far to the left for weak acids, and far to the right for strong acids.

Acids and Bases form **Conjugate Pairs**

When an acid's added to water, the equilibrium shown on the right is set up.

In the **forward reaction**, HA acts as an **acid** as it **donates** a proton. In the **reverse reaction**, A⁻ acts as a **base** and **accepts** a proton from the H_3O^+ ion to form HA. HA and A⁻ are called a **conjugate pair** — HA is the **conjugate acid** of A⁻ and A⁻ is the **conjugate base** of the acid, HA. H_2O and H_3O^+ are a conjugate pair too.

conjugate pair

$$HA + H_2O \rightleftharpoons H_3O^+ + A^-$$
acid   base   acid   base
conjugate pair

The acid and base of a conjugate pair can be linked by an **H⁺**, like this: $HA \rightleftharpoons H^+ + A^-$ or this: $H^+ + H_2O \rightleftharpoons H_3O^+$

Here's the equilibrium for aqueous HCl. $Cl^-_{(aq)}$ is the conjugate base of $HCl_{(aq)}$.

conjugate pair

$$HCl_{(aq)} + H_2O_{(l)} \rightleftharpoons H_3O^+_{(aq)} + Cl^-_{(aq)}$$
acid   base   acid   base
conjugate pair

An equilibrium with **conjugate pairs** is also set up when a **base** dissolves in water.

The base B takes a proton from the water to form **BH⁺** — so B is the **conjugate base** of BH⁺, and BH⁺ is the **conjugate acid** of B. H_2O and OH⁻ also form a **conjugate pair**.

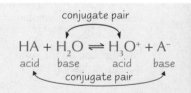

conjugate pair

$$B + H_2O \rightleftharpoons BH^+ + OH^-$$
base   acid   acid   base
conjugate pair

Acids and Bases

Water can Behave as an Acid AND a Base

Water can act as an **acid** by **donating** a proton — but it can also act as a **base** by accepting a **proton**.
So in water there'll always be both **hydroxonium ions** and **hydroxide ions** swimming around at the **same time**.

The equilibrium below exists in water:

$$2H_2O_{(l)} \rightleftharpoons H_3O^+_{(aq)} + OH^-_{(aq)} \quad \text{or more simply} \quad H_2O_{(l)} \rightleftharpoons H^+_{(aq)} + OH^-_{(aq)}$$

And, just like for any other equilibrium reaction, you can apply the equilibrium law and write an expression for the **equilibrium constant**:
(There's more about equilibrium constants on page 77)

$$K_c = \frac{[H^+][OH^-]}{[H_2O]}$$

Water only dissociates a **tiny amount**, so the equilibrium lies well over to the **left**. There's so much water compared to the amounts of H^+ and OH^- ions that the concentration of water is considered to have a **constant** value.

So if you multiply K_c (a constant) by $[H_2O]$ (another constant), you get a **constant**. This new constant is called the **ionic product of water** and it is given the symbol K_w.

$$K_w = K_c \times [H_2O] = [H^+][OH^-] \Rightarrow \boxed{K_w = [H^+][OH^-]}$$

The units of K_w are always $mol^2\,dm^{-6}$.

K_w always has the **same value** for an aqueous solution at a **given temperature**.

$$\text{At } 25\,°C \ (298\ K),\ K_w = 1.0 \times 10^{-14}\ mol^2\,dm^{-6}$$

You don't need to learn this value, you'll be given it in the exam.

A Neutral Solution has Equal H⁺ and OH⁻ Concentrations

A neutral solution is one in which $[H^+] = [OH^-]$.

If $[H^+]$ is greater than $[OH^-]$ the solution is **acidic**, and if $[OH^-]$ is greater than $[H^+]$ the solution is **alkaline**.

Practice Questions

Q1 What's the difference between a strong acid and a weak acid?
Q2 What is the conjugate base of $HCl_{(aq)}$?
Q3 What does K_w mean? Write down the formula for it.

Exam Questions

1 a) How did Brønsted and Lowry define: i) an acid, ii) a base. [2 marks]
   b) Show, by writing appropriate equations, how HSO_4^- can behave as:
      i) a Brønsted-Lowry acid, ii) a Brønsted-Lowry base. [2 marks]

2 Hydrocyanic acid (HCN) is a weak acid. Define the term 'weak acid' and write the equation for the
   equilibrium that occurs when HCN dissolves in water. [4 marks]

3 Ammonium nitrate (NH_4NO_3) is used as an artificial fertiliser.
   It is produced by reacting ammonia (NH_3) with nitric acid (HNO_3).
   a) Write an equation for this reaction showing the ions formed and use it to
      explain how ammonia is acting as a base in the reaction. [2 marks]
   b) Name a conjugate acid and base pair for this reaction.
      Explain your choice. [4 marks]

4 a) Write an equation to show how water dissociates to form a hydroxide and a hydroxonium ion. [2 marks]
   b) Write an expression for the ionic product of water (K_w) in terms of the concentration of
      hydroxide and hydroxonium ions. [2 marks]
   c) Pure water is neutral. What does this mean about the relative concentrations of
      hydroxide and hydroxonium ions? [1 mark]

Acids and bases — the Julie Andrews and Marilyn Manson of the chemistry world...

Don't confuse strong acids with concentrated acids, or weak acids with dilute acids. Strong and weak are to do with how much an acid ionises, whereas concentrated and dilute are to do with the number of moles of acid you've got per dm³. You can have a dilute strong acid, or a concentrated weak acid. It works the same way with bases too.

pH Calculations

Get those calculators warmed up — especially the log function key.

The *pH Scale* is a Measure of the *Hydrogen Ion Concentration*

The **concentration of hydrogen ions** can vary enormously, so those wise chemists of old decided to express the concentration on a **logarithmic scale**:

$$pH = -\log_{10}[H^+]$$

The pH scale normally goes from **0** (very acidic) to **14** (very alkaline). **pH 7 is neutral**.

For Strong Monoprotic Acids, *Hydrogen Ion Concentration = Acid Concentration*

Hydrochloric acid (HCl) and nitric acid (HNO_3) are **strong acids** so they ionise fully. They're also **monoprotic**, so each mole of acid produces **one mole of hydrogen ions**. This means the H+ concentration is the **same** as the acid concentration. So for 0.1 mol dm⁻³ hydrochloric acid, [H+] is **0.1 mol dm⁻³**. Its pH = $-\log_{10}[H^+] = -\log_{10} 0.1 = $ **1.0**.
Here are a few more examples for you:

1) Calculate the pH of 0.05 mol dm⁻³ nitric acid. $[H^+] = 0.05 \Rightarrow pH = -\log_{10} 0.05 = $ **1.30**

2) Calculate the pH of 0.025 mol dm⁻³ hydrochloric acid. $[H^+] = 0.025 \Rightarrow pH = -\log_{10} 0.025 = $ **1.60**

You also need to be able to work out **[H+]** if you're given the **pH** of a solution.
You do this by finding the **inverse $\log_{10}$ of –pH**, which is **10⁻ᵖᴴ**.

3) If an acid solution has a pH of 2.45, what is the hydrogen ion concentration, or [H+], of the acid? $[H^+] = 10^{-2.45} = $ **3.55 × 10⁻³ mol dm⁻³**

Use K_w to Find the *pH* of a *Base*

Sodium hydroxide (NaOH) and potassium hydroxide (KOH) are **strong bases** that **fully ionise** in water. They each have **one hydroxide per molecule**, so they donate **one mole of OH⁻ ions** per mole of base. This means that the concentration of OH⁻ ions is the **same** as the **concentration of the base**. So for 0.02 mol dm⁻³ sodium hydroxide solution, [OH⁻] is also **0.02 mol dm⁻³**.

But to work out the **pH** you need to know **[H+]** — luckily this is linked to **[OH⁻]** through the **ionic product of water**, K_w:

$$K_w = [H^+][OH^-] = 1.0 \times 10^{-14} \text{ mol}^2 \text{ dm}^{-6} \text{ at 298 K}$$

So if you know K_w and [OH⁻] for a **strong aqueous base** at a certain temperature, you can work out **[H+]** and then the **pH**

Example:
Find the pH of a 0.1 mol dm⁻³ solution of NaOH at 298 K.

$[OH^-] = 0.1 \text{ mol dm}^{-3} \Rightarrow [H^+] = \dfrac{K_w}{[OH^-]} = \dfrac{1.0 \times 10^{-14}}{0.1} = 1.0 \times 10^{-13} \text{ mol dm}^{-3}$

So pH = $-\log_{10} 1.0 \times 10^{-13} = $ **13.0**

To Find the *pH* of a *Weak Acid* you Use K_a (the *Acid Dissociation Constant*)

Weak acids **don't** ionise fully in solution, so the [H+] **isn't** the same as the acid concentration. This makes it a **bit trickier** to find their pH. You have to use yet another **equilibrium constant, K_a**.

For a weak aqueous acid, HA, you get the following equilibrium: $HA_{(aq)} \rightleftharpoons H^+_{(aq)} + A^-_{(aq)}$

As only a **tiny amount** of HA dissociates, you can assume that $[HA_{(aq)}]_{start} = [HA_{(aq)}]_{equilibrium}$.

So if you apply the equilibrium law, you get: $K_a = \dfrac{[H^+][A^-]}{[HA]}$

You can also assume that **all** the H+ ions come from the **acid**, so $[H^+_{(aq)}] = [A^-_{(aq)}]$. So $K_a = \dfrac{[H^+]^2}{[HA]}$ The units of K_a are mol dm⁻³.

Here's an example of how to use K_a to find the **pH** of a weak acid:

Calculate the hydrogen ion concentration and the pH of a 0.02 mol dm⁻³ solution of propanoic acid (CH_3CH_2COOH). K_a for propanoic acid at this temperature is 1.30×10^{-5} mol dm⁻³.

$K_a = \dfrac{[H^+]^2}{[CH_3CH_2COOH]} \Rightarrow [H^+]^2 = K_a[CH_3CH_2COOH] = 1.30 \times 10^{-5} \times 0.02 = 2.60 \times 10^{-7}$

$\Rightarrow [H^+] = \sqrt{2.60 \times 10^{-7}} = $ **5.10 × 10⁻⁴ mol dm⁻³** So pH = $-\log_{10}(5.10 \times 10^{-4}) = $ **3.29**

pH Calculations

You Might Have to Find the *Concentration* or K_a of a *Weak Acid*

You don't need to know anything new for this type of calculation. You usually just have to find **[H⁺]** from the pH, then fiddle around with the K_a **expression** to find the missing bit of information.

1) The pH of an ethanoic acid (CH_3COOH) solution was 3.02 at 298 K. Calculate the molar concentration of this solution. The K_a of ethanoic acid is 1.75×10^{-5} mol dm⁻³ at 298 K.

$$[H^+] = 10^{-pH} = 10^{-3.02} = 9.55 \times 10^{-4} \text{ mol dm}^{-3}$$

$$K_a = \frac{[H^+]^2}{[CH_3COOH]} \Rightarrow [CH_3COOH] = \frac{[H^+]^2}{K_a} = \frac{(9.55 \times 10^{-4})^2}{1.75 \times 10^{-5}} = \textbf{0.0521 mol dm}^{-3}$$

2) A solution of 0.162 mol dm⁻³ HCN has a pH of 5.05 at 298 K. What is the value of K_a for HCN at 298 K?

$$[H^+] = 10^{-pH} = 10^{-5.05} = 8.91 \times 10^{-6} \text{ mol dm}^{-3} \qquad K_a = \frac{[H^+]^2}{[HCN]} = \frac{(8.91 \times 10^{-6})^2}{0.162} = \textbf{4.90} \times \textbf{10}^{-10} \textbf{ mol dm}^{-3}$$

$pK_a = -log_{10} K_a$ and $K_a = 10^{-pK_a}$

pK_a is calculated from K_a in exactly the same way as pH is calculated from [H⁺] — and vice versa. So if an acid has a K_a value of 1.50×10^{-7}, its $\textbf{pK}_a = -\textbf{log}_{10}(\textbf{1.50} \times \textbf{10}^{-7}) = \textbf{6.82}$. And if an acid has a pK_a value of 4.32, its $\textbf{K}_a = \textbf{10}^{-4.32} = \textbf{4.79} \times \textbf{10}^{-5}$.

Notice how pK_a values aren't annoyingly tiny like K_a values.

Just to make things that bit more complicated, there might be a **pK_a** value in a question. If so, you need to convert it to K_a so that you can use the K_a **expression**.

3) Calculate the pH of 0.050 mol dm⁻³ methanoic acid ($HCOOH$) at 298 K. Methanoic acid has a pK_a of 3.75 at 298 K.

$$K_a = 10^{-pK_a} = 10^{-3.75} = 1.78 \times 10^{-4} \text{ mol dm}^{-3} \quad \longleftarrow \quad \text{First you have to convert the pK}_a \text{ to K}_a.$$

$$K_a = \frac{[H^+]^2}{[HCOOH]} \Rightarrow [H^+]^2 = K_a[HCOOH] = 1.78 \times 10^{-4} \times 0.050 = 8.9 \times 10^{-6}$$

$$\Rightarrow [H^+] = \sqrt{8.9 \times 10^{-6}} = 2.98 \times 10^{-3} \text{ mol dm}^{-3} \qquad pH = -\log 2.98 \times 10^{-3} = \textbf{2.53}$$

Sometimes you have to give your answer as a **pK_a** value. In this case, you just work out the K_a value as usual and then convert it to **pK_a** — and Bob's your pet hamster.

Practice Questions

Q1 Explain how to calculate the pH of a strong acid.

Q2 How could you calculate the pH of a strong base?

Q3 Explain how to calculate the pH of a weak acid.

Exam Questions

1 The value of K_a for a weak acid, HA, at 298 K, is 5.60×10^{-4} mol dm⁻³.
   a) Write an expression for K_a for the weak acid HA. [1 mark]
   b) Calculate the pH of a 0.280 mol dm⁻³ solution of HA at 298 K. [3 marks]

2 The pH of a 0.150 mol dm⁻³ solution of a weak monoprotic acid, HX, is 2.65 at 298 K.
   Calculate the value of K_a for the acid HX at 298 K. [4 marks]

3 a) Write an expression for the ionic product of water, K_w. [1 mark]
   b) At 298 K, K_w has a value of 1.0×10^{-14} mol² dm⁻⁶.
   Use this information to calculate the pH of a 0.0370 mol dm⁻³ solution of sodium hydroxide at 298 K. [3 marks]

My mate had a red Ka — but she drove it into a lamppost...

Strong acids have high K_a values and weak acids have low K_a values. For pK_a values, it's the other way round — the stronger the acid, the lower the pK_a. If something's got p in front of it, like pH, pK_w or pK_a, it tends to mean $-log_{10}$ of whatever. Not all calculators work the same way, so make sure you know how to work logs out on your calculator.

Buffers

Buffers are pretty important to life on Earth — without them it's possible that all the oceans and lakes would be too acidic or too alkali for any life at all — that's a bit of a scary thought for an intro line so thank goodness they do exist.

Buffers Resist Changes in pH

A **buffer** is a solution that **resists** changes in pH when **small** amounts of acid or alkali are added.

A buffer **doesn't** stop the pH from changing completely — it does make the changes **very slight** though.
Buffers only work for small amounts of acid or alkali — put too much in and they'll go "waah" and not be able to cope.
You can get **acidic buffers** and **alkaline buffers** — but you only need to know how the acidic type works.

Acidic Buffers are Made from a Weak Acid and one of its Salts

Acidic buffers have a pH of less than 7 — they're made by mixing a **weak acid** with one of its **salts**.
Ethanoic acid and **sodium ethanoate** ($CH_3COO^-Na^+$) is a good example:

The salt **fully** dissociates into its ions when it dissolves: $CH_3COO^-Na^+_{(aq)} \rightarrow CH_3COO^-_{(aq)} + Na^+_{(aq)}$.

Sodium ethanoate   *Ethanoate ions*

The ethanoic acid is a **weak acid**, so it only **slightly** dissociates: $CH_3COOH_{(aq)} \rightleftharpoons H^+_{(aq)} + CH_3COO^-_{(aq)}$

So in the solution you've got heaps of **ethanoate ions** from the salt, and heaps of **undissociated ethanoic acid molecules**

Le Chatelier's principle explains how buffers work:

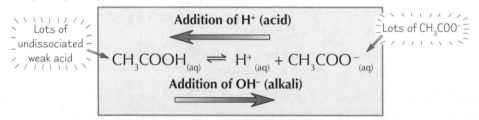

Lots of undissociated weak acid

Addition of H⁺ (acid)

Lots of CH_3COO^-

$$CH_3COOH_{(aq)} \rightleftharpoons H^+_{(aq)} + CH_3COO^-_{(aq)}$$

Addition of OH⁻ (alkali)

If you add a **small** amount of **acid** the **H⁺ concentration** increases. Most of the extra H⁺ ions combine with CH_3COO^- ions to form CH_3COOH. This shifts the equilibrium to the **left**, reducing the H⁺ concentration to close to its original value. So the **pH** doesn't change much.

The large number of CH_3COO^- ions make sure that the buffer can cope with the addition of acid.

There's no problem doing this as there's absolutely loads of spare CH_3COOH molecules.

If a **small** amount of **alkali** (e.g. NaOH) is added, the **OH⁻ concentration** increases. Most of the extra OH⁻ ions react with H⁺ ions to form water — removing H⁺ ions from the solution. This causes more CH_3COOH to **dissociate** to form H⁺ ions — shifting the equilibrium to the **right**. The H⁺ concentration increases until it's close to its original value, so the **pH** hardly changes.

Buffers are Really Handy

1) Most **shampoos** contain a pH 5.5 buffer. Soap gets your hair squeaky clean, but it's usually very **alkaline** — and alkalis tend to make hair look dull. So adding a slightly acidic buffer will keep your hair looking shiny.

2) **Biological washing powders** contain buffers too. They keep the pH at the right level for the **enzymes** to work.

3) **Cells** need a constant pH to allow the **biochemical reactions** to take place. The pH is controlled by a buffer based on the equilibrium between **dihydrogen phosphate** ions and **hydrogen phosphate** ions.

   $$H_2PO_4^- \rightleftharpoons H^+ + HPO_4^{2-}$$

   See page 54.

4) **Blood** needs to be kept at pH 7.4. It is buffered using carbonic acid. The levels of H_2CO_3 are controlled by **respiration**.

   and
   $$H_2CO_{3(aq)} \rightleftharpoons H^+_{(aq)} + HCO_3^-_{(aq)}$$
   $$H_2CO_{3(aq)} \rightleftharpoons H_2O_{(l)} + CO_{2(g)}$$

   By **breathing out CO₂** the level of H_2CO_3 is reduced as it moves this **equilibrium** to the **right**.
   The levels of HCO_3^- are controlled by the **kidneys** with excess being **excreted** in the urine.

5) Buffers are used in **food products** to control the pH. Changes in pH can be caused by **bacteria** and **fungi** and cause food to **deteriorate**. A common buffer is **sodium citrate**, which sets up an equilibrium between citrate ions and citric acid. **Phosphoric acid/phosphate ions** and **benzoic acid/benzoate** ions are also used as buffers.

Buffers

Here's How to Calculate the pH of a Buffer Solution

Calculating the **pH** of an acidic buffer isn't too tricky. You just need to know the K_a of the weak acid and the **concentrations** of the weak acid and its salt. Here's how to go about it:

Example: A buffer solution contains 0.40 mol dm^{-3} methanoic acid, HCOOH, and 0.6 mol dm^{-3} sodium methanoate, HCOO$^-$ Na$^+$. For methanoic acid, $K_a = 1.6 \times 10^{-4}$ mol dm^{-3}. What is the pH of this buffer?

Firstly, write the expression for the K_a of the weak acid:

$$HCOOH_{(aq)} \rightleftharpoons H^+_{(aq)} + HCOO^-_{(aq)} \Rightarrow K_a = \frac{[H^+] \times [HCOO^-]}{[HCOOH]}$$

Remember — these all have to be equilibrium concentrations.

Then rearrange the expression and stick in the data to calculate $[H^+_{(aq)}]$:

$$[H^+] = K_a \times \frac{[HCOOH]}{[HCOO^-]}$$

$$\Rightarrow [H^+] = 1.6 \times 10^{-4} \times \frac{0.4}{0.6} = 1.07 \times 10^{-4} \text{ mol dm}^{-3}$$

You have to make a **few assumptions** here:
- HCOO$^-$ Na$^+$ is fully dissociated, so assume that the equilibrium concentration of HCOO$^-$ is the same as the initial concentration of HCOO$^-$ Na$^+$.
- HCOOH is only slightly dissociated, so assume that its equilibrium concentration is the same as its initial concentration.

Finally, convert $[H^+_{(aq)}]$ to pH: $pH = -\log_{10}[H^+_{(aq)}] = -\log_{10}(1.07 \times 10^{-4}) = \mathbf{3.97}$ And that's your answer.

Practice Questions

Q1 What's a buffer solution?

Q2 How can a mixture of ethanoic acid and sodium ethanoate act as a buffer?

Exam Questions

1 A buffer solution contains 0.40 mol dm^{-3} benzoic acid, C_6H_5COOH, and 0.20 mol dm^{-3} sodium benzoate, $C_6H_5COO^-Na^+$. At 25 °C, K_a for benzoic acid is 6.4×10^{-5} mol dm^{-3}.

   a) Calculate the pH of the buffer solution. [3 marks]

   b) Explain the effect on the buffer of adding a small quantity of dilute sulfuric acid. [3 marks]

2 A buffer was prepared by mixing solutions of butanoic acid, $CH_3(CH_2)_2COOH$, and sodium butanoate, $CH_3(CH_2)_2COO^-Na^+$, so that they had the same concentration.

   a) Write a chemical equation to show butanoic acid acting as an acid. [1 mark]

   b) Given that K_a for butanoic acid is 1.5×10^{-5} mol dm^{-3}, calculate the pH of the buffer solution. [3 marks]

3 Carbonic acid is a weak acid. It dissociates in water according to this equation:

$$H_2CO_{3(aq)} \rightleftharpoons H^+_{(aq)} + HCO^-_{3\ (aq)}$$

   a) Give the name or formula of a chemical that you could add to a solution of carbonic acid to create a buffer solution. [1 mark]

   b) Explain how adding the chemical would create a solution that is resistant to small reductions in pH. [2 marks]

   c) Would the pH of this solution be above or below 7? Explain your answer. [2 marks]

   d) State one household product which might contain a buffer. [1 mark]

Old buffers are often resistant to change...

So that's how buffers work. They're really quite clever and it all seems quite important. In fact, I feel so inspired that I think I'm going to write a limerick *clears throat* 'Weak acid and salt make a buffer. Just mix the two with each other. They'll dissociate. Fight changes you make. But don't add too much or they're ~~bu~~...in trouble.' (It's a work in progress.)

Carbon Dioxide

Carbon dioxide is a gas. But it goes in the Oceans module because it goes in the sea... as do jellyfish and squid... and sharks... big ships... fishes... lots of them... and swimmers... hopefully not too near the sharks... hmm, well anyway...

Carbon Dioxide **Dissolves** in the **Oceans**

Carbon dioxide is **soluble** in water — between 1 and 3 g of it will dissolve in a litre of water, depending on temperature. This simple fact of chemistry has a massive impact on the environment — **huge amounts** of CO_2 can be stored in the **oceans** (just think about how much water they contain...) which affects things in and out of the seas.

Global warming is obviously a big environmental issue these days — it's generally accepted to be largely the result of **increasing CO_2 levels** in the atmosphere from **human activity**.

As the levels of CO_2 have been increasing, the **amount dissolved** in the oceans has also been **increasing**. This is good for us as it's likely to have helped **slow down** global warming.

But it's not all good news, sadly...

The seas are **naturally alkaline**. When CO_2 dissolves in water, it's slightly acidic because of this reaction:

$$CO_2 + H_2O \rightleftharpoons H^+ + HCO_3^-$$

So too much CO_2 being dissolved can affect the **overall pH** of the oceans which harms many species and **upsets ecosystems**. E.g. crustaceans and molluscs can't form and maintain their shells if conditions are too acidic. Other species that aren't directly harmed are also affected as **food chains** are disturbed.

There are Ways of **Reducing** the **Release** of **Carbon Dioxide**...

The oceans do their bit to help but can only do so much — it's really down to us humans to sort it out. Here are a few of the current ideas for tackling the CO_2 problem that you need to know about:

Use less fuel

Increasing the efficiency of devices such as vehicle engines, heating systems, industrial machines and domestic devices, means **less energy is needed**, so less fuel is burned and **less CO_2 released**. Governments can take steps to encourage the development and use of these new technologies, e.g. by putting cheaper taxes on more efficient cars.

Will's new vehicle was certainly green, but the fuel economy wasn't great.

Use different fuels

CO_2 is released when **fossil fuels**, oil, coal and gas, are burned.
An obvious way to reduce CO_2 emissions is to use alternative fuels that don't produce so much CO_2 — for example, **nuclear energy** and **hydrogen**.

Nuclear energy is already used extensively throughout the world. Some people believe that relying more on nuclear energy is the best way to reduce CO_2 emissions. But many people are opposed to this for various reasons...

— concerns over **health dangers**, e.g. possible links to leukaemia and other illnesses.

— concerns over the risks of **accidental leaks** or **major disasters** like Chernobyl.

— problems of **waste disposal**. The waste produced stays radioactive for hundreds of years, so systems are needed to store it **safely** and **permanently**.

— quite a bit of CO_2 is produced during the **mining**, **processing**, and **transportation** of the nuclear fuel.

Using **hydrogen** as a major fuel is a fairly new idea that could take off in the future. **Hydrogen fuel cells** could be used to power electric cars that would produce no pollution. Of course, if it were really that simple, we'd probably be doing it already...

— hydrogen is hard to **store** and **transport**. It can't be liquified easily without using expensive fridges and storing it as a gas under high pressure is dangerous.

— **huge investment** would be needed to set up a new supply infrastructure like we have for petrol.

— although hydrogen itself is a very **clean fuel** (the only by-product is water), producing it in the first place requires **energy**. If this ends up coming from fossil fuels then the problem hasn't really been solved.

Carbon Dioxide

...There are Also Ways of **Removing Carbon Dioxide** from the **Air**

So we've looked at ways of reducing the amount of CO_2 being released into the atmosphere.
Now here are some ideas you need to know about for **dealing with** the CO_2 that **has** and **is being** released.

Photosynthesis

You'll remember from your GCSE Biology that green plants use **photosynthesis** to convert CO_2 from the atmosphere and water into sugar and oxygen. This has maintained the **balance** of CO_2 and O_2 in our atmosphere for millions of years.

But once again, **humans** have **upset the balance**. Decades of large-scale **deforestation** have significantly reduced tree coverage around the globe, meaning less photosynthesis and less removal of CO_2. A good way to tackle this would be **reforestation** schemes — planting large areas of fast-growing trees to increase photosynthesis and CO_2 removal.

Carbon Capture and Storage (CCS)

This involves (as it says) **capturing CO_2** as we produce it, rather than simply releasing it into the atmosphere, and finding **somewhere to put it**.

One way would be to collect **CO_2** produced by **power stations** and pipe it into porous rock under the sea to be **stored**. This is potentially a good way for Britain to **reduce** its CO_2 emissions because there's a lot of porous rock under the North Sea and the old infrastructure from the oil fields could be used to transport it.

> You are sentenced to 10 years for the theft of the Big Diamond.

'Quick fingers' Maguire's excuse that it was only carbon capture wasn't fooling the judge.

Practice Questions

Q1   How is carbon dioxide dissolving into seawater both a good and a bad thing for the environment?

Q2   Outline some different ways to reduce the amount of CO_2 that we produce and describe any problems with them.

Q3   What does CCS stand for? Explain what it means.

Exam Questions

1   Many different schemes have been proposed to try to reduce the amount of carbon dioxide in the atmosphere.

   a)   Why is it important to reduce the levels of atmospheric CO_2?   [1 mark]

   CO_2 is released into the atmosphere when fossil fuels are burnt.
   One way of reducing the amount of CO_2 released into the atmosphere is to use alternative fuels.

   b)   Electric cars powered by hydrogen fuel cells do not release CO_2 from their engines.
        Give one disadvantage of using hydrogen fuel cells to power cars.   [1 mark]

   c)   Suggest two methods, other than using alternative fuels, that could be used to reduce
        the amount of carbon dioxide released into the atmosphere.   [2 marks]

2   A carbon sink is something that is able to store carbon-containing molecules for a long time.
   Both the oceans and plants are considered to be carbon sinks.

   a)   Explain why the oceans are considered a carbon sink and discuss
        the possible effects of this on global warming and ocean ecosystems.   [6 marks]

   b)   Briefly outline how plants are able to act as a carbon sink
        and comment on how human activity has impacted on this.   [4 marks]

You need to know this stuff — that's the inconvenient truth...

I'm sorry if you are a little squeamish. That was a bit of a gorey joke. Bum-bum. So it's the end of the Oceans section now. Just to recap — things that are found in the ocean... jellyfish, squids, sharks, big ships, lots of fishes, swimmers... hmmm I'm starting to struggle now... bottles... bits of wood... treasure, maybe.... oh, and CO_2 — that's the most important one.

Medicines

A spoonful of sugar helps the medicine section to sink in — but a choccy biscuit is even better...

Medicines Contain **Pharmacophores**

In virtually every cell of your body there are things called **receptors**. Some chemicals fit into these receptors and temporarily bond with them, which triggers a series of **biochemical reactions**. The chemicals have to be exactly the right **size and shape** to fit the receptor otherwise they don't bond and nothing happens.

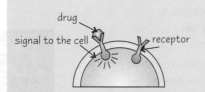

A **drug** is a molecule that is able to interact with one of these receptors. The part of the drug that gives it its activity is called the **pharmacophore**. Chemists try to design drugs with pharmacophores that fit exactly into target **receptors**.

The 'fit' of a **pharmacophore** into a **receptor site** depends on:

1) **Size** and shape — it's got to have a particular structure that will fit into the receptor site.

2) **Bond formation** — functional groups in the pharmacophore form **temporary bonds** with functional groups in the receptor. These are mostly **ionic** interactions or **intermolecular** forces e.g. hydrogen bonding. Covalent bonding is permanent, so would irreversibly block the receptor.

3) **Orientation** — if the pharmacophore has **optical** or **E/Z isomers**, then only one of the isomers will fit (see page 56).

To design a drug you need to consider if you want the drug to **increase** the response that happens naturally, or **decrease**

1) If you want a drug to increase the natural response you use an **agonistic** drug.
   This binds to the receptor and **triggers** a **response**.

2) If you want to decrease the response you use an **antagonistic** drug. This binds to the receptor and **blocks** it.

Chemists are Important in the **Design** and **Synthesis** of **New Medicines**

Here are some of the things chemists think about when they're trying to make a new drug to treat a disease:

Is there a natural compound already used to treat the disease?
Years ago foxglove leaves were used to treat heart failure — the drug's now been isolated and it's still used today.

Is there a compound in the body that's involved in the process?
This could give you a good starting point.

Molecule screening
This is where loads of molecules are tested to see if any of them bind to the target receptor.

Modifying the Compound
Now you've got something that interacts with the receptor site, you can modify its structure to make it fit better. This is where functional groups are added, removed or changed.

Testing the Compound
Once it's modified, you've got to test it to see if it works. This often happens again and again to make the best, safest drug possible.

Drug

Computer Modelling Techniques **Speed Up** Molecule Screening and Drug Design

Testing for a molecule that will fit a receptor perfectly takes loads of time and is expensive. It's sped up by screening the compounds in batches of 50-100, but this still takes **ages**, and there's no guarantee you'll find something that works.

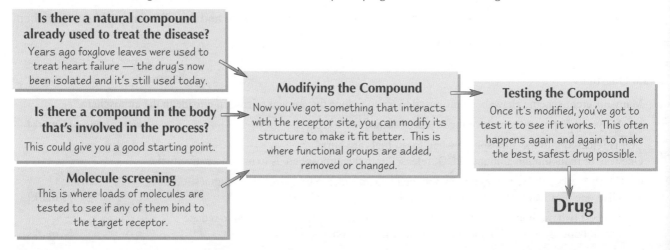

Computer 3D modelling can speed things up. **Databases** of 3D models of compounds can be searched to find compounds that may fit the **3D model of the target receptor site**, or to find ones containing particular structures and functional groups. This cuts down the number of compounds you need to test in the lab.

Classic molecule screening is like looking for a key to fit a lock. Rational drug design is like using the structure of the lock to make your own key.

Rational drug design is a bit different. It involves building a new compound from scratch using a 3D model of the receptor site.

Medicines

Modifying the Pharmacophore Changes the Pharmacological Activity

Once you know that part of a molecule is a **pharmacophore** you can tweak bits of it to make a drug **more effective** or to reduce its side effects. For example, **noradrenaline** is naturally found in the body and has been modified to treat different disorders.

Noradrenaline — expands airways and increases your heart rate and blood pressure

Salbutamol — treats asthma symptoms, without the raised heart rate and blood pressure

Isoprenaline — used to increase heart rate for some heart problems

Drug Testing Must be Ethical

All new drugs need to go through a lot of **testing** before they can be used. They have to be tested to see:

1) if the drug is **safe**.

2) if the drug actually **works**.

3) if the drug is **better** than existing drugs — if it's **more effective** or has **less side effects**.

All of these questions need to be answered in an **ethical way**.

In the UK, all new drugs are tested on **animals** by law. This is a controversial issue — some people think that animal testing is **wrong** because of the suffering that the animals are put through. Others would say that using animals is absolutely **necessary** to ensure that drugs are safe for human use.

New drugs also go through a series of **human trials** before being approved. In some trials, healthy volunteers are sought through adverts with money being offered as an incentive. But could this be seen as seeking out poor people who **need the money** to take the risks for others...

Some people think that **pharmaceutical companies** have too much **influence** over the drug approval process. They claim that test results can be easily **skewed** to obtain the desired result and that the companies use **marketing tricks** to push their products to market.

Practice Questions

Q1 What's a pharmacophore?
Q2 What three things does the fit of the pharmacophore into a receptor site depend on?
Q3 What's an agonistic drug? What's an antagonistic drug?

Exam Question

1 The structures of three non-steroidal anti-inflammatory drugs which share the same pharmacophore are shown below.

Ibuprofen

Naproxen

Fenoprofen

a) Explain the term pharmacophore. [2 marks]

b) Draw the structure of the pharmacophore found in these three compounds. [1 mark]

c) Identify a functional group that might make these compounds soluble in water. Explain your answer. [2 marks]

d) Suggest a way these compounds can bond to receptor sites. [2 marks]

e) The pharmacophore in these drugs is chiral.
   i) Mark the chiral centre with an asterisk on your diagram for part (b). [1 mark]
   ii) What implications will this have for the drug's pharmacological activity? [1 mark]

Why's there no aspirin in the jungle? The paracetamol...

That was a nice start to the section. To make a new drug sounds easy. You just need to find something that works and then modify it so it's better. But, finding a drug to treat something can still take ages because there's a lot of trial and error. And getting it to the market can take even longer because you've got to make sure it's as safe as possible.

Organic Functional Groups and Reactions

There's a whole load of organic chemistry coming up on the next few pages. But don't panic.
It's just drawing together stuff you've already seen.

Functional Groups are the Most Important Parts of a Molecule

Functional groups are the parts of a molecule that are responsible for the way the molecule reacts.
These are the main ones you need to know (which are all covered earlier in the book)...

Group	Found in	Prefix / Suffix	Example
$-C\overset{O}{\underset{OH}{}}$	carboxylic acids	carboxy– / –oic acid	ethanoic acid
$-C\overset{O}{\underset{Cl}{}}$	acyl chlorides	–oyl chloride	ethanoyl chloride
$-C-O-C-$ with O	acid anhydrides	–oic anhydride	ethanoic anhydride
$-C-O-$ with O	esters, polyesters	–oate	ethyl methanoate
$-C\overset{O}{\underset{H}{}}$	aldehydes	–al	propanal
$C=O$	ketones	–one	propanone

Group	Found in	Prefix / Suffix	Example
$-OH$	alcohols, phenols	hydroxy– / –ol	propanol
$-NH_2$	primary amines	amino– / –amine	methylamine
NH	secondary amines	–amine	aminomethane
$N-$	tertiary amines	–amine	trimethylamine
$-NO_2$	nitro benzenes	nitro-	nitrobenzene
benzene ring	aromatic compounds	phenyl– / –benzene	aminobenzene
$C=C$	alkenes	-ene	butene

The functional groups in a molecule give you clues about its **properties** and **reactions**.
For example, a **–COOH group** will (usually) make the molecule **acidic** and mean it will
form esters with alcohols. Molecules containing **ester groups** will have **distinctive smells**.

Use the Functional Groups for Classifying and Naming Compounds

Organic molecules can get pretty complicated, often with many functional groups. You need to be able to **pick
out** the functional groups on an unknown molecule, **name them** and **name the molecule** in a systematic way.

1) The **main functional group** is used as the **suffix** and the other functional groups are added as **prefixes**.

2) The table above shows the order of importance of the functional groups, with COOH being the most important,
   down to phenyl which is the least. (Note — alkenes are treated differently, with 'ene' always appearing in the suffix.

3) If you need to include more than one functional group prefix, then list them in alphabetical order.

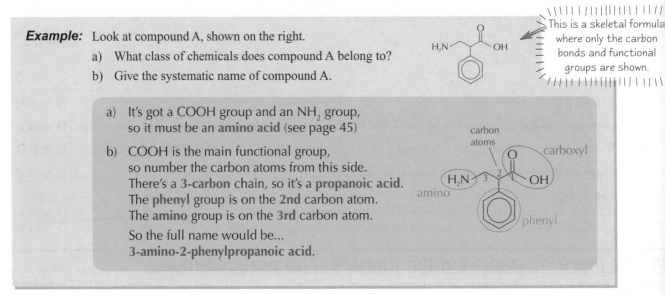

Example: Look at compound A, shown on the right.

　　a) What class of chemicals does compound A belong to?

　　b) Give the systematic name of compound A.

This is a skeletal formula where only the carbon bonds and functional groups are shown.

　　a) It's got a COOH group and an NH₂ group,
　　　　so it must be an **amino acid** (see page 45)

　　b) COOH is the main functional group,
　　　　so number the carbon atoms from this side.
　　　　There's a **3-carbon** chain, so it's a **propanoic acid**.
　　　　The **phenyl** group is on the **2nd** carbon atom.
　　　　The **amino** group is on the **3rd** carbon atom.

　　　　So the full name would be...
　　　　3-amino-2-phenylpropanoic acid.

Organic Functional Groups and Reactions

Organic Chemistry **Reactions** can be Classified into **Seven Types**

In organic chemistry you can **classify** all the different reactions based on what happens to the molecules involved. All of the reactions you have met at AS and A2 levels will fit into one of these seven types.

Reaction Type	Description	Functional groups that undergo this type of reaction
Addition	Two molecules join together to form a single product. Involves breaking a double bond.	$\diagdown$C=C$\diagup$ $-C\diagup^{O}_{\diagdown H}$ $\diagdown$C=O
Elimination	Involves removing a functional group which is released as part of a small molecule. Often a double bond is formed.	$-X$ (H–X eliminated) $-OH$ (H_2O eliminated) X = halogen
Substitution	A functional group on a molecule is swapped for a new one.	$-X$ $\hexagon$ (H replaced) $-OH$
Condensation	Two molecules get joined together with the loss of a small molecule, e.g. water. Opposite of hydrolysis.	$-C\diagup^{O}_{\diagdown OH}$ $-C\diagup^{O}_{\diagdown Cl}$ $-C\diagup^{O}_{\diagdown NH_2}$
Hydrolysis	Water is used to split apart a molecule creating two smaller ones. Opposite of condensation.	$-C\overset{O}{\underset{\|}{\|}}-O-$ $-C-\overset{O}{\underset{\|}{\|}}-O-C-\overset{O}{\underset{\|}{\|}}$ polyamides (e.g. nylon, proteins) polyesters (e.g. Terylene®, PET)
Oxidation	Oxidation is loss of electrons. In organic chemistry it usually means gaining an oxygen atom or losing a hydrogen atom.	$-\overset{H}{\underset{H}{C}}-OH \rightarrow -C\diagup^{O}_{\diagdown H} \rightarrow -C\diagup^{O}_{\diagdown OH}$ $-\overset{\|}{C}-OH \rightarrow \diagdown$C=O
Reduction	Reduction is gain of electrons. In organic chemistry it usually means gaining a hydrogen atom or losing an oxygen atom.	$-C\diagup^{O}_{\diagdown OH} \rightarrow -C\diagup^{O}_{\diagdown H} \rightarrow -\overset{H}{\underset{H}{C}}-OH$ $\diagdown$C=O $\rightarrow -\overset{\|}{C}-OH$

There are Six **Chemical Species** you Need to be Able to **Define**

These are all terms you'll have come across when you've been looking at the different reaction types and mechanisms. You need to make sure you can define them and use them if you're asked to talk about a particular reaction.

1) **Radical** — An atom, molecule or ion that has an unpaired electron.
2) **Electrophile** — Attracted to molecules with areas of high electron density where it accepts electrons.
3) **Nucleophile** — Attracted to regions of positive charge density e.g. δ+ C atoms in molecules with polar bonds (C–Halogen, C–O and C=O). It can donate a pair of electrons to form a dative covalent bond (so it must have a lone pair).
4) **Carbocation** — An organic ion with a positively charged carbon atom. They form when a bond breaks and the electrons move away from the carbon atom.
5) **Saturated molecule** — All the C–C bonds are single.
6) **Unsaturated molecule** — There is at least one C=C double bond.

Revise hard, y'all.

Meet Professor P. Orbital — he puts the 'func' into 'functional groups'.

Organic Functional Groups and Reactions

Organic Reactions Come Under Five Different Types of Mechanism

Here are the five reaction mechanisms you need to know. If you're asked to draw one remember to include all the curly arrows, dipoles and charges for full marks.

1) **Radical substitution** — covered at AS A molecule splits into two free radicals (initiation). The radicals react and are regenerated in a chain reaction (propagation). Radicals are removed by reacting with themselves (termination).	**Initiation** **Propagation** **Termination** $Cl\!-\!Cl \xrightarrow{UV} 2Cl^{\bullet}$ $H_3C\!-\!H + Cl^{\bullet} \longrightarrow H_3C^{\bullet} + HCl$ $2Cl^{\bullet} \longrightarrow Cl_2$ $Cl^{\bullet} + H_3C^{\bullet} \longrightarrow CH_3Cl$ $H_3C^{\bullet} + Cl\!-\!Cl \longrightarrow CH_3Cl + Cl^{\bullet}$ $2H_3C^{\bullet} \longrightarrow CH_3CH_3$.
2) **Electrophilic addition** — covered at AS The $\delta+$ of a polar molecule or a positive ion (electrophile) is attracted to the electrons in a double bond. The double bond opens up and the molecule or ion is added.	e.g. addition of bromine to ethene
3) **Nucleophilic substitution** — covered at AS The $\delta-$ of a polar molecule or a negative ion (nucleophile) is attracted to the $\delta+$ of a polar bond in a molecule. The nucleophile replaces an atom or group in the molecule.	e.g. reaction of hydroxide ions with 2-bromopropane
4) **Electrophilic substitution** — covered on page 86 Usually happens to aromatic compounds. The $\delta+$ of a polar molecule or a positive ion (electrophile) is attracted to an electron rich region and is substituted for an existing group.	e.g. formation of nitrobenzene
5) **Nucleophilic addition** — covered on page 15 The $\delta-$ of a polar molecule or a negative ion (nucleophile) is attracted to the $\delta+$ of a polar double bond. The double bond opens up and the nucleophile is added.	e.g. addition of CN^- to a ketone

A curly arrow with one head shows the movement of one electron.
A curly arrow with two heads shows the movement of two electrons.

Practice Questions

Q1 Draw the structures of these functional groups: i) carboxylic acid, ii) ester, iii) primary amine, iv) ketone.

Q2 Which functional groups undergo: i) elimination reactions, ii) substitution reactions, iii) reduction reactions?

Q3 Describe what happens in a: i) condensation reaction, ii) addition reaction.

Q4 Draw a reaction mechanism for a: i) nucleophilic substitution, ii) nucleophilic addition.

Exam Questions

1   Say whether the following are most likely to behave as electrophiles or nucleophiles, giving a reason in each case.
   a) H^+ b) NH_3 c) OH^- [6 marks]

2   a) Classify the reaction that occurs between each of the following as addition, elimination or substitution:
       i)   **HCN** and CH_3COCH_3 (propanone)
       ii) $CH_2\!=\!CH_2$ and **HBr**
       iii) CH_3CH_2Cl and **NaOH** (cold, dilute aqueous solution)   [3 marks]
   b) For each reaction, give the name or structural formula of the organic product(s) and say whether
       the species in bold is acting as an electrophile, nucleophile or neither.   [6 marks]

Holy organic reaction Baitman — that's a lotta chemistry...   Baitman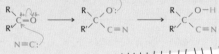

Well these pages aren't exactly short on information are they. The good news is that you've seen all of it before, either at AS or earlier in this book. So, if you can't remember all the details on something, flick back and have another read of it. Then close the book and start writing it all out until the pen runs dry.

Organic Synthesis

In your exam you may be asked to suggest a pathway for the synthesis of a particular molecule.
These pages contain a summary of some of the reactions you should know.

Chemists use **Synthesis Routes** to Get from One Compound to Another

Chemists have got to be able to make one compound from another. It's vital for things like **designing medicines**.
It's also good for making imitations of **useful natural substances** when the real things are hard to extract.

If you're asked how to make one compound from another in the exam, make sure you include:

1) any **special procedures**, such as refluxing.

2) the **conditions** needed, e.g. high temperature or pressure, or the presence of a catalyst.

3) any **safety** precautions, e.g. do it in a fume cupboard.

If there are things like hydrogen chloride or hydrogen cyanide around, you really don't want to go breathing them in.
Stuff like bromine and strong acids and alkalis are corrosive, so you don't want to splash them on your bare skin.

Most of these reactions are covered elsewhere in the book, so look back for extra details.

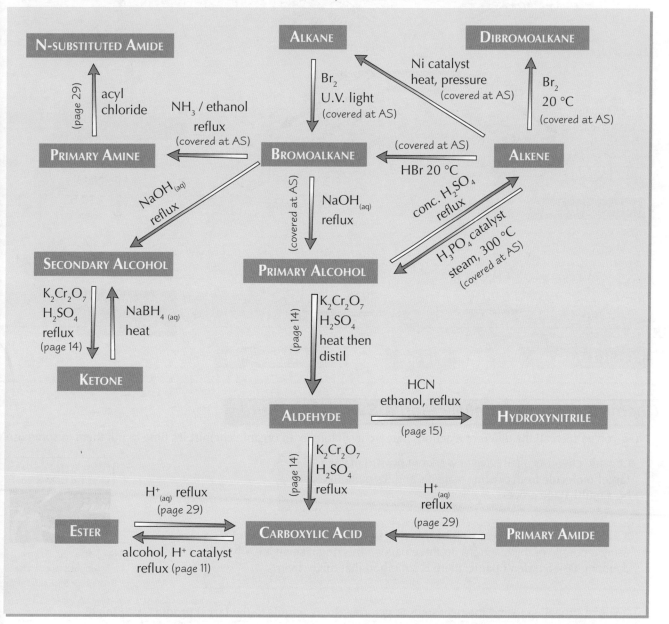

Organic Synthesis

There are Synthesis Routes for **Aromatic Compounds** too

There are not so many of these reactions to learn — so make sure you know all the itty-bitty details.
If you can't remember any of the reactions, look back to the relevant pages and take a quick peek over them.

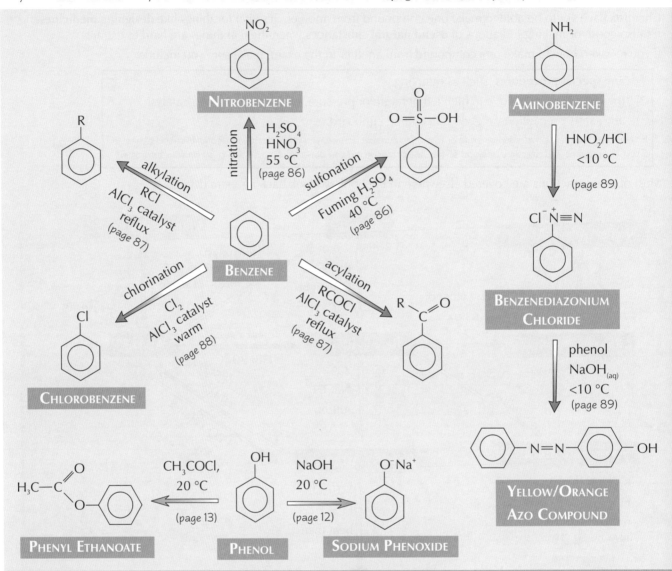

Chemists Have to Carefully **Plan** a **Synthetic Route**

Now you've seen all the different reactions that are available to an organic chemist it's time to put them to some use.

Organic chemists often have to work out how to **make** a **target molecule** from existing reagents and it's quite likely to be a **multi-stage** process.

It's also quite likely that **you** will be asked to synthesise a target molecule using a couple of the reactions on these pages. This might seem a really daunting task but **don't panic**, there is a method that might help...

If you're struggling to find the right steps to get from the **reactants** to the **target product**, you might find it easier to start with the product and **work backwards** — this is called **retrosynthesis**. You sometimes need a few steps before you get back to the basic reactants. But, once you can take it apart you can **reverse** all the **steps** and hey presto... you have your synthesis route.

An example of how to do this is on the next page.

Retro synths... that's what I'm talking 'bout.

We're starting to have som
doubts about the
Professor's qualifications

Organic Synthesis

Retrosynthesis is a Way of Planning a Synthetic Route

Example: Ethyl ethanoate is a solvent that has a pleasant fruity odour. Using your knowledge of organic reactions plan a synthesis route for ethyl ethanoate using ethanol as the only organic reagent.

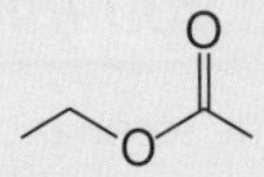

The first thing to do is **identify** any **functional groups** that the target molecule has. In this question the molecule has an **ester bond**. So a possible first retrosynthetic step would be to take the ethyl ethanoate apart into a carboxylic acid and an alcohol.

The retrosynthesis step uses the funny ⇒ arrow and the normal step uses a regular → arrow.

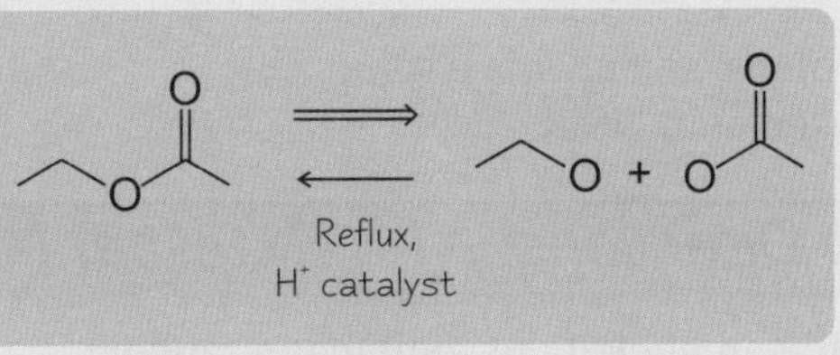

Reflux, H⁺ catalyst

The next stage is to work out how to create the carboxylic acid. You can make a carboxylic acid from an aldehyde — the aldehyde can be made from an alcohol, which is the starting reagent. So the last steps would be...

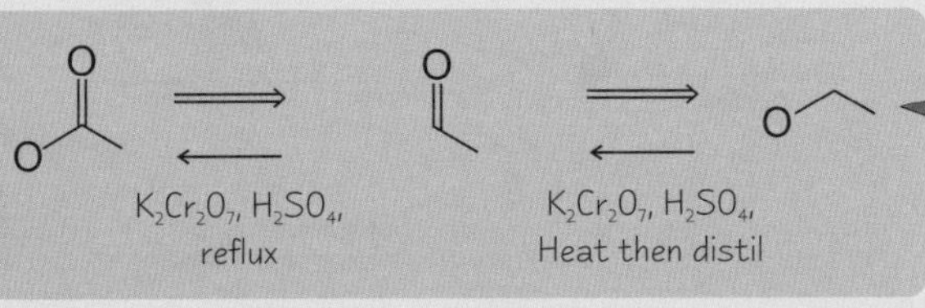

$K_2Cr_2O_7$, H_2SO_4, reflux

$K_2Cr_2O_7$, H_2SO_4, Heat then distil

The skeletal formula shows only the carbon skeleton without the H atoms.

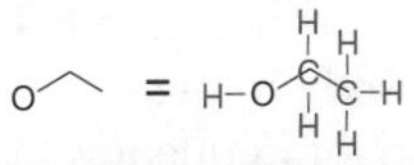

Retrosynthesis gets easier with practice. And knowing the organic reaction pathways makes a big difference. The approach is usually to try and **break up** the target molecule up into smaller, more easily synthesied bits. And look to **convert functional groups** until you have the starting reagents.

Practice Questions

Q1 How do you convert an ester to a carboxylic acid?

Q2 How do you make an aldehyde from a primary alcohol?

Q3 What do you produce if you reflux a primary amide with an acid?

Q4 How do you make an alkene from a primary alcohol?

Q5 How would you go about substituting an NO_2 group for a hydrogen atom on a benzene ring?

Exam Questions

1 Antifebrin was used as a painkiller and to treat fever before it was discovered to damage the liver. The structure is shown to the right. Part of a retrosynthesis for antifebrin involves breaking the bond shown in red. 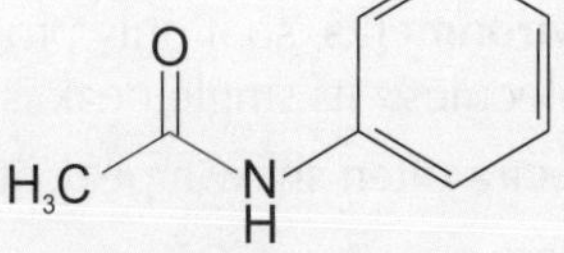
   a) Draw out the retrosynthetic step for this bond breaking, including the charges on the C and N atoms. [2 marks]
   b) i) State the reagents that could be used to perform this step forwards to create antifebrin. [2 marks]
      ii) Write out a balanced equation for the reaction. [1 mark]

2 How would you synthesise propanol starting with propane? State the reaction conditions and reagents needed for each step and any particular safety considerations. [8 marks]

I saw a farmer turn a tractor into a field once — now that's impressive...

There's loads of information here. Tons and tons of it. But you've covered pretty much all of it before, so it shouldn't be too hard to make sure it's firmly embedded in your head. If it's not, you know what to do — go back over it again. Then cover the diagrams up, and try to draw them out from memory. Keep going until you can do it perfectly.

NMR Spectroscopy — The Basics

NMR isn't the easiest of things, so ingest this information one piece at a time — a bit like eating a bar of chocolate (but this isn't so yummy).

NMR Gives you Information About an Organic Molecule's Structure

Nuclear magnetic resonance (NMR) spectroscopy tells you **how many hydrogens** there are in an organic molecule and how they're **arranged**. This lets you work out the **structure** of the organic molecule.

The reason NMR works is that nuclei with **odd** numbers of nucleons (protons and neutrons) have a **spin**. This causes them to have a weak **magnetic field** — a bit like a bar magnet.

Hydrogen nuclei are single **protons**, so they have spin. It's these that are normally looked at in NMR.

Protons Align in Two Directions in an External Magnetic Field

1) Normally, the protons (hydrogen nuclei) are spinning in **random directions** — so their magnetic fields **cancel out**.

2) But when a strong **external** magnetic field's applied, the protons align themselves either in the direction of the field (**aligned with it**), or in the opposite direction (**opposed to it**).

3) The aligned protons are at a slightly **lower** energy level than the opposed protons. But if they **absorb radio waves** of the right frequency, they can **flip** to the **higher** energy level. The opposed electrons can **emit** radio waves at the same frequency and **flip** to the **lower energy** level.

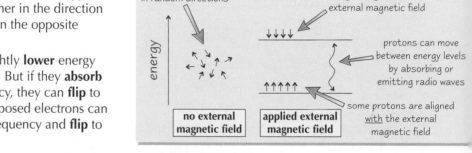

protons are spinning in random directions

some protons are aligned <u>against</u> the external magnetic field

protons can move between energy levels by absorbing or emitting radio waves

some protons are aligned <u>with</u> the external magnetic field

| no external magnetic field | applied external magnetic field |

4) There tends to be more aligned protons, so there's an **overall absorption** of energy. NMR spectroscopy **measures** this **absorption** of energy.

Protons with Different Environments Absorb Different Amounts of Energy

Protons are shielded from the external magnetic field by the surrounding electrons. The groups around a proton affect the amount of electron shielding — for example, the proton might be near something that withdraws electrons. So the **protons** in a molecule feel **different fields** depending on their **environment**. This means they absorb **different** amounts of energy, at **different frequencies**.

Chemical Shift is Measured Relative to Tetramethylsilane

So protons in different environments absorb energy of **different frequencies**. NMR spectroscopy measures these differences relative to a **standard substance** — the difference is called the **chemical shift (δ)**.

The standard substance is usually **tetramethylsilane** (**TMS**), $Si(CH_3)_4$. This molecule has 12 protons all with **identical environments**, so it only produces a **single** absorption peak — and this peak is well away from that of most other molecules. Its single peak is given a chemical shift value of 0.

Spectra often show a peak at $\delta = 0$ because some TMS is added to the test compound for calibration purposes.

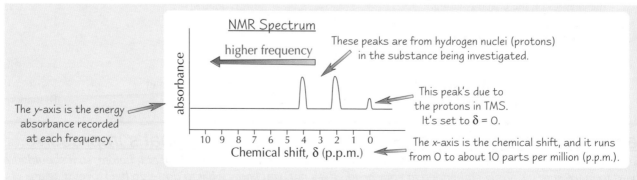

NMR Spectrum

higher frequency

These peaks are from hydrogen nuclei (protons) in the substance being investigated.

This peak's due to the protons in TMS. It's set to $\delta = 0$.

The *y*-axis is the energy absorbance recorded at each frequency.

Chemical shift, δ (p.p.m.)

The *x*-axis is the chemical shift, and it runs from 0 to about 10 parts per million (p.p.m.).

NMR Spectroscopy — The Basics

NMR Tells you the Number of Environments and the Number of Protons in Each

Each peak on an NMR spectrum is due to one or more protons in a **particular environment**.

The **relative area** under each peak tells you how many protons are in that environment.

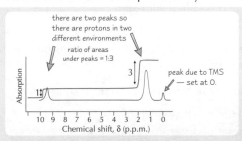

there are two peaks so there are protons in two different environments

ratio of areas under peaks = 1:3

3

peak due to TMS — set at 0.

Absorption

1

10 9 8 7 6 5 4 3 2 1 0
Chemical shift, δ (p.p.m.)

Example: NMR spectrum of ethanal, CH₃CHO
1) There are **two peaks** — so there are **two environments**.
2) The area ratio is **1:3** — so you know there's 1 proton in the environment at δ = 9.5 p.p.m. to every 3 protons in the other environment.

The red line on the diagram is the integration trace.
The height increases are proportional to the areas under the
trace and it tells you how many protons are in each environment.

Use a Table to Identify the Proton Causing the Chemical Shift

You use a table like this to **identify** which functional group each peak is due to.

Don't worry — **you don't need to learn it.** You'll be given one in your exam, so use it. The copy you get in your exam may look a little different, and have different values — they depend on the solvent, temperature and concentration.

The protons that cause the shift are highlighted in red.

Chemical shift, δ (p.p.m.)	Type of proton
0.8 – 1.3	R – CH₃
1.4 – 2.3	R – CH₂ – R
2.0 – 2.9	R – COCH₃
3.2 – 3.7	halogen – CH₃
3.6 – 3.8	R – CH₂ – Cl
3.3 – 3.9	R – OCH₂ – R
3.3 – 4.0	R – CH₂OH
0.5 – 4.5	R – OH
4.5 – 10.0	⬡ – OH
9.4 – 10	R – CHO
10.0 – 15.0	R – COOH

The example above shows that there's 1 hydrogen at δ = **9.5 p.p.m.** — this is due to an **R–CHO** group.

It also shows 3 hydrogens at δ = **1.3 p.p.m.** — an **R–CH₃** group.

Samples are Dissolved in Solvents Without Lone Protons

The sample's got to be dissolved in a solvent that has **no single protons** — or they'll show up as peaks on the spectrum and confuse things. **Deuterated solvents** are often used — their hydrogen atoms have been replaced by **deuterium**. Deuterium's an isotope of hydrogen that's got two nucleons (a proton and a neutron), so there's no overall spin on the nucleus. CCl_4 can also be used.

Practice Questions

Q1 Which part of the electromagnetic spectrum is absorbed in NMR spectroscopy?

Q2 What happens to the protons when they absorb energy?

Q3 What's a chemical shift?

Q4 What is a deuterated solvent, and why is it used?

Exam Question

1   Look at the NMR spectrum of a primary alcohol.
   a) Suggest a solvent that the alcohol might be dissolved in,
      and explain why this solvent can be used.   [3 marks]
   b) What are the approximate δ values for the three types of hydrogen atoms?   [1 mark]
   c) Suggest and explain a possible structure for the alcohol.   [4 marks]

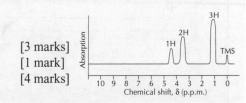

3H

2H

1H

TMS

Absorption

10 9 8 7 6 5 4 3 2 1 0
Chemical shift, δ (p.p.m.)

Aaaaaarrrrrghhhhhhhh....

Yep, I know, the ideas behind NMR are difficult, so don't worry if you have to read these pages quite a few times before they make sense. You've got to make sure you really understand the stuff on these two pages, cos there's more on the next two — and they aren't any easier. Keep bashing away at it though — you'll eventually go "aaaaaaaaaaahhhhh... I get it".

More NMR Spectroscopy

And now that you know the basics here's the really crunchy bit for you to get your teeth stuck in.

Spin-Spin Coupling *Splits* the *Peaks* in an NMR Spectrum

In high resolution NMR spectra, the peaks are **split** into **smaller peaks**. This is due to the **magnetic fields** of the **neighbouring single protons** interacting with each other, and is called **spin-spin coupling**. Only protons on **adjacent** carbon atoms affect each other.

These **multiple peaks** are called **multiplets**. They always split into the number of neighbouring protons plus one — it's called the **n + 1 rule**. For example, if there are **2 single protons** next door, the peak will be split into 2 + 1 = 3.

You can work out the **number** of **neighbouring single protons** by looking at how many the peak splits into:

If a peak's split into two (a **doublet**) then there's **one** neighbouring single proton.
If a peak's split into three (a **triplet**) then there are **two** neighbouring single protons.
If a peak's split into four (a **quartet**) then there are **three** neighbouring single protons.

One more fact to confuse things further: OH and NH **don't split** — they'll give a single peak.

For example, here's the NMR spectrum for **1,1,2-trichloroethane**:

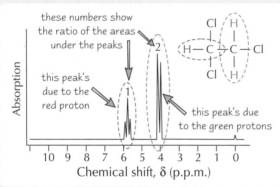

these numbers show the ratio of the areas under the peaks

this peak's due to the red proton

this peak's due to the green protons

The peak due to the green protons is split into **two** because there's **one proton** on the adjacent carbon atom.

The peak due to the red proton is split into **three** because there are **two protons** on the adjacent carbon atom.

An *NMR* Spectrum Gives us a Lot of *Information*

From an NMR spectrum you can tell these things:

1) The **different proton environments** in the molecule (from the **chemical shifts**).
2) The **relative number** of **protons** in each environment (from the **relative peak area**).
3) The **number of protons adjacent** to a particular proton (from the **splitting pattern**).

Yo! I'm still fresh!

Sadly, Professor Orbital is a little past his peak.

Using all this information you can predict **possible structures**, and sometimes the actual structure.

Example: Using the NMR spectrum below, predict the structure of the compound.

1) The peak at δ = **2.5 p.p.m.** is likely to be due to an **R–COCH₃** group, and the peak at δ = **9.5 p.p.m.** is likely to be due to an **R–CHO** group

2) From the areas, there's one proton in the peak at δ = **9.5 p.p.m.**, for every three in the peak at δ = **2.5 p.p.m.**. This fits nicely with the first bit — so far so good.

3) The quartet's got **three** neighbouring protons, and the doublet's got **one** — so it's likely these two groups are next to each other.

Now you know the molecule's got to contain...

...all you need to do is fit them together.

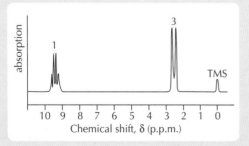

More NMR Spectroscopy

You Can Use *Data From Several Spectra* to *Work Out a Structure*

All the **spectroscopy techniques** that you've covered, mass spectrometry (page 23), IR (page 20) and NMR will **give clues** to the **identity of a mystery molecule**, but you can be more **certain** about a structure (and avoid jumping to wrong conclusions) if you look at **data from several different types of spectrum**.

Sorry, Prof — there's only space for one hip mascot around here...

Example: The following spectra are all of the same molecule. Deduce the molecule's structure.

The **mass spectrum** tells you the molecule's got a **mass of 44** and it's likely to contain a **CH$_3$ group**.

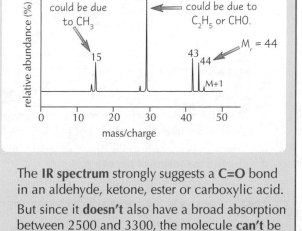

Mass Spectrum

could be due to CH$_3$

could be due to C$_2$H$_5$ or CHO.

M_r = 44

M+1

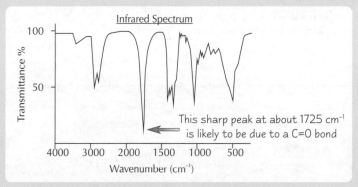

Infrared Spectrum

This sharp peak at about 1725 cm^{-1} is likely to be due to a C=O bond

The **IR spectrum** strongly suggests a **C=O** bond in an aldehyde, ketone, ester or carboxylic acid.

But since it **doesn't** also have a broad absorption between 2500 and 3300, the molecule **can't** be a carboxylic acid.

The **high resolution proton NMR spectrum** shows that there are **hydrogen nuclei in 2 environments**.

The peak at δ ≈ 9.5 is due to a **CHO group** and the one at δ ≈ 2.5 is probably **COCH$_3$**.
(You know that these can't be any other groups with similar chemical shifts thanks to the mass spectrum and IR spectrum.)

The **area** under the peaks is in the ratio **1 : 3**, which makes sense as there's **1 hydrogen in CHO** and **3 in COCH$_3$**.

The **splitting pattern** shows that the protons are on **adjacent carbon atoms**, so the group must be **HCOCH$_3$**.

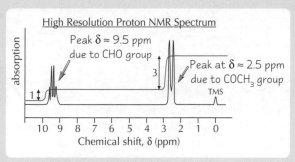

High Resolution Proton NMR Spectrum

Peak δ ≈ 9.5 ppm due to CHO group

Peak at δ ≈ 2.5 ppm due to COCH$_3$ group

TMS

Chemical shift, δ (ppm)

Putting all this together we have a molecule with a **mass of 44**, which contains a **CH$_3$** group, a **C=O** bond, and an **HCOCH$_3$** group.

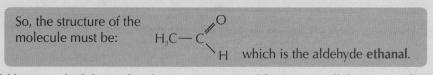

So, the structure of the molecule must be: H$_3$C—C   which is the aldehyde **ethanal**.

You probably could have worked the molecule's structure out **without** using all the spectra, but in more **complex examples** you might well need all of them, so it's good practice. And while we're on the subject, there are a couple **more examples** for you to practise on the next page — enjoy.

More NMR Spectroscopy

Practice Questions

Q1 Why does high resolution hydrogen NMR show peaks that are split?

Q2 Name three pieces of information that can be determined from an NMR spectrum.

Q3 Which type of spectrum gives you information on: i) the mass of the molecule, ii) the functional groups present?

Exam Questions   Use the NMR table from page 121 and the IR table from page 20 with these questions.

1   The NMR spectrum below is that of a haloalkane.

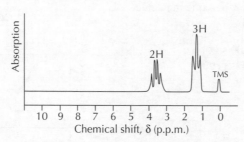

a)   What is the likely environment of the two protons with a shift of 3.6 p.p.m.?   [1 mark]

b)   What is the likely environment of the three protons with a shift of 1.3 p.p.m.?   [1 mark]

c)   The molecular mass of the molecule is 64. Suggest a possible structure and explain your suggestion.   [2 marks]

d)   Explain the shapes of the two peaks.   [4 marks]

2   The three spectra below were produced by running different tests on samples of the same pure organic compound.

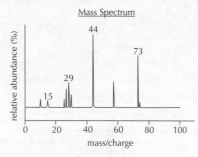
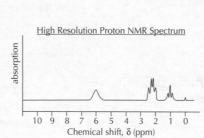
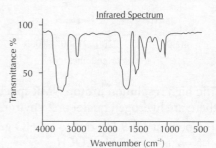

Use them to work out:

a)   The molecular mass of the compound.   [1 mark]

b)   The probable structure of the molecule. Explain your reasoning.   [6 marks]

3   The three spectra below were produced by running different tests on samples of the same pure organic compound.

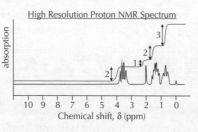
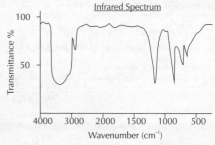

Use them to work out:

a)   The molecular mass of the compound.   [1 mark]

b)   The probable structure of the molecule. Explain your reasoning.   [6 marks]

Never mind splitting peaks — this stuff's likely to cause splitting headaches...

Is your head spinning yet? I know mine is. Round and round like a merry-go-round. It's not easy trying to get NMR spectroscopy firmly fixed in your head. And to make matters worse you need to remember the mass spec and IR stuff too. So, take it nice and slow, keep flicking back for reminders when you get stuck and it will eventually all click into place.

Practical and Investigative Skills

You're going to have to do some practical work too — and once you've done it, you have to make sense of your results...

Make it a **Fair Test** — Control your **Variables**

You probably know this all off by heart but it's easy to get mixed up sometimes. So here's a quick recap:

> **Variable** — A variable is a **quantity** that has the **potential to change**, e.g. mass.
> There are two types of variable commonly referred to in experiments:
> - **Independent variable** — the thing that you **change** in an experiment.
> - **Dependent variable** — the thing that you **measure** in an experiment.

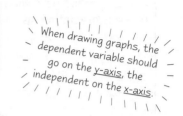
When drawing graphs, the dependent variable should go on the y-axis, the independent on the x-axis.

So, if you're investigating the effect of **temperature** on rate of reaction using the apparatus on the right, the variables will be:

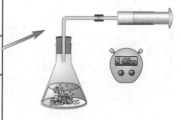

Independent variable	Temperature
Dependent variable	Amount of gas produced — you can measure this by collecting it in a gas syringe
Other variables — you MUST keep these the same	Concentration and volume of solutions, mass of solids, pressure, the presence of a catalyst and the surface area of any solid reactants

Know Your Different Sorts of **Data**

Experiments always involve some sort of measurement to provide **data**.
There are different types of data — and you need to know what they are.

> **Discrete** — you get discrete data by **counting**. E.g. the number of bubbles produced in a reaction would be discrete. You can't have 1.25 bubbles. That'd be daft. Shoe size is another good example of a discrete variable.

> **Continuous** — a continuous variable can have **any value** on a scale. For example, the volume of gas produced or the mass of products from a reaction. You can never measure the exact value of a continuous variable.

> **Categoric** — a categoric variable has values that can be sorted into **categories**. For example, the colours of solutions might be blue, red and green. Or types of material might be wood, steel, glass.

> **Ordered (ordinal)** — Ordered data is similar to categoric, but the categories can be **put in order**. For example, if you classify reactions as 'slow', 'fairly fast' and 'very fast' you'd have ordered data.

Organise Your Results in a **Table** — And Watch Out For **Anomalous** Ones

Before you start your experiment, make a **table** to write your results in.
You'll need to repeat each test at least three times to check your results are reliable.

This is the sort of table you might end up with when you investigate the effect of **temperature** on **reaction rate**.
(You'd then have to do the same for **different temperatures**.)

Temperature	Time (s)	Volume of gas evolved (cm³) Run 1	Volume of gas evolved (cm³) Run 2	Volume of gas evolved (cm³) Run 3	Average volume of gas evolved (cm³)
	10	8	7	8	**7.7**
20 °C	20	17	19	20	**18.7**
	30	28	20	30	**29**

Find the average of each set of repeated values.

You need to add them all up and divide by how many there are.

E.g.: (8 + 7 + 8) ÷ 3 = 7.7 cm³

Watch out for **anomalous results**. These are ones that don't fit in with the other values and are likely to be wrong. They're likely to be due to random errors — here the syringe plunger may have got stuck.
Ignore anomalous results when you calculate the average.

Practical and Investigative Skills

Graphs: *Line, Bar or Scatter* — Use the *Best Type*

You'll usually be expected to make a **graph** of your results. Not only are graphs **pretty**, they make your data **easier to understand** — so long as you choose the right type.

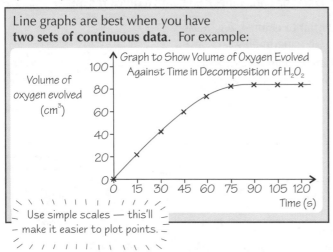

Line graphs are best when you have **two sets of continuous data**. For example:

Use simple scales — this'll make it easier to plot points.

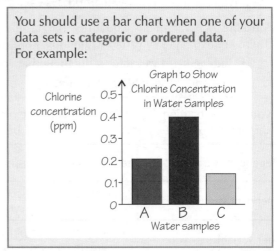

You should use a bar chart when one of your data sets is **categoric or ordered data**. For example:

Scatter plots are great for showing how two sets of data are related (or **correlated**).

Don't try to join all the points — draw a **line of best fit** to show the **trend**.

Scatter Graphs Show the Relationship Between Variables

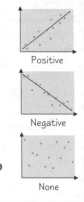

Correlation describes the **relationship** between two variables — the independent one and the dependent one.

Data can show:

1) **Positive correlation** — as one variable **increases** the other **increases**. The graph on the left shows positive correlation.

2) **Negative correlation** — as one variable **increases** the other **decreases**.

3) **No correlation** — there is **no relationship** between the two variables.

There are also pie charts. These are normally used to display categoric data.

Whatever type of graph you make, you'll ONLY get full marks if you:

• Choose a sensible scale — don't do a tiny graph in the corner of the paper.

• Label both axes — including units.

• Plot your points accurately — using a sharp pencil.

Correlation *Doesn't Necessarily* Mean *Cause* — Don't *Jump to Conclusions*

1) Ideally, only **two** quantities would **ever** change in any experiment — everything else would remain **constant**.

2) But in experiments or studies outside the lab, you **can't** usually control all the variables. So even if two variables are correlated, the change in one may **not** be causing the change in the other. Both changes might be caused be a **third variable**.

Watch out for bias too — for instance, a bottled water company might point these studies out to people without mentioning any of the doubts.

Example

For example: Some studies have found a correlation between **drinking chlorinated tap water** and the risk of developing certain cancers. So some people argue that this means water shouldn't have chlorine added.

BUT it's hard to control all the variables (e.g. lifestyle factors) between people who do drink tap water and people who don't.

Or, the cancer risk could be affected by something else in tap water — or by whatever the non-tap water drinkers drink instead...

Practical and Investigative Skills

Don't Get **Carried Away** When Drawing Conclusions

The **data** should always **support** the conclusion. This may sound obvious but it's easy to **jump** to conclusions. Conclusions have to be **specific** — not make sweeping generalisations.

Example

The rate of an enzyme-controlled reaction was measured at **10 °C, 20 °C, 30 °C, 40 °C, 50 °C and 60 °C**. All other variables were kept constant, and the results are shown in this graph.

A science magazine **concluded** from this data that enzyme X works best at **40 °C**. The data **doesn't** support this.

The enzyme **could** work best at 42 °C or 47 °C but you can't tell from the data because **increases** of **10 °C** at a time were used. The rate of reaction at in-between temperatures **wasn't** measured.

All you know is that it's faster at **40 °C** than at any of the other temperatures tested.

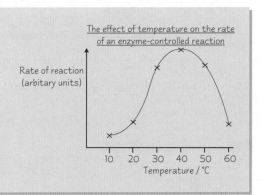

The effect of temperature on the rate of an enzyme-controlled reaction

Rate of reaction (arbitrary units)

Temperature / °C

Example

The experiment above **ONLY** gives information about this particular enzyme-controlled reaction. You can't conclude that **all** enzyme-controlled reactions happen faster at a particular temperature — only this one. And you can't say for sure that doing the experiment at, say, a different constant pressure, wouldn't give a different optimum temperature.

You Need to Look **Critically** at Your Results

There are a few bits of lingo that you need to understand. They'll be useful when you're evaluating how convincing your results are.

1) **Valid results** — Valid results answer the original question. For example, if you haven't **controlled all the variables** your results won't be valid, because you won't be testing just the thing you wanted to.

2) **Accurate** — Accurate results are those that are **really close** to the **true** answer.

3) **Precise results** — These are results taken using **sensitive instruments** that measure in **small increments**, e.g. pH measured with a meter (pH 7.692) will be **more precise** than pH measured with paper (pH 7).

   It's possible for results to be precise **but not** accurate, e.g. a balance that weighs to 1/1000 th of a gram will give precise results but if it's not **calibrated** properly the results won't be accurate.

   You may have to calculate the percentage error of a measurement.
   E.g. if a balance is calibrated to within 0.1 g, and you measure a mass as 4 g, then the percentage error is: (0.1 ÷ 4) × 100 = 2.5%.
   Using a larger quantity reduces the percentage error. E.g. a mass of 40 g has a percentage error of: (0.1 ÷ 40) × 100 = 0.25%.

4) **Reliable results** — **Reliable** means the results can be **consistently reproduced** in independent experiments. And if the results are reproducible they're more likely to be **true**. If the data isn't reliable for whatever reason you **can't draw** a valid **conclusion**.

   For experiments, the **more repeats** you do, the **more reliable** the data. If you get the **same result** twice, it could be the correct answer. But if you get the same result **20 times**, it's much more reliable. And it would be even more reliable if everyone in the class got about the same results using different apparatus.

Work **Safely** and **Ethically** — Don't Blow Up the Lab or Harm Small Animals

In any experiment you'll be expected to show that you've thought about the **risks and hazards**. It's generally a good thing to wear a lab coat and goggles, but you may need to take additional safety measures, depending on the experiment. For example, anything involving nasty gases will need to be done in a fume cupboard.

You need to make sure you're working **ethically** too. This is most important if there are other people or animals involved. You have to put their welfare first.

Answers

Unit 4: Module 1 — What's in a Medicine?

Page 5 — Acids, Bases and Bonding

1 a) $C_2H_5O^-$ (ethoxide ion) is the base *[1 mark]* because it accepts a proton in order to become C_2H_5OH *[1 mark]*.

b) Water is acting as an acid in this reaction *[1 mark]* because it loses H^+ to become OH^- *[1 mark]*.
The trick is to spot that C_2H_5OH has one more H than $C_2H_5O^-$ (so $C_2H_5O^-$ must have gained a proton in the reaction — which has come from H_2O).

2 a) Acids are proton donors *[1 mark]* and bases are proton acceptors *[1 mark]*.

b) No *[1 mark]*. It has no protons to donate *[1 mark]*.

c) (i) Base *[1 mark]*
(ii) Acid *[1 mark]*

Page 7 — More on Bonding

1 a)

[1 mark for a pair of shared electrons between the I and Cl atoms. 1 mark for the 6 non-bonding electrons (3 lone pairs) on each atom]

b) A covalent bond is a pair of electrons *[1 mark]* that is shared between two atoms *[1 mark]*. The atoms become more stable by sharing electrons because they achieve full outer shells of electrons *[1 mark]*.

c) There is a force of (electrostatic) attraction between the positive nuclei of the atoms and the negative electrons between them *[1 mark]*.

2 a) BH_3 is trigonal (triangular) planar *[1 mark]*.
NH_3 is trigonal (triangular) pyramidal *[1 mark]*.
They are different shapes because in NH_3 there is a lone pair on the central atom but not in BH_3 *[1 mark]*. (This could also be expressed as N has 5 electrons in its outer shell and B only has 3.)

b) Sodium chloride is ionic *[1 mark]* and silicon dioxide giant covalent (or giant molecular – must state 'giant') *[1 mark]*.
They could be distinguished from one another by trying to dissolve them in water *[1 mark]*. Sodium chloride would dissolve but silicon dioxide would not *[1 mark]*.
(Alternatively testing the electrical conductivity of their molten state *[1 mark]* – liquid sodium chloride conducts but silicon dioxide does not *[1 mark]*.)
When a question asks you to describe a test, it's important to state the results of the test and what the results tell you. Don't just name a test — you won't get full marks.

Page 9 — Organic Reactions

1 a) Alkene *[1 mark]* and alcohol *[1 mark]* functional groups.

b) Shake the compound with bromine (water) *[1 mark]*.
A would cause the colour to vanish *[1 mark]*.

c) Prop-2-en-1-ol *[1 mark]*

2 a) Ethene *[1 mark]*
Either pass ethanol vapour over Al_2O_3 *[1 mark]* heated to 400 °C *[1 mark]*. OR reflux ethanol *[1 mark]* with conc. H_2SO_4 *[1 mark]*.

b) Br_2 [1 mark] at 20 °C (or room temp) *[1 mark]*.

Page 11 — Carboxylic Acids and Esters

1 a) Esters *[1 mark]*

b) i) Ethanol *[1 mark]*

ii) *[correct C skeletal structure – 1 mark, correct structure of functional group – 1 mark]*
butanoic acid *[1 mark]*

iii) Water *[1 mark]*

Page 13 — Phenols

2 a) A is ethane-1,2-diol *[1 mark]*.

b) HOOC—⬡—COOH + 2NaOH → NaOOC—⬡—COONa + 2H₂O
[1 mark for correct Na salt, 1 mark for correct balancing.]

Page 13 — Phenols

1 a) *[1 mark]*

b) Hydrogen chloride gas/HCl *[1 mark]*
Just ignore the carboxyl group and pretend it's a phenol reacting with the acyl chloride.

2 TEST 1: Add sodium carbonate (or other suitable carbonate) *[1 mark]*. The carboxylic acid will fizz (CO_2 produced) *[1 mark]* but the phenol will not react *[1 mark]*.
TEST 2: Add iron(III) chloride *[1 mark]*. The carboxylic acid will not react *[1 mark]*, the phenol will produce a coloured solution *[1 mark]*.

3 a) Ethanoic acid *[1 mark]* and phenol *[1 mark]*

b) i) Structural formula:

Name: Ethanoyl chloride *[1 mark]*

ii) HCl *[1 mark]*

Page 15 — Aldehydes and Ketones

1 a) Oxidation *[1 mark]*

b) Ethanal *[1 mark]*. Functional group is carbonyl (C=O) *[1 mark]*.

c) i) If the ethanal is left in the reaction mixture it may oxidise further *[1 mark]* to form ethanoic acid *[1 mark]*.

ii) Propan-2-ol oxidises to a ketone *[1 mark]*, which cannot be oxidised any further *[1 mark]*.
Propan-2-ol oxidises to a ketone rather than an aldehyde because it's a secondary alcohol.

2 **X is butan-2-ol**

[1 mark for any secondary alcohol, 1 mark for name, 1 for structure]
Y is butanone

[1 mark for any ketone, 1 mark for name, 1 for structure]

3 i) A is ethanal *[1 mark]*, B is propanone *[1 mark]*, C is 2-methylpropanal *[1 mark]*

ii) A: ethanol *[1 mark]*, B: propan-2-ol *[1 mark]*, C: 2-methylpropan-1-ol *[1 mark]*

Page 17 — Reaction Type and Atom Economy

1 a) Ethane reaction: substitution *[1 mark]*
Ethene reaction: addition *[1 mark]*

b) Ethane reaction:
atom economy =
$[(2 × 12) + (5 × 1) + 35.5] ÷ [(2 × 12) + (6 × 1) + (35.5 × 2)]$
$= (64.5 ÷ 101) × 100 = $ **63.9%**
[1 mark for correct working, 1 mark for correct answer]
Ethene reaction:
atom economy =
$[(2 × 12) + (4 × 1) + (35.5 × 2)] ÷ [(2 × 12) + (4 × 1) + (35.5 × 2)]$
$= (99 ÷ 99) × 100 = $ **100%**
[1 mark for correct answer, with or without working]
This is an addition reaction, so you know the atoms economy must be 100%, you don't really need to work it out.

Answers

c) The ethene reaction has a higher atom economy since there is only one product (or there are no by-products) *[1 mark]* so all of the reactant atoms end up in the product (or none of the reactant atoms are wasted) *[1 mark]*.
Alternatively: The ethane reaction has a lower atom economy because some of the reactant atoms end up in HCl *[1 mark]* and are wasted *[1 mark]*.

2 M_r of $C_4H_2O_3 = (4 \times 12) + (2 \times 1) + (3 \times 16) = 98$
M_r of $CO_2 = 12 + (2 \times 16) = 44$
M_r of $H_2O = (2 \times 1) + 16 = 18$
Benzene oxidation:
Atom economy $= 98 \div [98 + (2 \times 44) + (2 \times 18)] \times 100 = $ **44.1%**
[1 mark for working, 1 mark for correct answer]
Butene oxidation:
Atom economy $= 98 \div [98 + (3 \times 18)] \times 100 = $ **64.4%**
[1 mark for working, 1 mark for correct answer]
The atom economies show that butene oxidation is less wasteful (higher economy) than benzene oxidation *[1 mark]* and therefore a more efficient use of resources (so more sustainable) *[1 mark]*.

Page 19 — Making Medicines

1 a) HS *[1 mark]* and COOH *[1 mark]*
b) The only difference between Molecule 1 and Molecule 2 is that the HS group is not present in Molecule 2 and this drug has very low activity compared to Molecule 1 *[1 mark]*.
In Molecule 3, although the HS group is there, the COOH group is missing and this drug also has very low activity *[1 mark]*.

2 a) 'Combinatorial chemistry' is a process of synthesising a large number *[1 mark]* of structurally similar (or related) *[1 mark]* molecules at the same time.
b) Because small differences in the structure of molecules can have large effects on their properties as a drug *[1 mark]* it is important to test many similar molecules to find the best combination of properties (or to find an effective drug with minimal side effects) *[1 mark]*.

Page 22 — Infrared Spectra and Chromatography

1 a) A's due to an O–H group in a carboxylic acid *[1 mark]*.
B's due to a C=O as in an aldehyde, ketone, acid or ester *[1 mark]*.
C's due to a C–O as in an alcohol, ester or acid *[1 mark]*.
D's also due to a C–O as in an alcohol, ester or acid *[1 mark]*.
b) The spectrum suggests it's a carboxylic acid — it's got a COOH group *[1 mark]*. This group has a mass of 45, so the rest of the molecule has a mass of 74 – 45 = 29, which is likely to be C_2H_5 *[1 mark]*. So the molecule could be C_2H_5COOH — propanoic acid *[1 mark]*.

2 a) X is a pure substance *[1 mark]*.
b) 1 and 2 *[1 mark]* since the spots present in mixture Y are at the same height (and so would have the same R_f values) as 1 and 2 *[1 mark]*.
c) R_f = spot distance ÷ solvent distance
$= 5.6 \div 8 = 0.7$
[1 mark for working, 1 mark for correct answer]
There are no units as it's a ratio.

Page 25 — Mass Spectrometry

1 a) 44 *[1 mark]*
b) X has a mass of 15. It is probably a methyl group/CH_3 *[1 mark]*.
Y has a mass of 29. It is probably an ethyl group/C_2H_5 *[1 mark]*.
c) $CH_3CH_2CH_3$ *[1 mark]*
d) If the compound was an alcohol, you would expect a peak with an m/z ratio of 17 *[1 mark]*, caused by the OH fragment *[1 mark]*.

2 a) Fragmentation *[1 mark]*.
b) $[CH_3CO]^+$ *[1 mark]*
c) 74 – 43 = 31 *[1 mark]*
This shows that H_3CO was lost from the molecule *[1 mark]*.

3 a) Low resolution mass spectrometry records m/z values as integers and both propane and ethanal have the same integer value for their M_r (44). *[1 mark]*
b) $M_r (C_3H_8) = (3 \times 12.0000) + (8 \times 1.0078) = 44.0624$ *[1 mark]*
$M_r (CH_3CHO) = (2 \times 12.0000) + (4 \times 1.0078) + 15.9949 = 44.0261$ *[1 mark]*
So the compound is ethanal *[1 mark]*.

Unit 4: Module 2 — The Materials Revolution

Page 27 — Electronegativity and Intermolecular Forces

1 a)

[1 mark for hydrogen bond shown between O of one molecule and H on the other, and 1 mark for δ^+ on all H atoms and δ^- on both oxygen atoms]
b) Permanent dipole-permanent dipole bonding *[1 mark]*

2 a) Oxygen *[1 mark]* Electronegativity decreases as you move down a group (and S is beneath O in Group 6) *[1 mark]*.
b)

[1 mark for δ^+ on the S atom, 1 mark for δ^- on all three O atoms]
c) SO_3 is non-polar overall *[1 mark]*. The three polar S=O bonds point in different directions, so their polarities cancel each other out *[1 mark]*.

Page 30 — Amines, Amides and Hydrolysis

1 a) A is 2-aminobutane *[1 mark]*
C is 1,2-diaminopropane *[1 mark]*
b) A is primary *[1 mark]*
B is tertiary *[1 mark]*
This isn't the same as classifying alcohols as primary, secondary or tertiary — to classify an amine, count how many carbon chains are attached to the N atom (1 = primary, 2 = secondary, 3 = tertiary).

2 a) $CH_3CH_2NH_{2(aq)} + HCl_{(aq)} \rightarrow CH_3CH_2NH_3^+Cl^-_{(aq)}$ *[1 mark]*
b) $CH_3CONH_{2(aq)} + HCl_{(aq)} + H_2O_{(l)} \rightarrow CH_3COOH_{(aq)} + NH_4^+Cl^-_{(aq)}$
[1 mark for ethanoic acid as a product, and 1 mark for correctly balancing equation using water and salt]

3 a) i) ethanoic acid *[1 mark]* and ethanol *[1 mark]*
ii) sodium ethanoate *[1 mark]* and ethanol *[1 mark]*
b) Dissolve the solid product in a minimum amount of hot solvent *[1 mark]*. Leave the saturated solution to cool slowly *[1 mark]*. Filter to remove the crystals of pure product *[1 mark]*. Wash the crystals in cold solvent, and then dry them *[1 mark]*.

Page 33 — Polymers

1 a)

[1 mark for correct diamine, 1 mark for correct dicarboxylic acid]
b) Polyamide *[1 mark]*. The polymer has an amide link (HN–CO) between the two monomers *[1 mark]*.

2 a) i)

[1 mark for ester link correct, 1 mark for rest of structure correct]
The oxygen atom at the right-hand end of the brackets could just as easily go on the left-hand end instead. As long as you have it there, it doesn't really matter which side it's on.
ii) Ester link *[1 mark]*.
b) It's called a condensation reaction because a water molecule is eliminated *[1 mark]*.
c) Any sensible advantage, e.g. reduces volume of waste going to landfill, or can be a source of energy/electricity *[1 mark]*.
Any sensible disadvantage, e.g. produces carbon dioxide, may produce toxic waste gases *[1 mark]*.

Page 35 — Polymer Properties

1 a) Polymer A *[1 mark]*
The more crystalline a polymer is, the stronger it is *[1 mark]*. Since HDPE is stronger than LDPE, it's likely to be the more crystalline polymer *[1 mark]*.

Answers

b) When you increase the crystallinity of a polymer, you force the polymer chains to lie closer together *[1 mark]*. The intermolecular forces between the chains will get stronger *[1 mark]*. This means that you will have to put more energy in to separate the chains, so the melting point of the polymer will increase *[1 mark]*.

c) Cold-drawing *[1 mark]*

2 a) In unplasticised PVC the polymer chains are closely packed together *[1 mark]*. So the intermolecular forces between the chains are very strong *[1 mark]*.
That's why PVC has a high glass transition temperature too.

c) Plasticiser molecules get in between the polymer chains, and reduce the effect of intermolecular forces *[1 mark]*, so chains can move around more *[1 mark]*. This makes PVC more flexible *[1 mark]*.

Unit 4: Module 3 — The Thread of Life

Page 37 — Rates of Reaction

1 a) E.g. Volume of $CO_{2(g)}$ *[1 mark]* using a gas syringe *[1 mark]* / Colour of $Br_{2(aq)}$ *[1 mark]* using a colorimeter *[1 mark]* / pH (since $H^+_{(aq)}$ produced) *[1 mark]* using a pH meter *[1 mark]* / mass of CO_2 lost *[1 mark]* using a mass balance *[1 mark]*.
You can follow the rate by monitoring any property that changes.

b) Plot a graph of $[Br_{2(aq)}]$ against time *[1 mark]*. Draw a tangent to the curve at a particular time *[1 mark]*. Calculate the gradient of the tangent *[1 mark]*.

2 a) Gas volume of $Z_{(g)}$ *[1 mark]* using, e.g. a gas syringe *[1 mark]*/ Loss of mass *[1 mark]* using, e.g. a mass balance *[1 mark]*.

b)

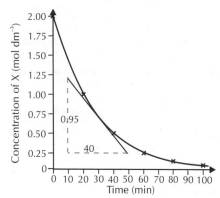

Rate after 30 minutes = 0.95/40
= 0.02375 *[1 mark]* mol dm^{-3} min^{-1} *[1 mark]*
Accept rate within range 0.02375 ± 0.005.
[1 mark for X concentration on y-axis and time on x-axis. 1 mark for points accurately plotted. 1 mark for best-fit smooth curve. 1 mark for tangent to curve at 30 minutes.]

Page 39 — Orders and Rate Equations

1 a) Rate = $k[NO_{(g)}]^2[H_{2(g)}]$ *[1 mark for correct orders, 1 mark for the rest]*
Sum of individual orders = 2 + 1 = 3rd order overall *[1 mark]*.

b) i) $0.00267 = k \times (0.004)^2 \times 0.002$ *[1 mark]*
$k = 8.34 \times 10^4$ dm^6 mol^{-2} s^{-1} *[1 mark for answer, 1 mark for units]*.
Units: $k = $ mol dm^{-3} s^{-1}/[(mol $dm^{-3})^2 \times$ (mol dm^{-3})] = dm^6 mol^{-2} s^{-1}.

ii) It would decrease *[1 mark]*.
If the temperature decreases, the rate decreases too.
A lower rate means a lower rate constant.

2 a) Rate = $k[CH_3COOC_2H_5][H^+]$ *[1 mark]*

b) $2.2 \times 10^{-3} = k \times 0.25 \times 2.0$
$k = 2.2 \times 10^{-3} \div 0.5 = 4.4 \times 10^{-3}$ mol dm^{-3} s^{-1} *[1 mark]*
The units are:
$k = $ (mol dm^{-3} s^{-1})/(mol dm^{-3})(mol dm^{-3})
$= mol^{-1}$ dm^3 s^{-1} *[1 mark]*

c) If the volume doubles, the concentration of each reactant halves to become 1 and 0.125 respectively. *[1 mark]*
So the rate = $4.4 \times 10^{-3} \times 1 \times 0.125 = 5.5 \times 10^{-4}$ mol dm^{-3} s^{-1} *[1 mark]*

Page 41 — Experimental Data and Rate Equations

1 a) Experiments 1 and 2: [X] doubles and the initial rate quadruples (with [Y] remaining constant) *[1 mark]*. So it's 2nd order with respect to [X] *[1 mark]*.
Experiments 1 and 3: [Y] doubles and the initial rate doubles (with [X] remaining constant) *[1 mark]*. So it's 1st order with respect to [Y] *[1 mark]*.
Always explain your reasoning carefully — state which concentrations are constant and which are changing.

b) rate = $k[X]^2[Y]$ *[1 mark]*

c) Any row of experimental data can be picked in this sort of question. In Experiment 1: $1.30 \times 10^{-3} = k \times 0.2^2 \times 0.2$ *[1 mark]*
$k = 0.163$ $dm^6 mol^{-2} s^{-1}$ *[1 mark for answer, 1 mark for units]*.
Units: $k = moldm^{-3}s^{-1}/[(moldm^{-3})^2 \times (moldm^{-3})] = dm^6mol^{-2}s^{-1}$.
Watch out — check the table of rate data carefully. In this case, the initial rate needs to be multiplied by 10^{-3}.

2 a) i) The three half-lives for reactant A are all 17s *[2 marks if all correct, or 1 mark for 2 correct]*.
The reaction is first order with respect to A *[1 mark]*.
You know this because the half-lives are constant.

ii) The three half-lives for reactant B are 21s, 37s and 59s *[2 marks if all correct, or 1 mark for 2 correct]*.
The reaction is second order with respect to B *[1 mark]*.
You know this because the half-lives increase.

b) Rate = $k[A][B]^2$
[1 mark for concentration terms — A and B appearing in square brackets. 1 mark for the rate constant, k. 1 mark for correct powers.]

Page 44 — Rates and Reaction Mechanisms

1 a) rate = $k[H_{2(g)}][ICl_{(g)}]$ *[1 mark]*

b) i) One molecule of H_2 and one molecule of ICl *[1 mark]*.
If the molecule is in the rate equation, it must be in the rate-determining step *[1 mark]*. The orders of the reaction tell you how many molecules of each reactant are in the rate-determining step *[1 mark]*.

ii) Incorrect *[1 mark]*. H_2 and ICl are both in the rate equation, so they must both be in the rate-determining step
OR the order of the reaction with respect to ICl is 1, so there must be only one molecule of ICl in the rate-determining step *[1 mark]*.

2 a) Rate = $k[CH_3CH_2CH_2Br][OH^-]$ *[1 mark for each correct term, including rate constant]*. The reaction is second order overall *[1 mark]*.

b) When all of the enzymes molecules are bound to reactant molecules (the enzyme is saturated) *[1 mark]*, adding more reactant can't make the reaction any faster because there are no enzyme molecules available to interact with the extra reactant *[1 mark]*.

Page 47 — Amino Acids and Proteins

1 a)

$$HOCH_2 - \overset{\overset{\displaystyle NH_2}{|}}{\underset{\underset{\displaystyle H}{|}}{C}} - COOH$$

[1 mark]

You'll need a cool head for this one. Start with a 3-carbon chain and then add the groups — you start numbering the carbons from the one with the carboxyl group.

b) i) Two amino acids joined together *[1 mark]* by a peptide/amide/–CONH– link *[1 mark]*.

ii)

$$H_2N - \overset{\overset{\displaystyle H}{|}}{\underset{\underset{\displaystyle H}{|}}{C}} - \overset{\overset{\displaystyle O}{||}}{C} - \overset{\overset{\displaystyle H}{|}}{N} - \overset{\overset{\displaystyle CH_2}{|} \overset{\displaystyle OH}{|}}{\underset{\underset{\displaystyle H}{|}}{C}} - COOH$$ *[1 mark]*

$$H_2N - \overset{\overset{\displaystyle CH_2}{|} \overset{\displaystyle OH}{|}}{\underset{\underset{\displaystyle H}{|}}{C}} - \overset{\overset{\displaystyle O}{||}}{C} - \overset{\overset{\displaystyle H}{|}}{N} - \overset{\overset{\displaystyle H}{|}}{\underset{\underset{\displaystyle H}{|}}{C}} - COOH$$ *[1 mark]*

The amino acids can join together in either order — that's why there are two dipeptides.

Answers

c) Hot aqueous 6 mol dm^{-3} hydrochloric acid/HCl **[1 mark]**, reflux for 24 hours **[1 mark]**.

2 a) Hydrolysis **[1 mark]**

b) Amino acids **[1 mark]**

c) (Paper) chromatography **[1 mark]**. Put a spot of the amino acid mixture on a pencil line at the bottom of a piece of paper, and stand the paper in a container with a solvent (just touching the paper but not the spot) **[1 mark]**. Allow the solvent to move nearly to the top of the paper, then remove the paper and mark where the solvent front has reached **[1 mark]**. Use a dye, e.g. ninhydrin, (allow UV or iodine) to reveal the spots **[1 mark]**. Calculate R$_f$ values and compare these to a table of known values **[1 mark]**.

Page 49 — DNA

1 a)

[1 mark for the correct attachment of deoxyribose to the phosphate. 1 mark for guanine correctly attached to ribose]

b) DNA codes for specific amino acids with sequences of three bases called base triplets **[1 mark]**. Different sequences of bases code for the different amino acids that make up a protein **[1 mark]**.

Page 51 — More DNA

1 a) By hydrogen bonds **[1 mark]** between bases **[1 mark]**.

b) Bases connect to one another in specific pairs **[1 mark]**, so the sequence of bases on the DNA strand defines the sequence of free nucleotides which connect to it **[1 mark]**.

c) TAACGT **[2 marks if all correct, 1 mark deducted for each mistake]**.

2 a) Sections of the DNA molecule vary from person to person. Genetic fingerprinting is a molecular technique which is able to break down and analyse these sections **[1 mark]**. It can be used to identify people based on samples of their DNA **[1 mark]**.

b) DNA profiles collected in the UK are stored on a national database, so there are concerns over e.g. who could access the information / what the information could be used for / the consequences of adding the DNA of innocent people to a database containing the DNA of criminals **[1 mark for any sensible concern]**.

Page 53 — RNA and Protein Synthesis

1 a) DNA does not contain uracil/only RNA contains uracil **[1 mark]**.

b) Four amino acids (or for three amino acids, plus partially for two others) **[1 mark]**. Each amino acid is coded for by a triplet of bases **[1 mark]**.

c) –TTCCACGTAGCT– **[2 marks for all correct, 1 mark deducted for each mistake.]**
Remember — thymine in DNA is replaced by uracil in RNA and that uracil pairs with adenine.

2 a) Transcription **[1 mark]** occurs in the cell nucleus **[1 mark]**.

b) A codon **[1 mark]**. The bases are complimentary pairs of those in DNA **[1 mark]**.

c) i) ribosome **[1 mark]**.

ii) Translation begins when a ribosome reads a start codon **[1 mark]**. As this codon is always the same, it always causes the addition of the same amino acid **[1 mark]**.
A tRNA has an anticodon at one end and glycine attached at the other **[1 mark]**. The anticodon on the tRNA involved is –CCA– (it's complementary to the mRNA codon) **[1 mark]**.
The tRNA anticodon binds to the codon on the mRNA **[1 mark]**. The same thing happens with the next codon and a peptide link is formed with the adjacent amino acid **[1 mark]**.

Page 55 — Enzymes

1 a) The enzyme only catalyses a specific reaction **[1 mark]** (or only works with a particular substrate).

b) Enzymes have an active site with a particular shape **[1 mark]**. Only a certain substrate will fit into this site **[1 mark]**.

2 a) i) Molecules have less (thermal/kinetic) energy **[1 mark]** at low temperatures, so collide less often and with less energy **[1 mark]**.

ii) Above optimum temperature the enzyme is denatured **[1 mark]**, the shape of the active site changes and so the substrate no longer fits into the active site **[1 mark]**.

b) pH **[1 mark]**.

3 a) Inhibitors **[1 mark]**.

b) A molecule may have a very similar shape to the substrate **[1 mark]** and so fit into the active site **[1 mark]**. This blocks the active site, preventing the substrate from entering **[1 mark]**.

Page 57 — Molecular Shapes and Isomerism

1 a) The property of having stereoisomers, which are molecules with the same molecular formula and with their atoms arranged in the same way **[1 mark]**, but with a different orientation of the bonds in space **[1 mark]**.

b) For example:

[1 mark for each correct structure, 1 mark for correct cis/trans labels.]

c) i) For example:

[1 mark for each correctly drawn structure — they don't have to be orientated in the same way as in the diagram above, as long as the molecules are mirror images of each other.]

ii) An asymmetric carbon/a chiral carbon/a carbon with four different groups attached **[1 mark]**.

2 a) A single C-C bond can rotate **[1 mark]** and so the groups above and below the line of the bond change all the time as the bond rotates **[1 mark]**. A C=C double bond can not rotate **[1 mark]**.

b) No **[1 mark]**. If one of the C atoms of the double bond is connected to two identical groups there can not be E/Z isomers **[1 mark]**.

Unit 4: Module 4 — The Steel Story

Page 59 — Titrations

1 Number of moles $MnO_4^- = (27.8 \times 0.0100) \div 1000$
$= 2.78 \times 10^{-4}$ **[1 mark]**
The reacting ratio $H_2O_2 : MnO_4^- = 5:2 = 2.5:1$ **[1 mark]**
So the number of moles $H_2O_2 = 2.78 \times 10^{-4} \times 2.5$
$= 6.95 \times 10^{-4}$ **[1 mark]**
The concentration of $H_2O_2 = (6.95 \times 10^{-4})$ moles/0.0150 dm^3 =
0.0463 mol dm^3 **[1 mark]** Answer should be to 3 significant figures **[1 mark]**

2 First measure out a fixed amount of acid/alkali using a pipette, to get an accurate measurement, and then put into a conical flask **[1 mark]**. Add an indicator e.g. phenolphthalein (OR methyl orange) to monitor the pH change **[1 mark]**. Fill the burette with alkali/acid and run it into the flask, roughly marking where the end point is **[1 mark]**. Reset the experiment with fresh alkali, acid and indicator. Repeat the titration, this time adding slowly to get accurate results **[1 mark]**. Repeat the titration to get similar results **[1 mark]**.
It doesn't matter if you put acid in the pipette and alkali in the burette or the other way round — the method will still be the same.

Answers

3 a) $(0.0200 \times 26.7) \div 1000 = 5.34 \times 10^{-4}$ **[1 mark]**
   b) ratio is 5:1 so $5.34 \times 10^{-4} \times 5 = 2.67 \times 10^{-3}$ **[1 mark]**
   c) mass of Fe $= 55.8 \times 2.67 \times 10^{-3} = 0.149$ g **[1 mark]**
   d) percentage $= (0.149 \div 0.150) \times 100 = 99.3\%$ **[1 mark]**

Page 61 — Redox

1 a) i) +1 **[1 mark]**
   ii) +2 **[1 mark]**
   iii) 0 **[1 mark]**
   b) Copper(I) oxide **[1 mark]**
   Copper(II) sulfate **[1 mark]**
   (NO marks for 'copper oxide' or 'copper sulfate')
   c) It is unchanged during the reaction **[1 mark]**
2 a) Oxidised **[1 mark]** because they are losing electrons **[1 mark]**
   b) +3 in $C_2O_4^{2-}$ **[1 mark]** and +4 in CO_2 **[1 mark]**
   c) $2MnO_4^- + 16H^+ + 5C_2O_4^{2-} \rightarrow 2Mn^{2+} + 8H_2O + 10CO_2$
   (allow $MnO_4^- + 8H^+ + 2.5C_2O_4^{2-} \rightarrow Mn^{2+} + 4H_2O + 5CO_2$)
   [1 mark for correct manganate(VII)/manganese(II) balancing, 1 mark for correct $C_2O_4^{2-}/CO_2$ balancing, 1 mark for correct H^+/H_2O balancing.]

Page 63 — Electrode Potentials

1 a)

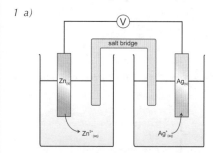

   [1 mark for correctly labelled electrodes, 1 mark for salt bridge, 1 mark for external circuit.]
   b) $+0.80$ V $- (-0.76$ V$) = +1.56$ V **[1 mark]**
   c) Any one of: the concentration of Zn^{2+} ions or Ag^+ ions was not 1.00 mol dm^{-3} / the pressure wasn't 100 kPa / the temperature wasn't 25 °C **[1 mark]**.
   d) $Zn_{(s)} + 2Ag^+_{(aq)} \rightarrow Zn^{2+}_{(aq)} + 2Ag_{(s)}$ **[1 mark]**
   e) The zinc half-cell. It has a more negative standard electrode potential **[1 mark]**.
2 a) $Zn_{(s)} + Ni^{2+}_{(aq)} \rightleftharpoons Zn^{2+}_{(aq)} + Ni_{(s)}$ **[1 mark]**
   $E^\circ = (-0.25) - (-0.76) = +0.51$ V **[1 mark]**
   b) $Ag^+_{(aq)} + Fe^{2+}_{(aq)} \rightleftharpoons Ag_{(s)} + Fe^{3+}_{(aq)}$ **[1 mark]**
   $E^\circ = (+0.80) - (+0.77) = +0.03$ V **[1 mark]**

Page 65 — Iron — Rusting, Recycling and Extraction

1 a) The Sn/Sn^{2+} system has a more positive (greater) standard electrode potential value than the Fe/Fe^{2+} system. **[1 mark]** This means that the iron would oxidise in preference to the tin and so the tin cannot act as a sacrificial protector. **[1 mark]**
   b) This is a sacrificial method of protection **[1 mark]** since the Zn/Zn^{2+} system has a more negative (lower) standard electrode potential value than the Fe/Fe^{2+} system. **[1 mark]** This means that the zinc would oxidise in preference to the iron. **[1 mark]**
2 The impure copper is used as the anode **[1 mark]** and a small piece of pure copper is used as the cathode **[1 mark]**. The electrolyte in the cell is a copper salt **[1 mark, accept named copper compound]**. At the anode the copper is oxidised $Cu_{(s)} \rightarrow Cu^{2+}_{(aq)} + 2e^-$ **[1 mark]**. The copper ions travel through the electrolyte to the cathode but the impurities fall to the bottom of the cell **[1 mark]**. At the cathode the copper ions are reduced back to copper $Cu^{2+}_{(aq)} + 2e^- \rightarrow Cu_{(s)}$ **[1 mark]**.

Page 67 — Transition Metals

1 a) $1s^2 2s^2 2p^6 3s^2 3p^6 3d^{10}$ or $[Ar]3d^{10}$ **[1 mark]**
   b) No, it doesn't **[1 mark]**. Cu^+ ions have a full 3d subshell **[1 mark]**.
   c) copper(II) sulfate ($CuSO_{4(aq)}$) **[1 mark]**

2 a) i) $1s^2 2s^2 2p^6 3s^2 3p^6 3d^{10}4s^2$ **[1 mark]**
   ii) $1s^2 2s^2 2p^6 3s^2 3p^6 3d^{10}$ **[1 mark]**
   iii) $1s^2 2s^2 2p^6 3s^2 3p^6 3d^5 4s^1$ **[1 mark]**
   iv) $1s^2 2s^2 2p^6 3s^2 3p^6 3d^3$ **[1 mark]**
   (allow use of shorthand [Ar] to represent $1s^2 2s^2 2p^6 3s^2 3p^6$ allow 4s and 3d to be reversed)
   b) A transition metal is one that has at least one stable ion **[1 mark]** with an incomplete/partially filled d-shell **[1 mark]**.
   Cu has one stable ion (the 2+ ion) with an incomplete d-shell (9 d electrons) **[1 mark]**. Zn has only one stable ion (2+) and this has 10 electrons in the d-subshell — the subshell is full **[1 mark]**.

Page 69 — Complex Ions

1 a) A = $[Cu(H_2O)_6]^{2+}$ **[1 mark]**, B = $[CuCl_4]^{2-}$ **[1 mark]**
   b) $[Cu(H_2O)_6]^{2+}_{(aq)} + 4Cl^-_{(aq)} \rightleftharpoons [CuCl_4]^{2-}_{(aq)} + 6H_2O_{(l)}$ **[1 mark]**
   c)

   $A = [Cu(H_2O)_6]^{2+}$ octahedral, $B = [CuCl_4]^{2-}$ tetrahedral.

   $A =$ octahedral, $B =$ tetrahedral.
   [1 mark for each correct diagram, 1 mark for each shape name]
2 a) Ligand substitution **[1 mark]** (accept 'ligand exchange')
   b) A lone pair of electrons **[1 mark]**.
   c) B only **[1 mark]**
   d) B is changing from octahedral **[1 mark]** to tetrahedral **[1 mark]**. The Cl^- ligands are bigger than the H_2O ligand **[1 mark]** so fewer of them can fit around the metal ion **[1 mark]**.

Page 71 — More on Transition Metals

1 a) i) A green precipitate forms **[1 mark]**
   ii) A brown/rust coloured precipitate forms **[1 mark]**
   b) $[Fe(H_2O)_6]^{2+} + 2OH^- \rightarrow [Fe(H_2O)_4(OH)_2] + 2H_2O$
   [1 mark for 2 OH^- ions, 1 mark for correct formula of precipitate. Allow $Fe(OH)_2$ for 2nd mark]
   $[Fe(H_2O)_6]^{3+} + 3OH^- \rightarrow [Fe(H_2O)_3(OH)_3] + 3H_2O$
   [1 mark for 3 OH^- ions, 1 mark for correct formula of precipitate. Allow $Fe(OH)_3$ for 2nd mark]
2 a) Both form a blue precipitate when first added to a solution of copper(II) ions **[1 mark]** but only excess ammonia solution will make this dissolve forming an (intense) blue solution **[1 mark]**.
   b) i) $[Cu(H_2O)_6]^{2+} + 2NH_3 \rightarrow [Cu(H_2O)_4(OH)_2] + 2NH_4^+$
   [1 mark for 2 ammonia molecules, 1 mark for correct formula of precipitate — allow $Cu(OH)_2$]
   ii) $[Cu(H_2O)_6]^{2+} + 4NH_3 \rightarrow [Cu(H_2O)_2(NH_3)_4]^{2+} + 4H_2O$
   [1 mark for 4 ammonia molecules, 1 mark for correct formula of complex ion formed — allow $[Cu(NH_3)_4]^{2+}$ — must have 2+ charge]
3 a) Heterogeneous means 'in a different phase from the reactants' **[1 mark]**.
   Homogeneous means 'in the same phase as the reactants' **[1 mark]**.
   b) The orbitals allow reactant molecules to make weak bonds to the catalyst **[1 mark]**.
   c) By changing oxidation state easily, transition metals can take in or give out electrons **[1 mark]** and so they can help transfer electrons from one reactant to another **[1 mark]**.
   (Accept answer in terms of catalyst helping to oxidise and reduce.)

Page 73 — Transition Metal Ion Colour

1 First select a filter that is the complement of the purple colour **[1 mark]**. Next, set the colorimeter to zero by measuring the absorbance of distilled water in a curvette **[1 mark]**. Then prepare a number of solutions of potassium manganate(VII) with known concentrations and measure their absorbances **[1 mark]**. Using these results draw a graph of absorbance vs concentration **[1 mark]**. Measure the absorbance of the unknown solution and use the graph to work out its concentration **[1 mark]**.
The complement colour to the purple potassium manganate(VII) is green.

Answers

2 a) *Magenta / red / blue [1 mark]. Since the solution appears green, it must be absorbing red and blue light [1 mark].*

b) *As a reference [1 mark] (allow 'to zero the colorimeter' or 'to measure the maximum intensity of light').*

c) *She will measure the absorbance of each standard solution [1 mark] and plot a calibration graph of absorbance against concentration [1 mark]. Then she can measure the absorbance of the solution of unknown concentration and use the graph to convert this to a concentration [1 mark].*

3 a)

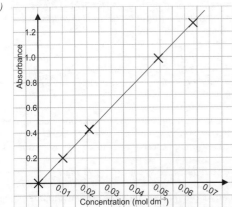

Appropriate scales for each axis [2 marks].
Vertical axis labelled 'Absorbance' [1 mark].
Horizontal axis labelled 'concentration' and in units of mol dm⁻³ [1 mark].
Points plotted correctly [1 mark].
Trendline drawn through points [1 mark].

b) *0.039 mol dm⁻³ [2 marks if within 0.002 either way, otherwise 1 mark if within 0.004 either way]*

Unit 5: Module 1 — Agriculture and Industry

Page 76 — Rates and Equilibria

1 a) *When the backward and forward reactions have reached the same rate [1 mark] and there is no change in the quantities of reactant and product in the mixture [1 mark].*

b) *Pushing in the plunger increases the pressure of the gas mixture [1 mark]. This causes the equilibrium position to shift to the right [1 mark] because there are 2 moles of gas on the left of the equation and only 1 on the right [1 mark]. The mixture now contains less of the brown NO_2 and more of the colourless N_2O_4 and so the colour appears fainter [1 mark].*

2 a) i) *The rate will increase [1 mark] because a higher temperature means faster particles that will collide more often, with more energy [1 mark].*

ii) *Position of equilibrium will move to the left [1 mark] because the forward reaction is exothermic, so the reverse reaction will be endothermic and the equilibrium will move to try to absorb heat [1 mark].*

Page 79 — Equilibrium Constants

1 a) $K_c = \dfrac{[CrO_4^{2-}]^2[H^+]^2}{[Cr_2O_7^{2-}][H_2O]}$

[1 mark for top expression correct, 1 mark for bottom expression correct]

b) $Cr_2O_7^{2-} + H_2O \rightleftharpoons 2CrO_4^{2-} + 2H^+$
Since there's 0.03 moles of $Cr_2O_7^{2-}$ at equilibrium, from the equation there must also be 0.03 moles of H_2O [1 mark].
0.07 moles of $Cr_2O_7^{2-}$ must have reacted [1 mark], which will give 0.14 moles of CrO_4^{2-} [1 mark] and 0.14 moles of H^+ [1 mark]
You can see from molar ratios in the equation that $Cr_2O_7^{2-}$ reacts to produce double the amount of CrO_4^{2-} and H^+.
If the total volume of the solution is 100 cm³, or 0.1 dm³, then the equilibrium concentrations are as follows:
$[H_2O] = 0.03 \div 0.1 = 0.3$ moldm⁻³ [1 mark]
$[CrO_4^{2-}] = [H^+] = 0.14 \div 0.1 = 1.4$ moldm⁻³ [1 mark]

c) *Concentration of $Cr_2O_7^{2-} = 0.05 \div 0.1 = 0.5$ moldm⁻³ [1 mark]*

$K_c = \dfrac{1.4^2 \times 1.4^2}{0.3 \times 0.3} = 42.7$ mol²dm⁻³

[1 mark for value, 1 mark for units]

2 a) *$p(O_2) = \frac{1}{2} \times 36$ [1 mark] = 18 kPa [1 mark]*

b) *$p(NO_2)$ = total pressure – p(NO) – p(O_2)*
= 99 – 36 – 18 [1 mark] = 45 kPa [1 mark]

c) $K_p = \dfrac{p(NO_2)^2}{p(NO)^2 p(O_2)}$ *[1 mark]* $= \dfrac{(45)^2}{(36)^2(18)}$ *[1 mark]*

= 0.0868 [1 mark] KPa⁻¹ [1 mark]

(Units = kPa²/(kPa² × kPa) = kPa⁻¹)

Page 81 — Nitrogen Chemistry

1 a) i) *–3 [1 mark]*
ii) *+5 [1 mark]*

b) *N is being oxidised [1 mark]. It is losing electrons/ gaining oxygen [1 mark].*

c) *$NH_4^+ + 3H_2O \rightarrow NO_3^- + 10H^+ + 8e^-$*
[1 mark for 3 moles of H_2O on left of arrow
1 mark for 10 moles of H^+ and 8 moles of e^- on right of arrow]

2 a) *$N_2 + O_2 \rightarrow 2NO$ [1 mark for left-hand side, 1 mark for right]*
(allow $0.5N_2 + 0.5O_2 \rightarrow NO$).

b) *N has an oxidation state of +2 in NO [1 mark].*

c) *A brown colour would appear (nitrogen dioxide is brown) [1 mark].*

Page 83 — The Chemical Industry and Food

1 *% atom economy = $\dfrac{12 + (3 \times 1) + 16 + 1}{12 + (3 \times 1) + 80 + 23 + 16 + 1} \times 100 = 23.7\%$*

[1 mark for product on top line, reactants on bottom. 1 mark for numbers correct on top line. 1 mark for numbers correct on bottom line. 1 mark for correct answer overall].

2 a) *To add extra nutrients to the soil, i.e. fertilisers [1 mark].*
To kill pests (weeds, insects, moulds), i.e. pesticides [1 mark].
To neutralise acid in soil/raise pH/control pH of soil [1 mark].

b) *Any two points with matching explanations from:*
Nitrates from fertiliser getting into rivers/lakes/drinking water [1 mark] causing excessive growth of plants (eutrophication)/harmful to health (of young children/babies)/blue baby syndrome [1 mark].
Pesticides may not only kill the pest/not selective [1 mark].
kill beneficial insects/plants/organisms/reduce biodiversity [1 mark].
Pesticides may not easily break down/may be too stable [1 mark].
Can build up in environment/accumulate in food chain/bioaccumulate [1 mark].

[4 marks in total, up to 2 for each problem]

Unit 5: Module 2 — Colour by Design

Page 85 — Benzene / Fats and Oils

1 a) i) *2 moles [1 mark]* ii) *240 kJ [1 mark]*

b) i) *3 moles [1 mark]* ii) *360 kJ [1 mark]*

c) *The delocalisation of electrons makes benzene more stable (it lowers the energy of the molecule) [1 mark] and so it released less energy when it reacts [1 mark].*

2 *The Kekulé structure cannot explain why all the C-C bond lengths in benzene are identical [1 mark], since C=C double bonds are shorter than single bonds [1 mark]. Also, the benzene molecule represented by the Kekulé structure should react in the same way as alkenes [1 mark] (i.e. by electrophilic addition), but benzene is actually much less reactive [1 mark] (and tends to react via electrophilic substitution).*

Answers

Page 88 — Reactions of Aromatic Compounds

1 a) (i)A: nitrobenzene *[1 mark]*
   B + C: concentrated nitric acid *[1 mark]*
   and concentrated sulfuric acid *[1 mark]*
   D: warm, not more than 55 °C *[1 mark]*
   When you're asked to name a compound, write the name, not the formula.
   (ii)This is an electrophilic substitution reaction with nitrobenzene as
   the electrophile. See page 88 for the mechanism.
   [1 mark for each of the three steps.]
   (iii) $HNO_3 + H_2SO_4 \rightarrow H_2NO_3^+ + HSO_4^-$ *[1 mark]*
   $H_2NO_3^+ \rightarrow NO_2^+ + H_2O$ *[1 mark]*
   b) (i) G: benzenesulfonic acid *[1 mark]*
   E + F: concentrated sulfuric acid, heat under reflux
   OR fuming sulfuric acid, warm
   **[1 mark for reagent, 1 mark for appropriate conditions
   for that reagent].**
   (ii) Sulfur trioxide/SO_3 *[1 mark]*
2 a) An ionic compound with a low melting point *[1 mark]*
   b) Any three from *[1 mark for each]*:
   Less vapour produced (accept 'less volatile')
   Less flammable
   Less toxic
   Reduce waste as can be re-used
   Enable lower temperatures to be used, so there's less demand on non-
   renewable fuels
   Enable lower temperatures to be used, so there's less pollution from
   burning fuels.

Page 91 — Dyes

1 a) i) Nitrous acid/HNO_2 *[1 mark]*
   $NaNO_{2(aq)} + HCl_{(aq)} \rightarrow HNO_{2(aq)} + NaCl_{(aq)}$ *[1 mark]*
   ii) Temperature below 10 °C *[1 mark]*

   b) i)   *[1 mark]*

   ii) Benzene rings *[1 mark]*, N=N/azo group *[1 mark]*,
   nitrogen lone pair *[1 mark]*.
   iii) Dye *[1 mark]*
   This is actually Butter Yellow, which was once used to colour
   margarine — until they found out it was carcinogenic (cancer-inducing)
   and banned it. Eeek...
2 a) i) Benzene rings *[1 mark]*, N=N/azo group *[1 mark]*,
   oxygen lone pairs *[1 mark]*.
   ii) $-SO_3^-Na^+$/sodium sulfonate group *[1 mark]*
   b) Ionic attraction *[1 mark]* between $-SO_3^-$ (in dye) *[1 mark]* and $-NH_3^+$
   (in protein) *[1 mark]*.

   c)   *[1 mark for each]*

Page 93 — Colour

1 a) The ligands split the 3d orbitals into two sets with different energies
   [1 mark]. Energy of a particular wavelength is absorbed by electrons
   in low-energy orbitals to move up to higher energy orbitals *[1 mark]*.
   The rest of the wavelengths are transmitted / reflected, making the
   compound appear pink *[1 mark]*.
   b) i) Colourless *[1 mark]*
   ii) A spectrometer *[1 mark]*
   c) i) Delocalised systems contain molecular orbitals that are close
   together in energy *[1 mark]* which allows them to absorb
   wavelengths / frequencies of visible light *[1 mark]*, resulting in
   coloured molecules.
   ii) Adding functional groups to a chromophore can increase the
   delocalisation *[1 mark]*, reducing the energy gap between molecular
   orbitals, so that different frequencies / wavelengths are absorbed
   [1 mark], changing the molecule's colour.

Page 97 — Identifying Materials Used in a Painting

1 a) The mixture is injected into a stream of carrier gas, which takes it
   through a tube over the stationary phase *[1 mark]*. The components
   of the mixture dissolve in the stationary phase *[1 mark]*, evaporate
   into the mobile phase *[1 mark]*, and redissolve, gradually travelling
   along the tube to the detector *[1 mark]*.

b) The peak at 5 minutes *[1 mark]*.
c) The mixture may contain another chemical with a similar retention
   time, which would give a peak at 5 minutes *[1 mark]*. He could run
   the separated components of the mixture through a mass
   spectrometer — this would allow him to confirm the presence of
   hexene *[1 mark]*.
2 a) Electrons are excited to higher energy levels *[1 mark]*. When they
   return to lower energy levels the excess energy is given off in the
   form of light *[1 mark]*.
   b) Energy levels are different in each atom *[1 mark]* and so the amount
   of energy given off during a transition between two levels is different
   [1 mark]. Since the frequency of light emitted depends on the
   energy, each element gives off a different set of frequencies *[1 mark]*.
   c) A *[1 mark]* and C *[1 mark]* are present. *[Deduct one mark for
   stating that B is present]*. You can tell this because the lines in the
   spectrum of the pigment match those in the spectra of A and C (but
   not B) *[1 mark]*.
3 a) The intensity of a monochromatic light beam is measured before
   and after passing through the solution *[1 mark]* and from this an
   absorbance value is plotted against frequency *[1 mark]*. A spectrum
   is produced by measuring absorbance over a range of frequencies
   [1 mark].
   b) Visible reflection / reflectance spectroscopy *[1 mark]*.
4 a) green *[1 mark]*.
   b) Because you can record a reflectance spectrum without removing
   any pigment from the painting *[1 mark]*. In atomic absorption
   spectroscopy a small sample of the pigment must be removed in
   order to prepare a solution of it *[1 mark]*
   c) It is possible to identify the exact chemical present in this spot of
   paint by comparing the reflectance spectrum produced to other
   reflectance spectra of know compounds *[1 mark]*.

Unit 5: Module 3 — The Oceans

Page 99 — Water and Dissolving

1   To boil water hydrogen bonds between water molecules must be
    broken *[1 mark]*. Since hydrogen bonds are very strong in
    comparison to other intermolecular forces they require a lot of energy
    to break, *[1 mark]* which is why the boiling point of water is very high
    when compared to similar molecules that are not capable of
    hydrogen bonding *[1 mark]*.
2   Water is a polar solvent *[1 mark]*. It forms a lot of bonds with the
    ions *[1 mark]* which releases enough energy to compensate for the
    energy needed to break the lattice apart *[1 mark]*. Hexane is a
    non-polar molecule *[1 mark]*. It would form only very weak bonds
    with the ions, *[1 mark]* which means there would not be not enough
    energy released to compensate for the energy taken in to break up
    the lattice *[1 mark]*.
3   Water is a polar solvent *[1 mark]*. Capsaicin is a non-polar molecule
    and cannot form bonds with the water *[1 mark]*. So it will not
    dissolve very easily in water *[1 mark]*.

Page 101 — Enthalpies and Dissolving

1 a) i) Lattice enthalpy *[1 mark]*
   ii) (Enthalpy change of) hydration/solvation *[1 mark]*
   b) i) $Br^-_{(g)} \rightarrow Br^-_{(aq)}$ *[1 mark]*
   ii) $KBr_{(s)} \rightarrow K^+_{(aq)} + Br^-_{(aq)}$ OR $KBr_{(s)} \rightarrow KBr_{(aq)}$ *[1 mark]*
   State symbols are vital in these equations

2
   Missing formulae = $Ca^{2+}_{(g)} + 2Cl^-_{(g)}$ *[1 mark]*
   Enthalpy changes:
   1 = enthalpy of solution (of $CaCl_2$) *[1 mark]*
   2 = lattice enthalpy (of $CaCl_2$) *[1 mark]*
   3 = enthalpy of hydration of Ca^{2+} (accept 'calcium ion') *[1 mark]*,
   2 × enthalpy of hydration of Cl^- *[1 mark]*

Answers

a)

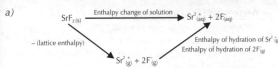

[1 mark for each of the 4 enthalpy changes labelled, 1 mark for a complete, correct cycle.]
Don't forget — you have to double the enthalpy of hydration for F^- because there are two in SrF_2.
b) $-(-2492) + (-1480) + (2 \times -506)$ **[1 mark]** $= 0$ kJ mol^{-1} **[1 mark]**

Page 103 — Entropy

a) Reaction is not likely to be spontaneous **[1 mark]** because there is a decrease in entropy **[1 mark]**.
Remember — more particles means more entropy. There are 1½ moles of reactants, and only 1 mole of products.
b) $\Delta S_{system} = 26.9 - (32.7 + 102.5)$ **[1 mark]**
$= -108.3$ **[1 mark]** J K^{-1} mol^{-1} **[1 mark]**
c) Reaction is not likely to be spontaneous **[1 mark]** because ΔS_{system} is negative/there is a decrease in entropy **[1 mark]**.
a) i) $\Delta S_{system} = 48 - 70 = -22$ J K^{-1} mol^{-1} **[1 mark]**
$\Delta S_{surroundings} = -(-6000)/250 = +24$ J K^{-1} mol^{-1} **[1 mark]**
$\Delta S_{total} = \Delta S_{system} + \Delta S_{surroundings} = -22 + 24 = +2$ J K^{-1} mol^{-1} **[1 mark]**
ii) $\Delta S_{surroundings} = -(-6000)/300 = +20$ J K^{-1} mol^{-1} **[1 mark]**
$\Delta S_{total} = \Delta S_{system} + \Delta S_{surroundings} = -22 + 20 = -2$ J K^{-1} mol^{-1} **[1 mark]**
b) It will be spontaneous at 250 K, but not at 300 K **[1 mark]**, because ΔS_{total} is positive at 250 K but negative at 300 K **[1 mark]**.

Page 105 — Acids and Bases

a) i) A proton donor **[1 mark]**
ii) A proton acceptor **[1 mark]**
b) i) $HSO_4^- \rightarrow H^+ + SO_4^{2-}$ **[1 mark]**
ii) $HSO_4^- + H^+ \rightarrow H_2SO_4$ **[1 mark]**
Weak acids dissociate (or ionise) a small amount **[1 mark]** to produce hydrogen ions (or protons) **[1 mark]**.
$HCN_{(aq)} \rightleftharpoons H^+_{(aq)} + CN^-_{(aq)}$ OR $HCN_{(aq)} + H_2O_{(aq)} \rightleftharpoons H_3O^+_{(aq)} + CN^-_{(aq)}$
[1 mark for correct formulas, 1 mark for equilibrium sign]
a) $NH_{3(aq)} + HNO_{3(aq)} \rightarrow NH_4^+{}_{(aq)} + NO_3^-{}_{(aq)}$
[1 mark, state symbols not needed for the mark]
Ammonia is acting as a base because it is taking a proton/H^+ ion from the acid **[1 mark]**
b) conjugate acid-base pair:
HNO_3 (acid) **[1 mark]** and NO_3^- (base) **[1 mark]**
They're a conjugate pair because HNO_3 donates a proton to form NO_3^- **[1 mark]**, and NO_3^- accepts a proton to form HNO_3 in the reverse reaction **[1 mark]**.
OR
NH_4^+ (acid) **[1 mark]** and NH_3 (base) **[1 mark]**
They're a conjugate pair because NH_3 accepts a proton to form NH_4^+ **[1 mark]** and NH_4^+ donates a proton to form NH_3 in the reverse reaction **[1 mark]**.
a) $2H_2O_{(l)} \rightarrow H_3O^+_{(aq)} + OH^-_{(aq)}$
[1 mark for two water molecules, 1 mark for correct equation]
b) $K_w = [H_3O^+][OH^-]$ **[2 marks – deduct 1 mark if $[H^+]$ used. Deduct 1 mark if $[H_2O]$ appears in equation]**
c) They are equal **[1 mark]**.

Page 107 — pH Calculations

a) $K_a = \dfrac{[H^+][A^-]}{[HA]}$ **[1 mark]**

b) $K_a = \dfrac{[H^+]^2}{[HA]}$ $\Rightarrow$ $[HA]$ is 0.280 mol dm^{-3} because very few molecules of HA will dissociate **[1 mark]**.
$[H^+] = \sqrt{K_a[HA]} = \sqrt{(5.60 \times 10^{-4})(0.280)} = 0.0125$ mol dm^{-3}
[1 mark]
$pH = -\log_{10}[H^+] = -\log_{10}(0.0125) = 1.90$ **[1 mark]**
$[H^+] = 10^{-2.65} = 2.24 \times 10^{-3}$ mol dm^{-3} **[1 mark]**
$K_a = \dfrac{[H^+]^2}{[HX]}$ **[1 mark]** $= \dfrac{[2.24 \times 10^{-3}]^2}{[0.15]}$
$= 3.34 \times 10^{-5}$ **[1 mark]** mol dm^{-3} **[1 mark]**

3 a) $K_w = [H^+][OH^-]$ **[1 mark]**.
b) $[OH^-] = 0.0370$ mol dm^{-3} **[1 mark]**
$[H^+] = K_w \div [OH^-] = (1 \times 10^{-14}) \div 0.0370 = 2.70 \times 10^{-13}$ **[1 mark]**
$pH = -\log_{10}[H^+] = -\log_{10}(2.70 \times 10^{-13}) = 12.57$ **[1 mark]**

Page 109 — Buffers

1 a) $K_a = \dfrac{[C_6H_5COO^-][H^+]}{[C_6H_5COOH]}$ **[1 mark]**

$\Rightarrow [H^+] = 6.4 \times 10^{-5} \times \dfrac{0.40}{0.20} = 1.28 \times 10^{-4}$ mol dm^{-3} **[1 mark]**

$pH = -\log_{10}[1.28 \times 10^{-4}] = 3.9$ **[1 mark]**
b) $C_6H_5COOH \rightleftharpoons H^+ + C_6H_5COO^-$ **[1 mark]**
Adding H_2SO_4 increases the concentration of H^+ **[1 mark]**.
The equilibrium shifts left to reduce concentration of H^+, so the pH will only change very slightly **[1 mark]**.
2 a) $CH_3(CH_2)_2COOH \rightleftharpoons H^+ + CH_3(CH_2)_2COO^-$ **[1 mark]**
b) $[CH_3(CH_2)_2COOH] = [CH_3(CH_2)_2COO^-]$,
so $[CH_3(CH_2)_2COOH] \div [CH_3(CH_2)_2COO^-] = 1$ **[1 mark]**
and $K_a = [H^+]$. $pH = -\log_{10}[1.5 \times 10^{-5}]$ **[1 mark]** $= 4.8$ **[1 mark]**
If the concentrations of the weak acid and the salt of the weak acid are equal, they cancel from the K_a expression and the buffer pH $= pK_a$.
3 a) Any highly soluble hydrogencarbonate (e.g. sodium hydrogencarbonate) or formula, e.g. $NaHCO_3$ **[1 mark]**
b) It supplies lots of HCO_3^- ions **[1 mark]**. These react with any added H^+ ions (to form H_2CO_3) **[1 mark]**
c) Below 7 **[1 mark]**. No matter where the position of equilibrium is, there will always be more H^+ ions than in pure water **[1 mark]**. (Accept reference to mixture being an 'acidic buffer')
d) Any sensible suggestion, e.g. shampoo, biological washing powders, soap, cosmetics, skin creams, etc. **[1 mark]**

Page 111 — Carbon Dioxide

1 a) Elevated levels of CO_2 are thought to be responsible for climate change/global warming/CO_2 is a greenhouse gas **[1 mark]**.
b) Hydrogen is hard/dangerous/expensive to store/transport OR it would be expensive to set up a supply infrastructure OR producing the hydrogen fuel uses energy (which might be produced by burning fossil fuels) **[1 mark]**.
c) Any two from:
Using less fuel/increasing energy efficiency of devices
Reforestation/planting trees/reducing deforestation
Carbon capture and storage
[1 mark for each method]
2 a) CO_2 will dissolve in water — the ocean acts as a carbon sink because it can store vast amounts of CO_2 **[1 mark]**. This has helped to slow/reduce increases in atmospheric CO_2 **[1 mark]**, which may have slowed down the effects of global warming due to CO_2 **[1 mark]**. It also increases the acidity of the oceans **[1 mark]**. This may harm or kill species which are pH sensitive **[1 mark]**. Other species will suffer due to food chains being disturbed **[1 mark]**.
b) Plants remove CO_2 from the atmosphere by photosynthesis **[1 mark]**, and store it as glucose and other carbon-based compounds **[1 mark]**. Deforestation has reduced green plant coverage on the Earth **[1 mark]**, reducing photosynthesis and the amount of CO_2 being removed from the atmosphere **[1 mark]**.

Answers

Unit 5: Module 4 — Medicines by Design

Page 113 — Medicines

1 a) The part of a drug that fits into a receptor *[1 mark]* and gives the drug its activity *[1 mark]*.

b)

[1 mark]

This is a skeletal structure so the C's and H's aren't shown.

c) –COOH/carboxyl group (accept OH) *[1 mark]*. This group can hydrogen bond with water *[1 mark]*.

d) Hydrogen bonding / dipole-dipole bonding *[1 mark]* between the carboxyl group and polar groups in the receptor site *[1 mark]*.

e) i)

[1 mark]

ii) Only one optical isomer/enantiomer will bind with the target receptor OR increased chance of side effects (because the other isomer bonds to another receptor elsewhere) *[1 mark]*.

Page 116 — Organic Functional Groups and Reactions

1 a) Electrophile *[1 mark]* because of positive charge *[1 mark]*.

b) Nucleophile *[1 mark]* because of lone pair of electrons on N *[1 mark]*.

c) Nucleophile *[1 mark]* because of negative charge *[1 mark]*.

2 a) i) addition *[1 mark]*

ii) addition *[1 mark]*

iii) substitution *[1 mark]*

b) i) $CH_3(CN)C(OH)CH_3$ or 2-hydroxy-2-methylpropanenitrile *[1 mark]*. Nucleophile *[1 mark]*

ii) CH_3CH_2Br or bromoethane *[1 mark]*. Electrophile *[1 mark]*

iii) CH_3CH_2OH or ethanol *[1 mark]*. Nucleophile *[1 mark]*

Page 119 — Organic Synthesis

1 a)

[1 mark for correct species formed, 1 mark for correct charges]

b) i) Aminobenzene / Phenylamine ($C_6H_5NH_2$) *[1 mark]* and ethanoyl chloride (CH_3COCl) *[1 mark]*

ii) $C_6H_5NH_2 + CH_3COCl \rightarrow C_6H_5NHCOCH_3 + HCl$ *[1 mark]*

2 Step 1: React propane with bromine *[1 mark]* in the presence of UV light *[1 mark]*. Bromine is toxic and corrosive *[1 mark]* so great care should be taken. Bromopropane is formed *[1 mark]*.
Step 2: Bromopropane is then refluxed *[1 mark]* with sodium hydroxide solution *[1 mark]*, again a corrosive substance so take care *[1 mark]*, to form propanol *[1 mark]*.

Page 121 — NMR Spectroscopy — The Basics

1 a) E.g. deuterated water/CCl_4 *[1 mark]*. This solvent has no single protons *[1 mark]*, so doesn't produce any peaks on the spectrum *[1 mark]*.

b) 1.0 p.p.m., 3.5 p.p.m. and 4.5 p.p.m. *[1 mark for all three]*.

c) The single hydrogen at $\delta = 4.5$ p.p.m. is the H atom in the OH group of the alcohol *[1 mark]*. The three hydrogens at a shift of 1 p.p.m. are likely to be in a CH_3 group *[1 mark]*. The two hydrogens at a shift of 3.5 p.p.m. are likely to be from a CH_2OH group *[1 mark]*. The structure's likely to be CH_3CH_2OH *[1 mark]*.

The CH_2OH group has three hydrogens, but only the two attached to the carbon cause this chemical shift. The one attached to the oxygen has a different chemical shift.

Page 124 — More NMR Spectroscopy

1 a) A CH_2 group adjacent to a halogen *[1 mark]*.
You gotta read the question carefully — it tells you it's a haloalkane. So the group at 3.6 p.p.m. can't have oxygen in it. It can't be halogen-CH either, as this has 3 hydrogens in it.

b) A CH_3 group *[1 mark]*.

c) CH_2 added to CH_3 gives a mass of 29, so the halogen must be chlorine with a mass of 35 *[1 mark]*. So a likely structure is CH_3CH_2Cl *[1 mark]*.

d) The quartet at 3.6 p.p.m. is caused by 3 protons on the adjacent carbon *[1 mark]*. The n + 1 rule tells you that 3 protons give 3 + 1 = 4 peaks *[1 mark]*.
Similarly the triplet at 1.3 p.p.m. is due to 2 adjacent protons *[1 mark]* giving 2 + 1 = 3 peaks *[1 mark]*.

2 a) Mass of molecule = 73 *[1 mark]*.
You can tell this from the mass spectrum — the mass of the molecular ion is 73.

b) Structure of the molecule: *[1 mark]*

Explanation: Award *1 mark* each for the following pieces of reasoning, up to a total of *[5 marks]*:
• IR spectrum shows strong absorption at about 3500 cm^{-1}, suggesting an amine or amide group.
• IR spectrum has trough at about 1700 cm^{-1}, suggesting C=O group.
• NMR spectrum has a quartet at $\delta \approx 2$, and a triplet at $\delta \approx 1$ — this splitting pattern matches a CH_2CH_3 group.
• Mass spectrum peak at m/z = 15 corresponds to CH_3 group.
• Mass spectrum peak at m/z = 29 corresponds to CH_2CH_3 group.
• Mass spectrum peak at m/z = 44 corresponds to $CONH_2$ group.

3 a) Mass of molecule = 60 *[1 mark]*.
You can tell this from the mass spectrum — the mass of the molecular ion is 60.

b) Structure of the molecule: *[1 mark]*

Explanation: Award *1 mark* each for the following pieces of reasoning, up to a total of *[5 marks]*:
• IR spectrum has a trough at 3300 cm^{-1}, suggesting an OH group.
• IR spectrum has a trough at 1200 cm^{-1}, suggesting a C–O group.
• Mass spectrum peak at m/z = 15 corresponds to CH_3 group.
• Mass spectrum peak at m/z = 17 corresponds to OH group.
• Mass spectrum peak at m/z = 29 corresponds to C_2H_5 group.
• Mass spectrum peak at m/z = 31 corresponds to CH_2OH group.
• Mass spectrum peak at m/z = 43 corresponds to C_3H_7 group.
• NMR spectrum peak at $\delta \approx 1$ corresponds to $-CH_3$.
• NMR spectrum peak at $\delta \approx 1.5$ corresponds to $-CH_2-$.
• NMR spectrum peak at $\delta \approx 2$ corresponds to –OH.
• NMR spectrum peak at $\delta \approx 3.5$ corresponds to $-CH_2OH$.
• NMR spectrum integration trace of 2, 1, 2, 3 matches the number of H atoms in $CH_3CH_2CH_2OH$.
• NMR spectrum has 4 peaks, so there's 4 proton environments.
• NMR spectrum has a sextuplet, a quartet, a triplet and a singlet — this splitting pattern matches the arrangement of H atoms in $CH_3CH_2CH_2OH$.

Index

Index